Ramsay's Catalog

British Model Trains

Second Edition

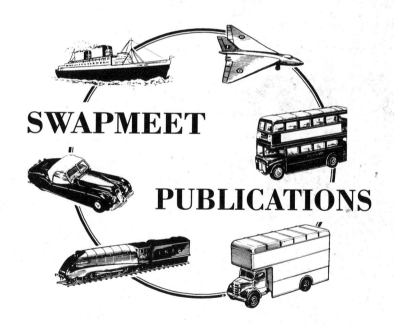

SWAPMEET

PUBLICATIONS

Swapmeet Publications
PO Box 47, Felixstowe, Suffolk, IP11 7LP
Phone (01394) 670700, Fax: (01394) 670730
Web site: www.swapmeet.co.uk   E-mail: info@swapmeet.co.uk

Swapmeet Toys and Models Ltd., t/a Swapmeet Publications

Reg. No. 1715966. Reg. Office: 36 Rembrandt Way, Bury St Edmunds, Suffolk. Directors: E. J. Ramsay, S. E. Ramsay, Co. Sec. M. J. Ramsay, BA.

Originator : John Ramsay

Editor : Pat Hammond

Technical Editor : John King

1st Edition published 1998
2nd Edition published 2000

Copyright © 2000 by John Ramsay

ISBN 09528352 – 5 – 8

Book designed by John King.
Origination by Swapmeet Publications, Felixstowe.
Printed by Page Bros. Ltd., Norwich.
Colour sections printed by Norwich Colour Print Ltd.

Front cover illustrations (top down):
(1) Bassett-Lowke open wagon behind a Bing SR 0-6-0
(2) Hornby Series 900 'Eton' (1937)
(3) Playcraft Class 29 D6100 (1961)
(4) Tri-ang Hornby Caledonian Single 123 (1971)
(5) Hornby (ex-Airfix) GWR Class 61XX Prairie Tank (1999)
(6) Lima Class 55 9016 ('Gordon Highlander') in Porterbrook purple (2000)

Contents

Acknowledgements

A work of this nature cannot be achieved by one man's efforts alone but depends upon many experts sharing their knowledge with us all. Special thanks go to Roy Chambers who wrote much of the original 0 gauge text. The text and lists that Roy and I prepared were then checked, corrected and expanded by a host of established experts whose very important contribution to this book I am pleased to acknowledge. I should particularly like to mention the following:

PETER BAKER – Lima
RICHARD BRADFORD – Wrenn
PAUL and JENNIFER BROOKES – MasterModels
ROY CHAMBERS – Hornby 0 gauge, Bassett-Lowke, Leeds, Milbro, Exley, Bonds, Bowman.
PETER CORLEY – various 00 gauge

JAMES DAY – Playcraft
MARTIN DOUBLEDAY – Lone Star
IAN DORRELL – Lone Star
MERL EVANS – Bachmann, Mainline and Airfix
BOB FIELD – Hornby Dublo
ROBERT FORSYTHE – Bassett-Lowke and Lima H0
PETER GOMM – Airfix, Mainline etc.
SIMON GOODYEAR – Milbro, Exley, Bonds
PETER GURD – Hornby Dublo and Bowman
CLIVE GEHLE – Lone Star
JACK HOLMES – Tri-ang 00
JOHN INGRAM – Bassett-Lowke
STEPHEN KNIGHT – Kitmaster and Playcraft
BOB LEGGITT – Playcraft
ALLEN LEVY – Ace Trains
ALAN BROWN – Ace Trains
QUENTIN LUCAS of Edward Exley Ltd – Exley

ROBERT NEWSON – Lone Star
DAVID PEACOCK – Leeds Model Company
DAVID O'BRIAN – Trix
TONY PRITCHARD – Dapol
PAUL ROUSE – Tri-ang TT
FLEETWOOD SHAW – Bassett-Lowke
GRAHAM SMITH-THOMPSON – Airfix, Mainline, Replica and Dapol
BARRY POTTER of Barry Potter Auctions
HUGO MARSH of Christie's South Kensington
TERRY DURRANT of Lacy, Scott & Knight Auctions
GLEN BUTLER of Wallis & Wallis Auctions
BRIAN GOODALL of Vectis Auctions
LEIGH GOTCH of Bonhams
PAUL CAMPBELL of Sotheby's
DICK HENRYWOOD of Dreweatt Neate Auctions
BRIAN LEE of Romsey Model Auctions

Pat Hammond, Editor

Foreword

The first edition of the British Model Trains Catalogue was a landmark publication and a testament to John Ramsay's tireless dedication and his mission to educate us all. With this new edition, credit goes first and foremost to the Editor, Pat Hammond, under whose guidance, twenty-eight experts have contributed to it. The original edition has remained unchallenged by competitors and it is fitting that it should only be surpassed by this new edition. The Catalogue has now become more like an encyclopaedia, with plenty of detailed historical background and many more manufacturers included.

I was first 'hooked' by pre-war Trix Twin in the 1960s, going on to collect Hornby-Dublo in the 1970s, which led to my start in the auction world twenty years ago. Thus I have seen the hobby change out of all recognition. The price gap between average and fine pieces has become a gulf, as the truly determined enthusiasts have refined their collections. The hobby is now bolstered by numerous societies dedicated to the great manufacturers, swapmeets, auctions and numerous publications for us to enjoy – and none more than this latest Catalogue.

My abiding impression is that collectors often enjoy the company they keep as much as the trains themselves. I am certain that this Catalogue will be a source of admiration around the swapmeet tables and model train societies of this country.

Hugo Marsh
Associate Director and Head of the Toy Department
Christie's

Preface

After completion of the second volume of my trilogy on the Rovex Company, I felt the urge to write a price guide as a compendium to the series. Consequently, when John Ramsay asked if I should like to have a go at rewriting his British Model Trains Catalogue, I jumped at the chance. For one thing, I welcomed the opportunity to write on a subject broader than Tri-ang Hornby, with which I am associated by most people who know me.

In actual fact, my interest has always been broad and long before I started writing my Rovex books I collected many different makes including: Hornby 0 gauge, Trix Twin, Hornby Dublo, Wrenn, Graham Farish, Airfix GMR, Mainline, Playcraft, MasterModels, Kitmaster kits, wooden stations and the products of the minor manufacturers in British 00 and H0 such as Stewart Reidpath, Gaiety, Ever Ready and Kirdon.

Although most of these collections have now gone in order to finance my Tri-ang Hornby reference collection, I have retained a strong interest in most British ranges. That interest was widened during my two years as editor of Model Railway Enthusiast during which I researched and wrote about subjects which were relatively new to me. Principal amongst these was Bassett-Lowke and the research I did for the six part series on the company left me fascinated both by the marque and the man.
I hope that the enthusiasm I have for all makes of British model railways spills over into this volume and particularly in the many potted histories which were great fun to write - not all, I hasten to add, were all my own work!

I have been particularly fortunate to have Roy Chambers to do most of the 0 gauge writing for me and his broad knowledge of the subject has provided excellent guidance. The help given by so many others is mentioned in greater detail later but, needless to say, this book is a combined effort and praise must go to all those involved. The design work is by John King who has been a delight to work with, as too has publisher John Ramsay whose good humour will be known to all who have met him. I consider that ours has become a well balanced and effective team.

Now enjoy the book!

Pat Hammond
Editor
Scarborough, July 2000

Welcome . . .

Welcome to the Second edition of the *British Model Trains Catalogue* which covers toy trains and model railway equipment made for the British market. You will find that the catalogue has been completely rewritten and reorganised to make it easier to use. If there are ways in which we can improve it further, we would be interested to hear your suggestions.

The comprehensive listing of all British railway models is a considerable (if not impossible) task to undertake and can only be done in stages. We, therefore, see this as a catalogue that will expand regularly as more lists are added. For this second edition we have tried to set a new standard of accuracy, comprehensiveness and ease of access and have concentrated on the comprehensive listing of locomotives.

Future additions to the catalogue will not only expand the number of brands covered but also go to greater detail in listing rolling stock and accessories. All will be to the new standard.

Your Help Needed!

While we have added a number of makes not previously covered and expanded others, there are several important makes of model trains we have yet to include. We would like to hear from anyone with expert knowledge of any make of toy or model train made for the British market who would be prepared to help with listing, pricing or checking drafts.

Needless to say there are bound to be mistakes in this edition of the catalogue but, where they exist, we are anxious to correct them and would welcome your notifying us of you may find.

You can either use the comments form that comes with the catalogue or write direct to:

The Editor,
British Model Trains Catalogue,
PO Box 199,
Scarborough
YO11 3GT

Illustrations and Captions

While the bulk of the illustrations have been supplied by Hammond Publishing, some have come from other sources including a number of auction houses. These are acknowledged in curved brackets at the end of the caption. I should like to express my gratitude for the help we have received in the supply of illustrations and to say that we are always interested in new sources.

Catalogue numbers of items illustrated, where known, are also shown in curved brackets after the item. The tables in which they are listed in the text of this catalogue are given in square brackets.

Beware of Prices

While everything possible has been done to obtain realistic prices, we stress throughout the catalogue that quoted prices can be misleading. There is a considerable difference between people's perception of value depending on whether they are buying or selling and the extent to which they want the item being sold. We provide prices to give a comparison between the scarcity of models and they should not be interpreted as the price you can expect to get for your model if you sell it. Dealers often have to undertake cleaning and servicing of second hand models they buy and can sometimes wait a long time before the right collector comes along who wants to buy it. They therefore rightly expect a good mark-up when they sell it.

Targets for the next Edition

So that this catalogue continues to expand and improve over the years, we have set ourselves targets. Before the next edition of the catalogue is published we plan the following:

1. Update listing of current ranges.
2. Update prices according to market changes as evidence becomes available.
3. Add lists of rolling stock where possible.
4. Add new sections including ones on Graham Farish 00 and N gauges, Hornby Minitrix and Bassett-Lowke Gauge 1.
5. Correct any inaccuracies that come to light.
6. Undertake further research into the histories of the companies covered by the catalogue.

Determining Value – The Impossible Task!

For Guidance Only
The first thing to remember about quoted prices is that they are for guidance only. Both at auction and on swapmeet stalls, prices vary enormously and who is to say what is the exact value of a given model. What is worth £200 to one collector may be worth only £150 (or even £100) to another buyer or seller.

Swapmeet Prices
On the whole, stall holders are very knowledgeable about what they sell but each tends to be a specialist. They sometimes find themselves with models that are outside their specialised area. If advice is not at hand they have to guess at the price to put on it. This can lead to bargains for knowledgeable buyers but can also cause frustration when the object is severely overpriced.

Remember, the price seen on a model at a swapmeet is not necessarily the price at which it sells. Most stall holders are prepared to haggle. So what is the true value of the model – the price at which he bought it in, the price he put on it or the price at which you finally buy it? Putting an accurate value to individual models is impossible. All we can do is show comparisons and that is all this price guide sets out to do.

Auction Prices
There is, usually, a fair gap between what you pay for a model and what you would expect to get for it when selling it again. We have set out prices at what we think the models will fetch at auction, prior to the addition of the buyer's premium. Even at auction, prices vary erratically depending on who is present bidding. As a result of this, we have had to deal with conflicting valuations from different auctions and, in each case, have tried to arrive at a compromise.

Our Valuations
Our valuations are based on mint boxed examples or, where a boxed example was not available (for example, if it was available only in a set), we have suggested the value of an unboxed example in mint condition (these are marked with an *).

Effect of Quality
Obviously, value falls as quality falls but not always by the same percentage. It depends how rare the model is and even what make it is. The lack of a box can reduce the value of a model by 40% or more. For poorer quality models the lack of a box has less impact on price.

Fluctuating Prices
Prices can fluctuate from year to year and from decade to decade. With the sale of the G&R Wrenn in the early '90s, the price of Wrenn models quickly escalated but, in the late '90s, fell to more modest levels. At auction, the sale of a famous comprehensive collection can bring out top bidders with the result that prices may rise on the day with rare and common items both selling at figures well above the norm.

High and Low Values
On the whole, the price gap between rare and common (or poor quality) items is ever widening. This means that rare and top quality models are a much better investment than common or poor quality models.

Train Packs
Nowadays, some manufacturers sell their models in train packs. These consist of a locomotive and some coaches or wagons but no track etc. The mint/boxed price quoted is for the complete train pack while the good/unboxed price is for the locomotive only. Multiple units (DEMUs, EMUs etc.) as sold as train packs. Here, once again, the mint/boxed price is for a complete pack but on this occasion the good/unboxed price is for the complete 2-car or 3-car unit without its packaging.

How to use this Catalogue

The catalogue has been designed as a reference work and, as such, a high priority has been the ease with which models can be traced. Having said that, it helps if you have some idea as to what the model is. It is also principally a reference work for locomotives and, with a few exceptions, there is little likelihood that you will be able to use it to identify a coach, wagon or lineside accessory. We are working on that information which will appear in future editions of the catalogue.

Most models today have the manufacturer's name on them but this was not so in the case of minor manufacturers in days gone by. Nor is it always the case with non-proprietary models, for it is quite possible that your model was not originally bought ready made but was either scratch built or made from a kit. Such models are not covered by the catalogue, that is with exceptions such as Kitmaster kits which are particularly collectable in their unmade state.

Determine the size
If you do not know the name of the manufacturer, a good starting point is to look at the size of the model. Railway models are governed in size by the gauge of the track they were made to run on. The book is laid out with the largest gauges first and the smallest last. You can determine the gauge of the model by measuring the distance between the backs of the wheels and referring to the section on Scales and Gauges.

Having determined the gauge, turn to the Contents page where you will find listed all the makes of that gauge that have been included, together with the number of the page on which their listing starts. The list is not comprehensive and there is always a chance that the make of the model you are trying to identify has not yet been covered by the catalogue. You will notice that '00' and 'H0' are referred to as 'scale' and not 'gauge'. This is because both 00 and H0 models use the same gauge track but 00 models are made to a scale of 4mm:1ft and H0 models to 3.5mm:1ft. The former are, therefore, slightly larger than the latter when you compare like subjects. If, having found the right part of the catalogue, you are still not sure of the make, compare the model with pictures in that section.

Looking for the Number
Having found the section you want, it does help if you know the name of the prototype that has been modelled. This will allow you to find the correct table for that model and search through it for the model variation that matches your own. If this is not the case, note the number on the side of the locomotive (or its tender) and check through the tables until you find it. This is particularly easy to do in the case of Lima locomotives as these almost all have modern TOPS numbering and so they have been listed in numerical order.

Lima is, however, the exception to the rule. With three of the largest product ranges (Hornby 0 gauge, Bassett-Lowke and Rovex/Tri-ang/Hornby) we have provided 'loco search' tables. All the known numbers carried by models in each of these groups have been listed in numerical order alongside the number of table(s) in which they will be found. You will find that this is a very fast way of tracing your model.

Understanding the Tables
In 99% of cases, all the models listed in each table are structurally the same and differ only in the livery they carry or in minor added detail. You will find that the table gives you the catalogue number (if known), the name and number of the locomotive, its basic colour, the livery it carries together with other distinguishing features, the years it was available in shops and a range of prices you might expect to pay for one (see Determining Value).

Some of the information is in code form in order to save space. Where those codes are specific to that model the codes are shown under the title of the table but where the codes are common to many models they may be listed in the introduction to the section or will be found in this main introduction section under Codes and Explanations.

The tables also contain information about limited and special editions (Ltd Edn and Sp Edn). Where known, this information includes the number made and (in brackets) the shop or organisation that commissioned it.

The history of British train manufacture

In the Beginning

The first commercially built model railways were imported into Britain from Germany in 1902 and were made for Bassett-Lowke by the German companies, Bing, Carette and Märklin. Up until the First World War, the most popular gauge was 1¾" (known as gauge 1) but after the war, gauge 0 really came into its own.

The war was to have a dramatic effect on the model railway industry as post-war anti-German feeling made German imports unpopular and Bassett-Lowke Ltd were forced to manufacture more of their products themselves. It also created an opportunity for other British manufacturers to enter the fray.

The most successful of these was Meccano Ltd, a company that had been founded in 1908 to manufacture the Meccano engineering construction system. They introduced their toy trains in 1920 and these took their name of the Company's founder – Frank Hornby – and were sold as 'Hornby Trains'. Hornby, from the start, chose to manufacture in 0 gauge and early models constructed with Meccano nuts and bolts soon gave way to tinplate tab and slot construction.

First 00 Scale System

As early as 1922, Bassett-Lowke introduced to Britain a tabletop railway made in Germany by Bing and considered to be 00 gauge – i.e., half the size of the popular 0 gauge. Within a very short time this was available as an electric system. The Bing company was to fall victim to the rise of Nazi power in Germany and trading became very difficult. Out of these difficulties came a more commercial small scale system known as Trix and this was introduced to Britain in 1936, again with the assistance of Bassett-Lowke.

Within a very short time it was being made by a satellite company of Bassett-Lowke at Northampton. Meccano Ltd could see the way the wind was blowing and quickly responded with their own 00 system which they called Hornby Dublo. This was launched in 1938 and, unlike the Trix Twin system, was initially available in clockwork form as well as electric.

Post WW2

The Second World War brought to an end all commercial model railway production but post-war Britain saw major changes in both demand and response. It was soon clear that 0 gauge was no longer the leading scale and over the years production

of it gradually declined. The new top gauge was 00 and it was to remain so to the present day.

Hornby Dublo returned after the war but while it was the market leader for a while Meccano Ltd did not recognise the importance of expanding it fast to meet the growing demands from the public. The gap in demand was quickly filled by a new system called Tri-ang Railways which was made by Rovex Scale Models Ltd, a subsidiary of Lines Bros.

The New Contender

The Tri-ang system had several advantages that would play in its favour during the struggle for market domination that lay ahead. It was a two rail system making the track look more realistic; it used plastic mouldings that could show much more detail, it was a lot cheaper while still being reliable and the range expanded quickly to offer the public plenty of choice when building a layout. Within a few years it had become the market leader.

The early post-war years saw many other companies trying to break into the model railway market. Principal amongst these was Graham Farish who marketed an 00 system with some very attractive models but which, initially, were not too reliable mechanically.

Trix in the meantime failed to respond quickly enough to the demand for realism and slowly faded. The business changed hands a few times and new investment resulted in some nice models being produced. One of its problems became obvious in the late '50s and that was its adoption of the Continental HO scale instead of British 00. This meant that when some excellent models started to arrive they looked out of scale when mixed with those of other makes.

Meanwhile Tri-ang's onslaught was injuring Hornby Dublo and although Meccano Ltd made major improvements to their range, including a 2-rail system and use of plastic mouldings, its response came too late to save the Company which was being bombarded on other fronts at the same time.

Big Take-overs

In 1964 Meccano Ltd was taken over by Lines Bros. who renamed their own model railway system 'Tri-ang Hornby' and sold the Hornby Dublo tools to another of their subsidiaries - G&R Wrenn. For the next decade Tri-ang Hornby virtually had the market to itself. The only competition came from a Trix system, which limped along, and Playcraft which was made by Jouef in France and marketed in Britain by Mettoy Ltd. The late '60s saw a bid by Lima to break into the British market but they made the mistake of using the smaller HO scale. Although by the early 1970s Lima had changed to 00 scale, their day had not yet dawned.

In 1971, the Lines Bros. Group fell apart. Rovex, the member of the group making Tri-ang Hornby, was sold to Dunbee Combex Marx (DCM) and Tri-ang Hornby was renamed Hornby Railways. Wrenn became an independent company again and continued to manufacture Wrenn Railways for the next 20 years using the former Hornby Dublo tools. The British part of Meccano Ltd (based in Liverpool), who no longer made trains, was sold to Airfix while Meccano France (based in the Tri-ang factory in Calais) was acquired by General Mills who also owned Palitoy.

New Competition
Both Airfix and Palitoy judged that there was a place in the market for better quality model railways and decided to fill it. The Airfix and Mainline (Palitoy) systems were both launched in the mid '70s but it had taken them two years from announcing their intentions to supplying shops and this gave Rovex the breathing space they required to respond with their Hornby Railways system. By 1980 it was a three horse race with Hornby closely chased by Mainline and Airfix and Lima coming up on the outside. Meanwhile, trailing some way behind, was British Trix and Playcraft now out of view. This seems an appropriate point at which to stop and look at what else was happening.

Smaller Scales
Tri-ang had seen a need to experiment with yet smaller scales and in 1957 had launched their TT system. This never really caught on although it was well developed as a system and was supported by manufacturers of accessories. It had died in the mid '60s.

The even smaller scale of 000 or N gauge was tried by Lone Star as a push-along system in 1957 with an electric system following in 1960. Lines Bros. were invited to buy the system but refused and it died out in the 1970s. Lima had produced a more sophisticated N gauge system which they had offered to Lines Bros. in the 1960s and they agreed to market it through their subsidiary, G&R Wrenn. This was sold as Wrenn Micromodels for many years.

Following the purchase of Rovex in 1971 by Dunbee Combex Marx they entered into an agreement with the German Trix company to import their Minitrix system (formerly made at Wrexham by Trix Trains) and sell it as Hornby Minitrix. New models were produced to Rovex's requirements, leaving Rovex free to concentrate on developing Hornby Railways. The arrangement was quite successful and lasted several years.

The only British company to really grasp the N gauge nettle was Graham Farish. Remember them? We last saw them in the 1950s with a nice but not too successful 00 system. This had limped along through the '60s with much shrinkage until they turned their attention to developing an N gauge system at the end of the '60s. In a virtual vacuum, but with a steadily growing demand for good N gauge models at reasonable prices, the Grafar N gauge system has expanded and now offers considerable choice to the N gauge modeller. Many small companies have developed to provide accessories, resprays etc. on the back of this system.

Before returning to 00 gauge it is worth mentioning that 0 gauge virtually petered out in the mid '60s as Hornby, Bassett-Lowke and Leeds production ground to a halt. Despite this, in the mid 1960s, Tri-ang produced their toy-like Big Big trains, the tools for which were later sent to Russia, and Lima produced some acceptable models of British outline.

The Tools Merry-go-round
In 1980 DCM were in the receivers' hands and the future of the Hornby Railway system was once again in question. The same year Airfix went bust and its railway system was taken over by Palitoy and its models absorbed into the Mainline system. By 1981, Hornby were up and running again, now for the first time in 30 years as an independent company. Ten glorious years of expansion followed. During the 1980s Lima firmly took hold of the modern image locomotive market bringing out models of many of the better known subjects. Then, in 1990, it all changed again!

In 1984, General Mills, who owned Palitoy, had given up toy production and the assets of their Mainline system, including the Airfix tools, were sold to another up and coming company called Dapol Ltd who were by then producing their own new, high quality, models of locomotives. However, Palitoy had not owned the tools for the manufacture of their Mainline models as these belonged to Kader of China who had made them.

(continues overleaf)

Enter the Dragon

Kader were interested in expanding their model railway manufacturing and in 1988 took control of the American model company, Bachmann. In 1989 they formed Bachmann Industries Europe Ltd to develop and market models in Europe through bases in Britain and Germany. The Bachmann Branchline range was launched in Britain in 1990, using the former Mainline tools. Building on these, Kader were soon manufacturing models to a quality never before seen in Britain. This was the Blue Riband range.

Once again Hornby found their commanding place in the market threatened and had to respond. To allow them to expand their range fast, and quickly improve the quality of their models, they needed to buy ready to use new tools. For these they turned to Dapol Ltd. As we have seen, Dapol had produced some high quality models of their own but also held, and used, the former Airfix tools they had bought from Palitoy. In 1996

Hornby purchased both lots of tools and this gave them four years breathing space in which to develop their own new models. In the summer of 2000, the first of these arrived in the shops. with the promise that all new Hornby models would be to the new standard.

Today the market is dominated by Hornby, Bachmann and Lima with Graham Farish looking after N gauge. Both Hornby and Bachmann depend on China supplying their needs, but what will it be like ten years from now? We will have to wait and see.

This has been a simplified history of the principal manufacturers of ready-to-run models and toy trains and it fails to reflect the enormous contribution made to the industry by the scores of smaller firms that specialise in kits, materials and accessories. Without them it would be a far less interesting hobby and we hope to cover the products of more of them in future editions.

The history of collecting model trains

The collecting of toy trains did not really get under way in Britain until the late 1960s when operators of Hornby 0 gauge were looking for additional stock. One way in which the exchange of models was effected was through the organisation of meetings by groups of enthusiasts and this lead to the invention of a new word in the English language - the Swapmeet.

Out of this growth in interest, the Hornby Railway Collectors Association was formed in 1969 and following a period of sometimes heated argument through the pages of the Association's magazine, membership was extended to Hornby Dublo collectors, some of whom had formed the Dublo Circle. The HRCA has steadily grown over the years and is by far the largest club of its kind in the UK. It has also spawned a number of satellite organisations abroad.

The mid 1970s saw a growing interest in collecting of other makes of toy trains and the formation, in 1975, of two more organisations. The first of these was the Tri-ang Hornby Collectors Club which survived for many years, chronicling the diversities of the range, before disbanding. The other new organisation was the Trix Twin Railway Collectors Association which has flourished and remains a well supported organisation producing its own spares and special models for members.

It was not until 1978 that collectors in Britain had an organisation that catered for 'any make, any age, any gauge'. This is the by-line of the Train Collectors Society which has stuck to its principles and not tried to set close restrictive limits to its member's interest. The result is a very friendly society that does not take itself, or its hobby, too seriously. Other specialised clubs followed with the Kitmaster Collectors Club in 1980, the Bassett-Lowke Society in 1991, the Graham Farish Circle in 1994, the Lima Collectors Society in 1995, the Wrenn Railways Collectors Club in 1998 and, finally, the Tri-ang Society, with its fairly broad interest in the products of the Lines Bros. Group, in 1999.

Recent years have seen a growing recognition, by the manufacturers, of the expanding market for new models made specially for collectors. As a result, Hornby, Lima, Bachmann, Dapol and Grafar are all embarked on a programme of producing collectors editions of their models. Some, like Bachmann, Lima and Hornby also have their own collectors clubs and Hornby has established collectors centres that exclusively receive some of their limited editions.

Outside the scope of this book are those British clubs that cater for collectors of foreign makes. These include the Fleischmann Model Railway Club and the Lionel Collectors Club UK.

Collectors Clubs

Anyone interested in collecting railway models should consider joining one of the growing number of specialist collecting clubs. The following are relevant to the systems covered by this guide:

Train Collectors Society
This is a society with a broad interest in toy and model train collecting and has the motto 'Any Make. Any Gauge, Any Age'. Founded in 1978, the Society publishes a quarterly magazine and is currently developing a spares and information service. It holds three major gatherings each year but members also exhibit at other events.
Contact : James Day, Tel: 020 8209 1589
Web site : www.traincs.demon.co.uk

Airfix Collectors Club
The Club caters for collectors of any Airfix product including the model railway range and publishes a newsletter called Constant Scale.
Contact : Jeremy Brook, 29 Elley Green, Neston, Nr. Corsham, Wiltshire SN13 9TX
Web site : www.djairfix.freeserve.co.uk

Bachmann Collectors Club
For some years the Company sponsored a club called Bachmann Times which operated at arms-length. In 2000 the club was reformed in-house as the Bachmann Collectors Club. Members receive a quarterly magazine called Bachmann Times. For further information, write to the Club at Bachmann Industries Europe Ltd, Moat Way, Barwell, Leicestershire LE9 8EY.

Bassett-Lowke Society
The Bassett-Lowke Society caters for those who collect and operate Bassett-Lowke models. It publishes a quarterly magazine called 'Lowko News' and organises events to which members may take their stock to run. For further information ring 01359 251127.

Hornby Collectors Club
This is a club supported by Hornby Hobbies for subscribing customers. The club was formed in 1997 and publishes a full colour bimonthly magazine. Through the Club, members have the opportunity to purchase special collectors editions of models produced by Hornby.
Contact : Fiona Baulard-Cato, Tel: 01223 208308
Web site : www.hornby.co.uk

Hornby Railway Collectors Association
The HRCA was founded in 1969 and caters for collectors of both Hornby 0 gauge and Hornby-Dublo. It is the largest of the clubs listed here and has overseas associate organisations. The Association publishes 11 issues of its magazine each year and has a very well developed spares service.
Contact : Bob Field, Tel: 0115 962 5693

Kitmaster Collectors Club
Enthusiasts of the Kitmaster kit range are well catered for by the Kitmaster Collectors Club which was founded in 1980. The Club publishes a magazine called 'Signal' twice a year and includes in the subjects covered the railway kits by Airfix and Dapol.
Contact : fax: 01787 478226.
Web site : www.kitmaster-club.org.uk

Leeds Stedman Trust
The Leeds Stedman Trust is an organisation run by David Peacock to help collectors and operators of LMC models to keep them running by supplying spare parts. It is not a club but you can be placed on a mailing list for the annual price list of parts.
Contact : E-mail: dpeacock@btconnect.com

Lima Collectors Society
The Society was founded in 1995 for collectors of Lima 00 and H0 railway models produced for the British market. A bimonthly newsletter is distributed to members and a complete listing of Lima's British products is available and is regularly updated through the newsletter.
Contact : Peter Baker, Tel: 01782 519267

Tri-ang Society
The Tri-ang Society was formed in 1999 and caters for all Tri-ang products including Tri-ang Railways, Tri-ang Hornby, Tri-ang Railways TT, Big-Big Trains and Minic Motorway. The Society has a quarterly magazine and arranges displays at various model shows and vintage events.
Contact : Miles Rowland, Tel 0161 976 5059
Web site : www.tri-angsociety.co.uk

Trix Twin Railway Collectors Association
The Trix Twin Railway Collectors Association (TTRCA) was founded in 1975 and caters for enthusiasts of Trix Twin, Trix Express, Trix Trains and the models of Liliput UK. It publishes a quarterly magazine called 'Trix Twin Gazette' and offers a spares service to its members. For enquiries concerning membership, telephone: 0116 271 5943.

Wrenn Railways Collectors Club
The Club was founded in 1998 and caters for the collectors of all products of G&R Wrenn Ltd. It publishes a bimonthly magazine and organises gatherings for its members, contributing displays at various vintage events.
Contact : Barry Fentiman, Tel: 01628 488455
Web site : www.wrennrail.freeserve.co.uk

Codes and Explanations

Abbreviations

While some sections in the catalogue have their own set of abbreviations, the following codes are common throughout the guide:

Ltd Edn = Limited Edition. These are usually initiated by the manufacturer.
Sp Edn = Special Edition. These are usually commissioned by a shop or other interested party.

The following codes are used for decals carried by models:

BRa = 'BRITISH RAILWAYS'.
BRb = lion astride wheel.
BRc = lion holding wheel (in a roundel on multiple units and coaches and a few diesel hydraulics). This is also known as the 'ferret and dart board' logo!
BRd = lion in crown (briefly used on West Coast Main Line electrics).
BRe = double arrow.
BReLL = double arrow (large logo)
IC = InterCity.
ICs = InterCity with swallow motif.
NSE = Network Southeast.

The following are abbreviations used for railway companies:

BR = British Railways
CLR = Central London Railway
CR = Caledonian Railway
GCR = Great Central Railway
GER = Great Eastern Railway
GNR = Great Northern Railway
GWR = Great Western Railway
LBSCR = London Brighton & South Coast Railway
LMS = London Midland & Scottish Railway
LNER = London North Eastern Railway
LNWR = London North Western Railway
LSWR = London South Western Railway
LT = London Transport
LYR = Lancashire & Yorkshire Railway
M&GN = Midland & Great Northern Railway
MR = Midland Railway
NBR = North British Railway
NER = North Eastern Railway
NLR = North London Railway
SECR = South East & Chatham Railway
SER = South Eastern Railway
SR = Southern Railway

Italics

Text shown in italics (in the 'Details' column) is that which appears on the model being described in addition to the names and numbers shown in the 'Name/Number' column. We have tried to get these right but there are many cases where we did not have access to a model or picture and in those cases we had to make calculated guesses.

Motors

All locomotive models are electrically powered unless otherwise stated.
c/w = clockwork

Prices

Unless otherwise stated, the first price column, in tables that have them, gives the value of a 'good unboxed' example and the second column 'near mint and boxed'. In the case of train packs the value quoted is for the complete pack i.e., locomotive and coaches/wagons.

* An asterisk in the second price column indicates that the model cannot be found in mint solo boxed form (possibly because it comes from a boxed set) and so the price of a mint unboxed one is given.

NPG = No Price Given. This is used where we have no idea of the likely price a model would sell for.

(see also separate section on Determining Value – The Impossible Task!)

Detail

The absence of detail in the description of a model is not evidence that the detail is not carried by the model. Furthermore, a feature may be mentioned on one model but not on another that also carries it. Information is provided only where it is felt that it may be helpful.

Listing order

The listing of models is not always done in the same way as, in each case, we have chosen an order of listing that best suits the subject and makes it easiest for you to find what you are looking for. The method of listing is explained at the start of each section.

Production dates

We have also adopted different systems for dating models but this has been determined by the level of information available. Wherever possible we have shown the span of years when a model was available but in some cases models were produced in batches and did not carry over from year to year. This is particularly common today as manufacturers can sell more models by constantly changing their livery or the number they carry. In these cases a single year applies i.e., the year the batch was released.

Beware! The existence of an illustration of a model in a catalogue is not evidence that it was available. However, in the case of some of the earlier toy trains we have had to use catalogue entries as a guide to availability as no other evidence exists.

Code 3 models

A Code 3 model is one that has been finished outside the factory by a secondary 'manufacturer'. These are often retailers who buy a quantity of a certain model and re-release it in a modified form. To count as a Code 3 it has to have been produced in the modified form in quantity and to a common specification. This means that one off modifications do not count. Batches of 50 upwards are more usual. These often have a numbered certificate to authenticate them and to indicate how many of them were modified. These have their own niche market.

'Not made'

This means that the model did not reach full production. However, it can be confusing when examples of the model turn up. This is usually because, prior to production starting, a small batch of samples was made as is commonly the case where the models are manufacture is in the Far East. These samples often find their way on

to the market where they can command a high price if the model did not go into full production. This is where it pays to know your subject so that you can recognise the genuine article when you see it.

Pre-production models

This is a similar situation except that the models rarely look like production models. They were samples of which one, two or even three were made to help the company to decide whether to manufacture the subject.

With completely new models, the sample may have been built by a model maker using plasticard or may be assembled from a proprietary model kit. It may even have been scratch built using some parts from an existing model in the range. Where it was a proposal to release an existing model in a new livery, a production model will have been taken off the production line and resprayed and detailed.

Pre-production samples were often finished on one side only and the writing and logos are often skilfully hand painted. One of the spare samples would have gone to the studio preparing the catalogue. Further models were often needed for testing but these did not need to be properly finished as it was the performance of the model that mattered.

Pre-production models (prototypes, samples and testing models) sometimes come on the market but the first problem is proving that they are what they claim to be. While many collectors would like to buy them, uncertainty about authenticity is a disincentive to do so. This is really an area of collecting which requires a lot of experience in handling examples in order to recognise the genuine from the false. Where the provenance is good they can fetch a high price and four figures have been quoted in some cases. Where there is no provenance, they may be purchased quite cheaply but there is a risk you could burn your fingers.

Scales and gauges

A useful guide and comparison chart appears on page 268.

Further reading

When toy train collecting was in its infancy, there was a dearth of information about manufacturers and model ranges with the result that any book, however simple, that included text or pictures about toy trains was pounced on by knowledge hungry collectors. Two such books were 'Older Locomotives (1900-42)' [ISBN 17-213208-8] by Peter Gomm and 'Recent Locomotives (1947-70)' [ISBN 17-213209-6] by Peter Randall. Both were published in 1970 by Thomas Nelson and Sons Ltd in their Troy Model Club Series for collectors and such was the demand for them that even libraries could not guarantee supplying you with a copy on loan.

While books on British manufacturers remained scarce, those on the international scene started to appear in the '70s. 1972 saw the release in Britain of the English language edition of Gustav Reder's 'Clockwork, Steam and Electric'. This is a classic study of early toy train making and is a must for anyone with an international interest in the subject. A better illustrated book with more of a British slant is 'A Century of Model Trains' [ISBN 0-517-184370] by Allen Levy and published in 1974 by Crescent Books. Another international book which is good for its mouth watering coloured photographs is Udo Becher's 'Early Tin Plate Model Railways' [ISBN 0-85242-669-0] which was published by Argus Books in 1980. A much more general history of toy manufacturing is the very detailed 'The Toy Collector' [ISBN 0-8015-7846-9] by Louis H Hertz and published in 1976 by Hawthorn Books Inc. of New York.

Books specifically for the British collector took a step forward with F.R.Gorham's compilation of extracts from Hornby catalogues published between 1927 and 1932. Titled 'Hornby Book of Trains' [ISBN 0-0902888-20-X] it was released by the Oxford Publishing Co. in 1973. This idea of using extracts from old publications was adopted by The Cranbourne Press Ltd. for their booklets. These were made up from Meccano Magazine and Tri-ang catalogue pages and included 'Main Line Ending' by Peter Randall (Hornby 0 Gauge), 'Hornby Dublo Trains 1938-1939' by Ronald Truin and 'A Short History of Tri-ang Railways' by Tony Stanford.

Little more was available for several years and then, suddenly, there was an explosion of publishing in the late '70s starting in 1977 with the excellent 'Collectors Guide to Model Railways' [ISBN 0-85242-529-5] by James Joyce. This remains, today, one of the best broad-brush studies of the British model railway industry, despite the fact that it needs bringing up to date. It was published by Argus books as, too, was 'Toyshop Steam' [ISBN 0-85242-583-X] by Basil Harley, which was released the following year.

That same year saw the release of the first volume of a series of books that was to set the benchmark for specialist books on individual subjects. I refer, of course, to The Hornby Companion Series by New Cavendish and edited by Allen Levy. Volume 1 'The Products of Binns Road - A General Survey' [ISBN 0-904568-06-7] by Peter Randall provided us with the first study of Meccano Ltd and, for the first time, included full colour reproductions of three catalogues. The series went on to cover individual toy ranges from this important company as well as their paperwork and publications. There were also compendia published for some of the volumes which provided check lists of products made.

Volume 2 of The Hornby Companion Series was devoted to Meccano super models but Volume 3 was the much awaited 'Hornby Dublo Trains 1938-1964' [ISBN 0-904568-18-0] by Michael Foster. I distinctly remember the excitement with which I waited for my volume to arrive and then shutting myself away for a week to study it. It was a book which more than anything else encouraged me to become a writer for New Cavendish Books.

Volume 4 was Mike & Sue Richardson's famous treatise on Dinky Toys and this was followed by what I think is the best written book in the whole series. It is of course Volume 5 'The Hornby O Gauge System' [ISBN 0-904568-35-0] by Chris & Julie Graebe. A better researched and illustrated book would be hard to find. The series went to seven volumes plus five compendia and several of the books have run to second editions.

A magazine popular at the time among collectors was the 'History of Model & Miniature Railways' which built up into two bound volumes. The close-up photography for this was to spawn a number of look-alike books one of which was 'The World of Model Trains' [ISBN 0-86124-009-X] edited by Patrick Whitehouse and Allen Levy and published by Bison Books in 1978.

A remarkable book of this period was the 'International Model Railways Guide' [ISBN 3-920877-16-0] which was a German publication, written in three languages (German, French and English). This was, in effect, a large catalogue of model railway manufacturers around the world illustrating in colour many (but not all) of the models available at the time (1978-79). I979 also saw the publication of 'Mechanical Toys' [ISBN 0-600-363-317] by Charles Bartholomew and published by Hamlyn, but this had only limited information about toy trains.

Of special interest to Tri-ang Hornby collectors was 'The Hornby Book of Trains 25 Year Edition' [ISBN 0-9506586-0-X] which was published in 1979. It was edited by S.W.Stevens-Stratten and chapters on everything from real trains to the manufacturing process at Margate were largely written by staff at the factory. The book was followed in 1983 by 'The Art of Hornby' [ISBN 0-7182-3037-X], written by Richard Lines, which looked at catalogue and leaflet designs by Meccano Ltd for their Hornby Series and Hornby Dublo as well as for Tri-ang Hornby and Hornby Railways.

An important reference series started in 1980 was 'Cade's Locomotive Guide' [ISBN 0-905377-07-9] which was written by Dennis Lovett and Leslie Wood. This ran to three volumes [ISBN 0-905377-11-7] [ISBN 0-905377-15-X] and was later re-released in a combined volume. The aim of the series was to provide background information about the real locomotives that are the subjects of models. After each account there were details and photographs of relevant models.

By now articles on model railway collecting were beginning to appear in the model railway press although these remained few and far between. One exception was a series by Peter Gomm called 'Tinplate Topics' which was a regular feature in Model Railway News for several years and looked principally at Hornby 0 gauge. It was directly as a result of this that I considered writing

a series on the lesser scales and wrote to Railway Modeller with my idea. Having been turned down by them I approached Chris Leigh who was then editor of Model Railway Constructor and he was much more helpful offering me a regular slot which we called 'Collector's Corner'. This started in 1984 and ran for several years. Another attempt at a 'world catalogue' had come in 1983, this time in English, with the publication of 'The World Guide to Model Trains' [ISBN 0-7221-8824-2] which was compiled by Peter McHoy with the help of Chris Ellis and was published by Sphere Books Ltd.

A new major work appeared in 1984 when Roland Fuller's 'The Bassett-Lowke Story' [ISBN 0-904568-34-2] reached the shops. This excellent book, published by New Cavendish Books, contained a considerable number of archive photographs and is a valuable reference work. For quality coloured photographs, the series by Salamanda Books Ltd cannot be beaten. The volume called 'The Collector's All-Colour Guide to Toy Trains' [ISBN 1-85501-025-9] (1985) was compiled by Ron McCrindell and contains excellent pictures of many rare items; most of which are in superb condition having been drawn from several famous collections.

Now for three New Cavendish books from the early 1990s. The first of these looked at the whole field of British toy manufacturers and, although railway content was small when compared with the rest, the detail provided is so good that it is a 'must' for any toy collector's library. This is 'British Tin Toys' [ISBN 0-904568-86-5] by Marguerite Fawdry which was published in 1990 and it covers more than just tin toys!

The next is my own book 'Tri-ang Railways' [ISBN 0-904568-57-1] which New Cavendish Books published in 1993. It is the first in a trilogy about the Rovex company better known today as Hornby Hobbies. This first volume deals with the years from 1950 to 1965 when the product was known as Tri-ang Railways.

This was followed the next year by Tony Matthewman's beautiful volume 'The History of Trix H0/00 Model Railways in Britain' [ISBN 0-904568-76-8]. For me the book comes a close second to Chris & Julie Graebe's Hornby 0

(continues overleaf)

Gauge book for the excellence of its research and presentation. This, like 'Tri-ang Railways' (and its sequel), was produced in landscape format to match the Hornby Companion Series.

A small book, also released in 1994, was the Shire Album Series No.255 'Toy Trains' [ISBN 0-7478-0087-1] by David Salisbury. And another book published that year was 'Model Trains - The Collector's Guide' [ISBN 1-85422-780-7] by Chris Ellis. Published by Magna Books, it contains an easy to follow history and some good photographs.

1996 brought with it Jeff Carpenter's privately produced volume 'Bing's Table Railway' [ISBN 1-900-897-008], published by Diva Publishing, which provides not only a full account of the small Bing system but also the histories of many other miniature trains such as those by Karl Bub, Distler and Jep Mignon.

November 1993 had seen the launch of Model Railway Enthusiast which was a model railway magazine with some articles for collectors. In February 1998 content for collectors was raised to 50% of the magazine and in November 1999 to 100% when the magazine was renamed Model Railway Collector.

1998 saw the release of my second book 'Tri-ang Hornby' [ISBN 1-872727-58-1], again by New Cavendish Books, and also the first edition of 'Ramsay's British Model Trains Catalogue' [ISBN 0-9528352-3-1], published by Swapmeet Publications. In 1999, Irwell Press published Steven Knight's excellent study of Kitmaster kits in 'Let's Stick Together' [ISBN 1-871608-90-2]. It was also in 1999 that 'Wenman Joseph Bassett-Lowke' [ISBN 1-900622-01-7] was published by Rail Romances who at the same time released a video recording based on films taken by W.J.Bassett-Lowke, including footage in the factory. The book had been written by his niece Janet Bassett-Lowke.

Finally, in 2000, the first of a series of planned volumes called 'A History of Locomotive Kits' [ISBN 0-9537720-0-4] by Robert Forsythe was published by Amlor Publishing. This covers kits by K's, Nu-Cast, Wills and South Eastern Finecast.

Thus from a dearth of books in 1970, today we have quite a library to choose from and there is every indication that the choice will continue to grow.

D & J Fairs

Promotors of
MAJOR TOY and TRAIN COLLECTORS FAIRS NATIONWIDE

See the Collectors Press for full details
of our forthcoming events at:

LONDON • EXETER • DONCASTER
HARROGATE • NEC BIRMINGHAM • DONINGTON PARK

Visit our website at www.d-jfairs.co.uk or send a S.A.E. for a programme of events to JOHN WEBB at the address below

JULIE & JOHN WEBB

Toy and Train Fairs Nationwide

Now in our 14th year of promoting Toy and
Train Collectors Fairs for your enjoyment.
We advertise in all the Collectors Press for our events at:

BEVERLEY • BISHOPS STORTFORD • BRENTWOOD
BURY St EDMUNDS • CLEETHORPES • COLCHESTER
HALIFAX • HEYWOOD • HUDDERSFIELD • HUNTINGDON
IPSWICH • KINGS LYNN • LINCOLNSHIRE • MANSFIELD
MORLEY • NEWMARKET • NORWICH • SPALDING
RUSHDEN • WISBECH • WYMONDHAM • YORK

For more information and a full programme of events send a S.A.E. to:

JOHN WEBB, Rosebank House, Bardney, Lincs., LN3 5UF
or Tel/Fax 01526 398198

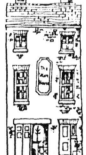

LACY SCOTT AND KNIGHT

The largest regular diecast, tinplate, lead and steam model auctions in the country

Examples of items which have successfully passed through our auctions

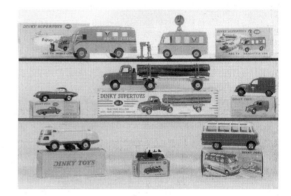

- Four major sales per year of 1,500 lots
- Free on-site parking
- Payments to vendors within 10 working days
- Refreshments on sale days

Auction Centre
10 Risbygate Street, Bury St Edmunds, Suffolk, IP33 3AA
Tel: 01284 748600   Fax: 01284 748620
Catalogue website: www.lsk.co.uk

When replying to advertisements, please mention 'Ramsay's Catalogue'.

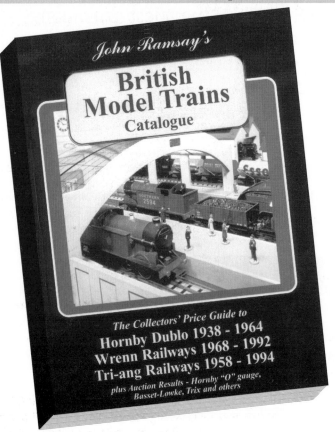
When replying to advertisements, please mention 'Ramsay's Catalogue'.

Ace Trains

History

Ace Trains originated from an original arrangement to produce a limited run of electric Hornby replica 4-4-4 tank locomotives in Southern livery - the colour scheme most in demand with collectors. The parties to this arrangement were Ron Budd (the importer of Darstead Märklin style coaches) and Andries Grabowsky who acquired the Darstead business in the early 1990s.

This arrangement did not come to fruition and Allen Levy agreed to take on and expand the 4-4-4 project which was designated E/1. A company named Alchem Trains Ltd was formed in 1995 which commenced trading under the name ACE Trains.

The production and assembly of the E/1, of which both AC and DC versions were made, was initially concentrated in Taiwan and later at the Grabowsky family factory in Madras, India. The E/2, a 4-4-2 derivative of the E/1, was developed in DC only with an isolating switch allowing it to stand on the track without picking up power. The locomotives were designed to run on all types of 3-rail tinplate standard track including that by Hornby, Märklin, Bing, JEP and MDF and have an interchangeable rear coupling.

The C/1 coach range, covering more railway systems than any former manufacturer, came on the market in 1999. The tin printing for this range was carried out by Cyril Luff in Wales who produced some of the last Hornby 0 gauge and Hornby Dublo tin printed sheets. A five-car Merseyside Express set became the last lithographed toy train product of the twentieth century. The Company introduced the first of a range of EMU units early in 2000.

Ace Trains identified a gap in the market and have been successfully filling it. They have established a market not only in the UK but around the world and have agents in a number of countries. What then of the future? A small batch of clerestory roofed LNER (ex-Great Eastern) C/1's and a similar batch of LMS (ex-Midland) C/1's is soon to be delivered. A clerestory roof for existing GWR C/1 stock will also be available in sets of 3. These will be 2001 releases. Future plans include a series of six coupled locomotives and a range of tankers and other goods vehicles. We look forward to including these in future editions of this catalogue.

Further Reading

The product range is too new to have had a book written about it but there have been articles in the HRCA Journal from February 1996 onwards. There have also been articles in Classic Toy Trains (USA), British Railway Modelling and Trains RM (Japan).

Locomotives

Motors – About 10 locos were supplied with 12V DC motors then the Company standardised their DC motor at 24 v. As all Ace Trains locomotives run on 6 - 20V and draw 0.7amp the distinction became academic.

Couplings – All couplings (on locos and coaches) are replaceable except the front hook on the LMS and Metropolitan EMU's and the front buffer couplings on the E/1 and E/2 locos. The southern EMU units have replaceable couplings throughout but the coaches are without buffers as per the originals.

Ace Trains GWR 4-4-4T (EGW/1) [table 1]. (Ace Trains)

Ace Trains LMS 4-4-4T (ELM/1) [table 1]. (Ace Trains)

A4 COMING DOWN THE LINE
2001 ...the best gauge O tinplate trains made today

A4 Pacific
'Dwight D Eisenhower',
'Mallard' etc.
(available 2001)

All EMU sets have remote control in DC and manual forward/ reverse in AC. All sets with isolating switches

E/1 Caledonian
(sold out)
C/1 CR coach
(sets £165 & singles £58.75)

C/1 rear lighting sets available October 2000 £10.95

CIE/Met interurban 4 car set £295

CIE/LMS interurban 3 car set £295

For release in first half of 2001 the ACE E/3 0-6-0 and tender in all the big four versions and pre grouping liveries including SJDR, SECR.LBSCR, CR. NBR. and GER. BR versions of SR, LMS. LNER, GWR and ex LNER/ NBR all in black with BR Lion symbol. All locos for AC/DC operation as above.

All our locos and rolling stock have an interchangeable coupling facility. Details of second half 2001 releases available in December 2000

Southern 3 car EMU available before Xmas 2000 £315

Merseyside Express 5 car set £300

Full range of French E/1 locomotives and coaches available • French E/1 4-4-4 locos in Etat, Nord. PO and Est liveries available

ESSO

ACE Series I Tankers

A Series of 21 different liveries and variations will be issued during 2001 at regular intervals

acetrains
P.O.Box 2985
London W11 2WP
Tel: 020 7727 1592
Fax: 020 7792 4029
Send for colour catalogue £3.00
All major credit cards accepted
ACE Trains is a registered trade mark

VISA MasterCard

All prices exclude shipping and insurance. Canadian distribution via Britannia Models Vancouver Canada

Email: trainsw11@aol.com   Web: www.acetrains.com

Locomotives

Cat.No.	Name / Number	Colour	Details	Years	£	£

1.   4-4-4 Tank Engine   This model is based on the No.2 Tank Engine in the pre-war Hornby Series, which went out of production in 1929. The original models were available only with a clockwork mechanism but the E/1 locomotives by Ace Trains have 20v electric mechanisms with remote control in AC/DC.   ** Also in DC only with isolating switch.

Cat.No.	Name / Number	Colour	Details	Years	£	£
ESB/1	E492 ***	black	*Southern*, gloss or matt **	96	NPG	270
ESG/1	B604 ***	green	*Southern*, gloss or matt **	96	NPG	280
ELM/1	4-4-4	maroon	*LMS*, gloss or matt **	96	NPG	300
EMB/1	4-4-4	black	*LMS*, gloss or matt	96	NPG	300
ELG/1	4-4-4	green	*LNER*, gloss or matt	96	NPG	280
ELB/1	4-4-4	black	*LNER*, matt	96	NPG	300
EGW/1	7202	green	*Great* (crest) *Western*, gloss or matt	96	NPG	300
ECR/1	4-4-4	blue	*C* (crest) *R*, gloss or matt **	96	NPG	350
EMR/1	108	maroon	*Metropolitan*, gloss or matt	96	NPG	265
EET/1	2-2-2	black	*ETAT*, matt	96	NPG	293
EPO/1	2-2-2	grey	*PO*, matt	96	NPG	293
EPL/1	-	red	*PLM*, matt	96	NPG	350
END/1	-	brown	*Nord*, matt	96	NPG	293
END/1	-	green	*Nord*, matt	96	NPG	293
EES/1	-	black	*EST*, matt	96	NPG	293
EES/2	-	brown	*EST*, matt	96	NPG	293
ENZ/1	-	black	*NZR*, matt	96	NPG	325

*** 44 of the E/1 series in Southern livery were given factory produced names at the request of customers (1996/97).

2.   4-4-2 Tank Engine   The E/2 series of locomotives are DC only and are fitted with a neutral switch allowing them to stand stationary on live track.

Cat.No.	Name / Number	Colour	Details	Years	£	£
E/2LB	22	brown	*LB&SCR*, gloss	98	NPG	300
E/2S	2001	green	*Southern*, gloss	98	NPG	300
E/2LN	40	black	*L&NWR*, gloss	98	NPG	325
E/2LM	6822	maroon	*LMS*, gloss	98	NPG	250
E/2BR	32085	black	*British Railways*, gloss	98	NPG	295
E/2NZR	-	green	*NZR*, gloss, Sp Edn (Railmaster Exports, NZ)	98	NPG	325

3.   3-Car Electric Units   All units comprise a powered motor coach (DC only) with 3rd class accommodation, a first class coach and a dummy 3rd class motor coach. All are tin printed and have punched out windows.

Cat.No.	Name / Number	Colour	Details	Years	£	£
C1E/LM	Broad Street - Richmond	maroon	*LMS* 3-car unit	99	NPG	295
C1E/Met	Baker Street - Harrow	brown	Metropolitan 4-car unit	99	NPG	295
C1E/S	1528/1664/1783	green	*Southern* 3-car unit *V* and *L* route boards carried	00	NPG	295

Ace Trains BR 4-4-2T (E/2BR) [table 2]. (Ace Trains)

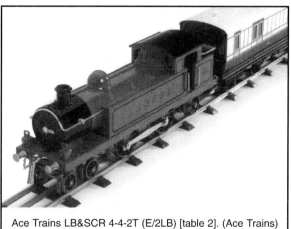

Ace Trains LB&SCR 4-4-2T (E/2LB) [table 2]. (Ace Trains)

Coaches

4.   35cm Non-Corridor   Tin printed. Some of the French coaches have clerestory roofs. Colours: 'aub' = aubergine, 'choc' = chocolate.

C/1	-	maroon	*LMS*	99	NPG	59
C/1	21397	teak	*LNER* all 1st	99	NPG	59
C/1	1948	teak	*LNER* all 3rd	99	NPG	59
C/1	21508	teak	*LNER* brake 3rd	99	NPG	59
C/1	-	choc + cream	*GWR*	99	NPG	59
C/1	-	green	*Southern*	99	NPG	59
C/1	-	brown	Metropolitan	99	NPG	59
C/1	-	brown+white	*LBSCR*	99	NPG	59
C/1	-	plum+ white	Caledonian	99	NPG	59
C/1	M43277	maroon	BR composite	99	NPG	59
C/1	M43279	maroon	BR all 3rd	99	NPG	59
C/1	M43278	maroon	BR brake 3rd	99	NPG	59
C/1	-	brown+white	LNWR	99	NPG	59
C/1	-	maroon	NZR, Sp Edn (Railmaster Exports, NZ)	99	NPG	59
C/1F	-	green	*Etat*, sold in sets of 3	99	NPG	175
C/1F	-	aub + black	Est, sold in sets of 3	99	NPG	175
C/1F	-	grn/brn + black	*Est*, sold in sets of 3	99	NPG	175
C/1F	-	brn+blk	*Est*, sold in sets of 3	99	NPG	175
C/1F	-	green	*PO*, sold in sets of 3	99	NPG	175
C/1F	-	green	*Nord*, sold in sets of 3	99	NPG	175
C/1F	-	green	*SNCF*, I and II class coaches available, sold in sets of 3	99	NPG	175
C/1 Bge	-	khaki	French outline	99	NPG	55

The actual price of the coaches is £58.75 each or £165 for three consisting of a 1st, 3rd and brake 3rd. A special HRCA 30th Anniversary set was done priced £50 per coach or £150 the set of three.

5.   Merseyside Express Sets   These coaches have domed roofs and litho silver windows. They have Merseyside Express name boards in the printing design except where indicated.

C2	4195	maroon	*LMS* composite	99	NPG	60
C2	4195	maroon	*LMS* all 3rd	99	NPG	60
C2	4799	maroon	*LMS* Restaurant Car	99	NPG	60
C2	4183	maroon	*LMS* all 1st	99	NPG	60
C2	26133	maroon	*LMS* brake 3rd	99	NPG	60
C2	4195	maroon	*LMS* composite, no name boards	99	NPG	60
C2	4195	maroon	*LMS* all 3rd, no name boards	99	NPG	60
C2	26133	maroon	*LMS* brake 3rd, no name boards	99	NPG	60

Merseyside Express coaches are also sold as boxed sets of 5 for £300.

Ace Trains LMS 3-car electric unit (C1E/LM)
[table 3]. (Ace Trains)

Ace Trains LMS Merseyside Express coach set (C2)
[table 5]. (Ace Trains)

WALLIS & WALLIS

EST. 1928

WEST STREET AUCTION GALLERIES, LEWES, SUSSEX, ENGLAND BN7 2NJ
TEL: +44 (0)1273 480208 FAX: +44 (0)1273 476562

Britain's Specialist Auctioneers of Diecast Toys, Model Railways, Tin Plate Toys & Models.

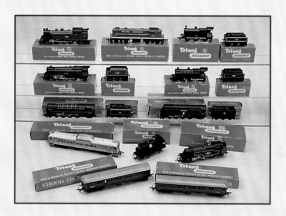

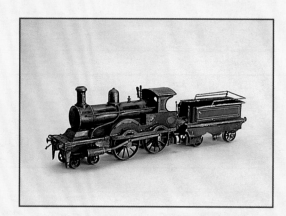

We hold 8 regular Toy Auctions every year at approximately 6 week intervals. Each sale includes railway, diecast, figures etc. A fully illustrated catalogue is available, price £6.50 incl. postage worldwide, and full subscription rates and entry forms are available on request.

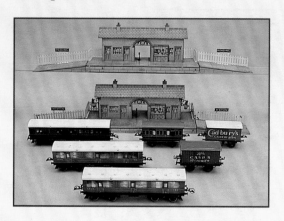

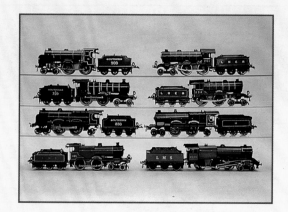

Ten back number catalogues, with prices realised, are available price £20.00, or send for a single sample catalogue, price £2.00.

email: grb@wallisandwallis.co.uk   web site: http://www.wallisandwallis.co.uk

O Gauge

Hornby No.1
loco with nickel
plated footplate
c1920
[table 10]

Bassett-Lowke 2265
'Princess Elizabeth'
c1932
[table 32]

Hornby Compound 1185
with early
unlined tender
c1929
[table 16]

Bassett-Lowke 6100
'Royal Scot'
with Fowler tender
c1929
[table 67]

Bassett-Lowke
Jubilee 5701
'Conqueror'
c1936
[table 69]

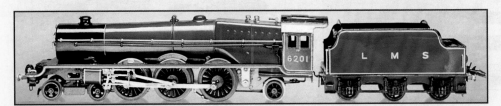

Hornby Princess
Royal 6201
'Princess Elizabeth'
c1938
[table 19]

Bassett-Lowke
Princess Coronation 6232
'Duchess of Montrose'
c1939
[table 79]

Pictures supplied by Barry Potter Auctions.

1. Hornby No.2 engine shed.
2. Hornby No.2 signal gantry.
3. Hornby No.1 footbridge without signals.

4. Hornby No.1E electric lamp standard.
5. Bassett-Lowke LMS Stanier Mogul LMS 2945 [table 56].
6. Bassett-Lowke standard 0-6-0 LNER 156 [table 54].

7. Hornby No.1 tank engine GWR 4560 c1931 [table 9a].
8. Hornby No.2 special tank engine GWR 2221 c1936 [table 15].
9. Hornby No.3 tender locomotive GWR 4073 'Caerphilly Castle' c1936 [table 17].
10. Hornby No.2 special tender locomotive LNER 201 'Bramham Moor' c1936 [table 16].

11. Hornby No.3 tender locomotive LMS 6100 'Royal Scot' c1936 [table 17].
12. Hornby No.2 Pullman car c1930 with small coat of arms [table 4b].
13. Hornby No.2 special Pullman composite 'Verona' c1935 [table 3c].
14. Hornby No.2-3 special Pullman 'Zenobia' c1929 [table 3c].
15. Hornby No.3 Pullman c1927 with large coat of arms [table 4b].

Pictures supplied by Wallis & Wallis Auctions, Lewes.

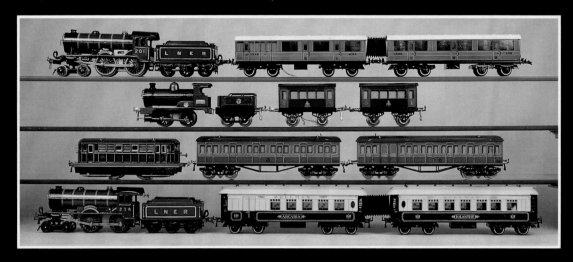

Bassett-Lowke

History

Wenman Joseph Bassett-Lowke was born in December 1877 and was a member of the boiler making family, J.T.Lowke & Co Ltd. After the death of Tom Lowke, his wife had married one Absalom Bassett who adopted her son Joseph Tom Lowke. He got on well with his stepfather and when he married and had three sons of his own he gave them all 'Bassett' as their middle name. All three sons, however, grew up using the surname Bassett-Lowke. Wenman, for some reason took the name Whynne but was often referred to simply as 'WJ'.

Whynne Bassett-Lowke trained in the family business but wanted to strike out on his own. With his father's book keeper, Harold Franklin, he founded his own model engineering company in 1899 while still serving an apprenticeship with his father. This became a limited company in 1910 with a factory base in Northampton. The Company was never large although its output was considerable. This was achieved by contracting out work to other companies that Bassett-Lowke became associated with. One of these was Winteringham Ltd, which had been established by George Winteringham in 1908 as a subsidiary, and this became Bassett-Lowke's main manufacturer.

In 1900 WJ had been to the Paris Exhibition and been much impressed by the products of German manufacturers such as Märklin, Carette and Bing. A year later, all three had agreed to manufacture models to Bassett-Lowke's design for the latter to sell in the UK. The first supply arrived in 1901 and the first locomotive was a gauge 3 model of a LNWR 4-4-0 named 'Black Prince'. WJ supplemented the supplies he received from Germany with models built in his limited facilities although, initially, these were mainly freelance subjects. By 1904 a range of 40 locomotives were being offered!

The German supplies ceased during the First World War but Bing and Märklin both produced models to Bassett-Lowke's requirements after the war. However, by now, anti-German feelings were affecting sales and Bassett-Lowke Ltd were pushed into manufacturing more themselves at Northampton and through their associated companies such as those of Stuart Turner and John Claret

Model railways in gauges 0, 1, 2 and 3 were only part of the Bassett-Lowke business. They also made stationary engines, model ships and miniature railways. A man who came closely linked with Bassett-Lowke for many years was Henry Greenly and he was responsible for the design of some of their engines. Another famous name associated with Bassett-Lowke was the model maker E.W.Twining who illustrated catalogues for them and later joined the Company.

Year by year the Bassett-Lowke catalogue grew and was split into different interest sections. Besides a large range of railway locomotives, rolling stock, accessories, track and sets being offered, there were the drawings and parts to enable you to construct your own models in one of a number of gauges. Models were also available with a choice of power units; namely steam, clockwork or electric. The range of locomotives available before and immediately after the First World War was considerable and some were available for many years. Amongst the favourites were the Precursor tank, 'George the Fifth', 'Sydney', Deeley

---

Milestones

1899	Bassett-Lowke sets up his company with Harry Franklin.
1899	B-L produces his first mail order catalogue at the age of just 22.
1900	Paris Exhibition and B-L enters into an import agreements with Stefan Bing and George Carette.
1901	B-L takes delivery of his first supply from Bing.
1901	Henry Greenly appointed Consulting Engineer and Designer to B-L.
1902	Track developed by George Winteringham.
1902	First comprehensive catalogue produced containing railway items.
1905	First exhibition stand at the Model engineering Exhibition in London.
1905	Model Railway Handbook first published.
1907	'Lowko' motor introduced.
1908	Winteringham Ltd formed as a subsidiary.
1908	B-L opens his first shop in Holborn, London.
1910	Bassett-Lowke Ltd becomes a public company.
1912	First Continental retail agency opens in Paris.
1919	Mass production plant installed for small gauge models.
1920-23	Wintringham's trademark appears on some items.
1922	Introduction of Bing Table Top Railway.
1922	Edinburgh shop opens.
1922	First American agency established in New York.
1924	Smallest model railway in the world made for Queen's dolls house.
1927	BDV gift coupon scheme sells 30,000 locos.
1927	Manchester shop opened.
1931	Robert Bindon Blood joins B-L, later to design many of the better models.
1932	Franz Bing emigrates to England.
1932	Trix Ltd founded in the UK with WJ Bassett- Lowke as a Director.
1935	Launch of Trix Twin Railway.
1941	Founding of Precision Models Ltd.
1946	Reappearance of models after the war.
1949	50th Anniversary celebrations.
1950	New BR livery appears on a B-L locomotive.
1953	Death of W.J.Bassett-Lowke.
1963	Last Bassett-Lowke catalogue released.
1965	Bassett-Lowke Ltd ceases trading.
1968	Bassett-Lowke Railways produce some prototype models.
2000	Corgi Classics re-launch the range.

Compound (which was also available as a kit from 1909), GNR Atlantic and the Great Central locomotive 'Sir Sam Fay'. In the early 1920s, Bassett-Lowke and Henry Greenly were instrumental in introducing 00 scale to Britain in the form of the Bing Table Top Railway. This started life as a clockwork system but was soon available with electric motors. In the mid 1930s they made a home at Northampton for the refugee Trix system, also from Germany.

A different approach to marketing had been made in 1927 through Godfrey Phillips B.D.V.cigarettes, when sons were encouraged to get their fathers to smoke themselves to death to collect enough tokens for the Bassett-Lowke model of the 'Duke of York'! Bassett-Lowke made 30,000 locomotives for this promotion. It was in October this year that Bassett-Lowke opened a shop at 28 Corporation Street, Manchester.

As the years passed the demand for the larger gauges fell away and 0 gauge became the mainstay of Bassett-Lowke Ltd. Likewise, interest in electric traction grew and that in steam and clockwork lessened especially after the Second World War.

Some of the finest and most famous Bassett-Lowke locomotives were built during the late 1920s and 1930s; many designed by Robert Bindon Blood. Popular subjects included 'Flying Scotsman', 'Royal Scot', 'Lord Nelson', a Jubilee, 'Princess Elizabeth', a Duchess, a range of A4s with different names, a Midland Compound, the 0-6-0 and 0-4-0 Standard tanks and, of course, the much loved Moguls.

Production ceased during the Second World War and restarted sometime after the cessation of hostilities. The new British Railways livery made its appearance on a Bassett-Lowke model in 1950 and, the following year, the 4-4-0 'Princess Elizabeth' was replaced by 'Prince Charles'. Notable post-war locomotives were the Rebuilt Royal Scot, 'Spitfire' (Castle), 'Britannia', the Classes 5, 8F and 9F and 'Deltic'.

The final catalogue was published in 1963 and trading ceased in 1965; although there was an unsuccessful attempt at reviving the Company in the late 1960s. The name and intellectual assets of the company were later acquired by Corgi; a fact which provided an interesting link with the past. Corgi had been a product of Mettoy, a company which started life in 1933 in the basement and ground floor of the Winteringham factory. At the time Winteringham Ltd was, of course, the production arm of Bassett-Lowke Ltd!

At the 2000 British Toy and Hobbies Fair at Olympia, Corgi Classics launched the first of a new range of Bassett-Lowke 0 gauge locomotives and the subject chosen for the relaunch was a steam powered Mogul. We wait with interest to see how successful these will be.

Further Reading
The standard work is 'The Bassett-Lowke Story' by Roland Fuller and published by New Cavendish Books (ISBN 0-904568-34-2). This is thought to be out of print but available through the public library service. A recently published book of value to researchers is 'Wenman Joseph Bassett-Lowke' by his niece Janet Bassett-Lowke and published by Rail Romances (ISBN 1-900622-01-7). This same publisher has also released a video tape showing footage taken by WJ himself which includes factory scenes.

Collectors Club
The Bassett-Lowke Society caters for those who collect and operate Bassett-Lowke models. The Society publishes a quarterly magazine called 'Lowko News' and organises events to which members may take their stock to run. For further information about the Society, ring 01359 251127.

Locomotives (O Gauge)
Dates – The dates when models were available are very difficult to determine so long after the event and should not be taken too seriously. They also ignore breaks in availability during the two world wars when the Company was engaged in war work.

Prices – There is very limited information about prices of Bassett-Lowke models except through auctions. Where auction prices are known, the latest is given but it should be remembered that some of these are now 4 or 5 years old. These will be added to as more information becomes available. The two prices show the range for a model in good condition.

Codes – These codes are peculiar to this section:
(F) = Freelance design. Also, 'Standard' normally implies freelance.
(B) = Made by Bing for Bassett-Lowke.
(C) = Made by Carette for Bassett-Lowke.
(L) = Made by Leeds Model Company for B-L.
(M) = Made by Märklin for Bassett-Lowke.
(H) = Made by Hunt for Bassett-Lowke.
litho = lithographed (printed as opposed to painted) locomotives .

Listing – The models have been separated into gauges (only gauge 0 is included in this edition) and then separate tables have been prepared for each model type. The tables are arranged so that tank engines are listed first followed by tender engines, diesels and electrics. The smallest engines (judged by the number of driving wheels (or large wheels)) are listed first starting with 0-4-0s and finishing with 2-10-0s. If you are unsure what type of locomotive you have, check the running number on the side of the locomotive or its tender against the number key and it will tell you in which table to look. Models made for Bassett-Lowke by Bing, Carette, Märklin, Leeds and Hunt which are included in these lists may be identified by a letter code as indicated above.

Loco Search

In order to help you find your Bassett-Lowke 0 Gauge locomotive, we have listed below, in the left column, the numbers that appear on the side of models (running numbers) and, in the right column, the table in the following locomotive list where you will find the model.

Loco No.	Table	Loco No.	Table	Loco No.	Table	Loco No.	Table	Loco No.	Table	Loco No.	Table
1	88	483	40	1190	39	2838	72	5071	73	8851	51
10	3	504	9	1425	49	2848	72	5320	35	8872	50
11	12	504	42	1442	49	2871	62	5374	13	8937	13
23	90	504	43	1448	53a	2945	56	5524	62	13000	55
25	3	513	34	1456	54	3064	93	5552	69	13007	56
33	57	513	35	1652	94	3400	39	5573	69	41109	39
36	3	601	41	1864	57	3410	44	5600	66	41125	39
41	10	650	24	1902	33	3433	44a	5701	69	41611	13
44	10	773	51	1927	31	3536	20	5712	69	41613	13
45	9	773	76	1930	31	3611	9	5765	15	42603	21
63	3	850	75	1931	31	3611	18	6000	74	42608	21
73	13	851	62	2066	58	3800	45	6027	74	42980	56
77	37	864	60	2241	11	3801	45	6100	19	43871	54
78	13	866	60	2265	32	4072	53	6100	67	45126	71
78	16	903	61	2350	48	4079	73	6105	19	45295	62
88	3	910	47	2495	62	4256	54	6200	77	46100	68
89	12	930	52	2509	81	4331	59	6201	77	46232	79
94	17	947	13	2510	81	4390	42	6202	77	48209	85
100	2	955	26	2511	81	4420	25	6220	78	60103	80
101	2	982	57	2512	81	4431	59	6225	78	62078	32a
103	80	999	30	2524	20	4460	51	6232	79	62136	32a
112	1	1000	38	2526	20	4460	63	6285	28	62453	32a
142	36	1017	2	2531	20	4472	51	6311	7a	62759	28
211	1	1036	39	2536	20	4472	64	6508	51	63871	54
251	49	1063	39	2603	20	4472	80	6508	65	64193	54
298	14	1067	39	2603	21	4481	2	6560	94	68211	13
335	13	1082	39	2663	35	4489	81	6750	25	70000	82
433	13	1106	4	2664	35	4490	81	6810	10	92220	87
440	27	1108	39	2670	22	4498	81	7083	92		
441	5	1113	39	2700	55	4853	70	8851	25		

Bing for Bassett-Lowke c/w LB&SCR I2 Class 4-4-2T (4/0) [table 12] and c/w GWR Short Precursor 4-4-0T [table 9].
(Barry Potter Auctions)

Cat.No.	Name / Number	Colour	Details	Years	£	£
1.	**Class S14 0-4-0T** (Bing for Bassett-Lowke)					
53/0	112	black	LNWR, (steam)	21-29	NPG	NPG
53/0	112	green	GNR, (steam)	21-29	NPG	NPG
53/0	112	red	MR, (steam)	21-29	NPG	NPG
53/0	112	brown	NER, (steam)	21-29	NPG	NPG
53/0	112	blue	CR, (steam)	21-29	NPG	NPG
21/0	112	green	GNR, (c/w)	20-29	NPG	NPG
21/0	112	blue	CR, (c/w)	20-29	NPG	NPG
21/0	112	black	LNWR, (c/w)	20-29	NPG	NPG
21/0	112	crimson	MR, (c/w)	20-29	NPG	NPG
21/0	112	green	GWR, (c/w)	20-29	350	550
21/0	112	crimson	*LMS*, (c/w)	24-29	NPG	NPG
21/0	112	green	*L&NER*, (c/w)	24-29	NPG	NPG
37/0	211	green	GNR, (elec)	20-29	NPG	NPG
37/0	211	black	LNWR, (elec)	20-29	NPG	NPG
37/0	211	blue	CR, (elec)	20-29	NPG	NPG
37/0	211	red	MR, (elec)	20-29	NPG	NPG
2.	**Peckett 0-4-0ST** (Carette for Bassett-Lowke)			?	NPG	NPG
3104/0	100	crimson	MR, (c/w)		NPG	NPG
3104/0	101	black	LNWR, (c/w)	07-09-?	350	500
3104/0	101	crimson	MR, (c/w)	07-09-?	350	500
3104/0	101	green	GNR, (c/w)	07-?	450	600
3104/0	1017	green	(c/w)	24-34	250	300
3104/0	1017	green	(elec)	24-34	450	550
	4481	green	(elec)	24-34	300	400
3.	**Standard Tank 0-4-0T**					
	10	black	*LMS*, (DC elec)	37-?	250	310
	25	black	*LMS*, litho (elec)	37-?	NPG	NPG
4730/0	25	black	*LMS*, litho (c/w)	37-?	NPG	NPG
4730/0	36	black	*LNER*, litho (c/w)	37-?	NPG	NPG
4730/0	36	black	*LMS*, litho (c/w)	37-?	150	200
	36	black	*LNER*, litho (elec)	37-?	NPG	NPG
	36	black	*LMS*, litho (elec)	37-?	250	400
4730/0	63	black	*Southern*, litho (c/w)	37-?	NPG	NPG
	63	black	*Southern*, litho (elec)	37-?	NPG	NPG
	88	green	*LNER*, (DC elec)	37-?	NPG	NPG
	88	black	*LNER*, (DC elec)	37-?	250	300
4.	**Class 11XX Class Dock Tank 0-4-0T**					
	1106	green	*GWR* (only about 3 made) (elec)	61-63	NPG	NPG
5.	**Class 0 Passenger Tank 0-4-4T** (Bing for Bassett-Lowke)					
	441	green	*NER*, (c/w)	14-19	NPG	NPG
6.	**GNR Suburban Tank 0-4-4T** (Märklin for Bassett-Lowke)					
	?	green	*GNR*, (c/w)	07-?	NPG	NPG
7.	**Class M7 Tank 0-4-4T** (Bing for Bassett-Lowke)					
	109	green	LSWR, (c/w)	09-13	700	850
7a.	**2-4-2T** (Bing for Bassett-Lowke)					
	3611	green	*GWR*, (c/w)	11-13	1800	2000

Märklin for Bassett-Lowke electric LMS 4MT 2-6-4 tank (913/0)
[table 20]. (Barry Potter Auctions)

Bassett-Lowke steam Enterprise Express 4-4-0 (6690/0)
[table 28]. (unknown)

Bing for Bassett-Lowke c/w S14 0-4-0T (21/0) [table 1].
(Barry Potter Auctions)

Carette for Bassett-Lowke c/w
Peckett 0-4-0ST (3104/0) [table 2].
(Barry Potter Auctions)

8. 4-4-0T (Freelance) (Bing for Bassett-Lowke)

		green	*GNR*, (c/w)	20-26	NPG	NPG
23593/0		black	*L&NWR*, (c/w)	20-26	NPG	NPG
		red	*MR*, (c/w)	20-26	NPG	NPG
		blue	*CR*, (c/w)	20-26	NPG	NPG
		green	*GWR*, (c/w)	20-26	NPG	NPG
		brown	*NBR*, (c/w)	20-26	NPG	NPG

9. Short Precursor Tank 4-4-0T (Bing for Bassett-Lowke)

	-	green	GNR, (c/w)	21-?	NPG	NPG
	-	blue	CR, (c/w)	21-?	NPG	NPG
	-	green	*Great Western*, (c/w)	21-?	400	500
	-	red	MR, (c/w)	21-?	NPG	NPG
	45	crimson	*LMS*, (c/w)	11-20	300	560
	504	green	*LNER*, (c/w)	?	500	860
	3611	black	*LNER*, 4-4-0T (c/w)	23-?	300	400

10. Precursor Tank 4-4-2T

	41	yellow	*M&GN*, (elec)	64	NPG	NPG
	44	black	*L&NWR*, (M)(c/w)	09-10	400	500
3101/0	44	black	*L&NWR*, (B) (c/w)	11-20	300	400
3101/0	44	black	*L&NWR*, (c/w)	21-c23	250	350
	44	black	*L&NWR*, (elec)	21-c23	250	350
	44	black	*L&NWR*, (B) (elec)	11-20	300	400
	44	black	*L&NWR*, (M) (elec)	09-10?	400	500
	6810	black	*L&NWR*, (c/w)	21-?	NPG	NPG
3101/0 2/0	6810	crimson	*LMS*, (c/w)	25-c30	200	350
	6810	black	*L&NWR*, (elec)	21-c23	NPG	NPG
2/0 3101/0	6810	crimson	*LMS*, (elec)	25-c30	250	400

11. County Tank 4-4-2T

	2241	green	*GWR*, (one-off) (elec)	c50	NPG	NPG

12. LBSCR I2 Class 4-4-2T (Bing for Bassett-Lowke)

4/0	11	umber	*LB&SCR*, (c/w)	11-25	300	500
	11	umber	*LB&SCR*, (elec)	11-25	400	550
	89	umber	*LB&SCR*, (elec)	69	450	600

13. Standard Tank 0-6-0T (Freelance)

All the 0-6-0 standard tanks were lithographed. Some electric locomotives were fitted with a super reduction gear (40:1) for shunting and locos can be found with automatic (track operated) couplings. Likewise, some models are found with smoke units driven by a cam on the front axle. The LMS versions had a capuchon on the chimney. Pre-war electric models did not have key holes or control rod holes in the cab rear plate while post-war examples usually did, until late production orders. Catalogue number 4305/0 was used until 1940 for electric locos fitted with junior permag mechanisms.

3305/0	5374	black	LMS lined red (c/w)	33-38	200	300
4305/0	5374	black	LMS lined red (elec)	33-38	300	400
4305/0	5374	black	LMS lined red, Walschaerts valve gear (elec)	33-38	400	600
3305/0	61	black	*LMS* lined red (c/w)	38-50	200	300
5305/0	61	black	*LMS* lined red (elec)	38-50	300	400
5505/0	61	black	*LMS* lined red (elec 20V AC)	38-50	300	400
3305/0	78	black	*LMS* lined red (c/w)	38-50	200	300
5305/0	78	black	*LMS* lined red (elec)	38-50	300	400
3305/0	335	black	*LNER* lined red (c/w)	33-38	200	300

Cat.No.	Name / Number	Colour	Details	Years	£	£
5305/0	335	black	*LNER* lined red (elec)	33-38	300	400
3305/0	433	black	*LNER* lined red (c/w)	38-50	200	300
5305/0	433	black	*LNER* lined red (elec)	38-50	300	400
3305/0	947	black	*Southern* lined green (c/w)	38-50	300	350
5305/0	947	black	*Southern* lined green (elec)	38-50	350	450
3305/0	68211	black	BRb lined red (c/w)	51-67	200	300
5305/0	68211	black	BRb lined red (elec)	51-67	350	450
2305/0	68211	black	BRb lined red (2-rail elec)	51-67	350	450
3305/0	41611	black	BRb lined red (c/w)	51-67	200	300
5305/0	41611	black	BRb lined red (elec)	57-67	350	450
2305/0	41611	black	BRb lined red (2-rail elec)	51-67	350	450
-	41611	black	BRb lined red (2/3-rail elec) Nu-Scale***	57-67	350	450
3305/0	?	black	*LMS* lined red (c/w)	59-61	300	400
5305/0	?	black	*LMS* lined red (elec)	59-61	400	500
2305/0	?	black	*LMS* lined red (2-rail elec)	59-61	400	500
3305/0	?	black	*LNER* lined red (c/w)	59-63	300	400
5305/0	?	black	*LNER* lined red (elec)	59-63	400	500
2305/0	?	black	*LNER* lined red (2-rail elec)	59-63	400	500
-	41613-41617**	blue	Longmoor Military Railway (*LMR*) (elec)	?	400	700
5305/0	9033	black	*LNER* lined red (elec)	48-50	400	500

** used for training at Longmoor Military Railway. It is understood that they were numbered in sequence from 41613 to 41617.
*** Nu-Scale models were more detailed with lamp brackets and reprofiled wheels.

14. Ex-Burry Port Hudswell Clark 0-6-0T

Cat.No.	Name / Number	Colour	Details	Years	£	£
	298	black	prototype only (steam)	68	NPG	NPG

15. Class 57XX Pannier Tank 0-6-0PT (Hunt for Bassett-Lowke) (*** Made to order.)

Cat.No.	Name / Number	Colour	Details	Years	£	£
		green	*GWR*, (2/3 rail elec)	?-63	NPG	NPG
	5765	green	*GWR*, (elec)	50-63***	NPG	NPG

16. Class 3P Suburban Tank 2-6-2T

Cat.No.	Name / Number	Colour	Details	Years	£	£
	78	black	*LMS*, (c/w)	40-?	750	1000
	78	black	*LMS*, 2P (elec)	40-?	750	1000

17. LMS Prairie Tank 2-6-2T

Cat.No.	Name / Number	Colour	Details	Years	£	£
	94	black	*LMS*, (c/w)	?	2000	2750
	94	black	*LMS*, (elec AC)	?	2000	2750

18. Class 36XX Class 2-6-2T (Bing for Bassett-Lowke)

Cat.No.	Name / Number	Colour	Details	Years	£	£
	3611	green	GWR, (c/w)	11-13	1800	2600
	3611	green	GWR, (elec)	13-16	1800	2600

19. GWR 61XX Class Prairie 2-6-2T

Cat.No.	Name / Number	Colour	Details	Years	£	£
	6100	green	GWR, (elec 2/3 rail) hand built	55-63	750	1000
3609/0	6105	green	GWR, (c/w)	37-41?	750	1000
5609/0 A4609/0	6105	green	GWR, (elec AC and DC versions)	37-41?	750	1000

20. Stanier 4MT Tilbury Tank 2-6-4T

Cat.No.	Name / Number	Colour	Details	Years	£	£
913/0/C	2524	black	*LMS*, (M) (c/w)	35-?	2000	2300
913/0/D 913/0/A	2524	black	*LMS*, (M) (elec AC and DC versions)	35-?	2000	2600
913/0/C	2526	black	*LMS*, (M) (c/w)	c37	2500	3000
913/0/D 913/0/A	2526	black	*LMS*, (M) (elec AC and DC versions)	c37	2250	3000
913/0/C	2531	black	*LMS*, (M) (c/w)	c39	2000	2500
913/0/D 913/0/A	2531	black	*LMS*, (M) (elec AC and DC versions)	c39	2000	2500
913/0/C	2536	black	*LMS*, (M) (c/w)	c37	2000	2500
913/0/D 913/0/A	2536	black	*LMS*, (M) (elec AC and DC versions)	c37	2000	2500
913/0	2603	black	*LMS*, 4P (elec AC and DC versions)	40-c50	1000	2000
913/0/C	3536	?	*LMS*, 4P (c/w)	c36	NPG	NPG

21. LMS Stanier Suburban 4MT Tank 2-6-4T

Cat.No.	Name / Number	Colour	Details	Years	£	£
	2603	black	*LMS*, (c/w)	40-c50	1000	2000
	42603	black	BRb, (c/w)	c50-?	1200	1750
	42603	black	BRb, (elec)	c50-?	1500	1750
3618/0	42608	black	BRb, (c/w)	c52-c59	800	1200
5618/0	42608	black	BRb, (elec 2/3 rail)	c52-63	1000	1200

22. Bowen-Cooke 4-6-2T (Bing for Bassett-Lowke)

Cat.No.	Name / Number	Colour	Details	Years	£	£
	2670	black	*L&NWR*, (c/w)	14-?	750	1000

23. Der Adler 2-2-2 (Märklin for Bassett-Lowke)

	'Der Adler'		(elec)	35-?	NPG	NPG

24. Johnson Spinner 4-2-2 (Bing for Bassett-Lowke)

	650	crimson	*MR*, litho (c/w)	14-?	400	500
	650	red	*MR*, litho	14-?	400	500

25. Freelance 0-4-0

4734/0	4420	green	*GWR*, (B?) (c/w)	c28	NPG	NPG
4735/0	6750	crimson	*LMS*, (B?) (c/w)	c28	NPG	NPG
4732/0	8851	green	*LNER*, (B?) (c/w)	c28	NPG	NPG
4733/0			*Southern*, (B?) (c/w)	c28	NPG	NPG

26. Charles Dickens 2-4-0 (Märklin for Bassett-Lowke)

	955 'Charles Dickens'	black	*L&NWR*, (c/w)	03-?	1500	2000
	955 'Charles Dickens'	black	*L&NWR*, (elec)	03-?	1500	2000

27. Standard Express 4-4-0 (Freelance) (Bing for Bassett-Lowke)

48/0	440	green	*LSWR*, (steam)	22-29	NPG	NPG
48/0	440	blue	*CR*, (steam)	22-29	NPG	NPG
48/0	440	black	*L&NWR*, (steam)	22-26	NPG	NPG
48/0	440	red	*MR*, (steam)	22-29	NPG	NPG
48/0	440	green	*GNR*, (steam)	22-29	NPG	NPG
48/0	440	green	*GWR*, (steam)	22-29	NPG	NPG

28. Enterprise Express 4-4-0 (Freelance)

-	-		Loco kit (steam)	31-?	NPG	NPG
6690/0	6285	red	number on tender (steam)	31-40	NPG	NPG
6690/0	6285	green	number on tender (steam)	31-40	NPG	NPG
6690/0	6285	green	*LNER*, (steam)	31-40	200	350
6690/0	6285	black	(steam)	31-40	300	500
6690/0	62759	green	BRb, lined white (steam)	c54	250	300
6690/0	62759	blue	BRb lined orange (steam)	c54	350	400
6690/0	62759	black	BRb lined orange (steam)	c54	250	300

29. Bogie Express 4-4-0 (Freelance) (Bing for Bassett-Lowke)

61/250/0		green	*GWR*, (steam)	11	NPG	NPG
61/250/0		red	*LMS*, (steam)	24-26	NPG	NPG
61/250/0		green	*LNER*, (steam)	24-26	NPG	NPG
61/250/0		green	*GWR*, (steam)	24-26	NPG	NPG

30. Midland Compound 4-4-0 (Bing for Bassett-Lowke)

17/0	999	crimson	MR, (c/w)	10-30	600	750
-	999	crimson	MR, (steam)	10-30	400	450

31. Duke of York 4-4-0 (Freelance)

All examples of this model have a lithographed body. Only LMS versions carried a company designation. The 1927 locos had coupling rods with 'marine' Bing style big ends while later coupling rods were of a simplified shape. Electric models with a key hole have been converted to electric operation after purchase.

61/4710/0	1927 'Duke of York'	light green	LNER, lined black + white (c/w)	27-29	250	400
61/4710/0	1927 'Duke of York'	dark green	SR & GWR, lined blk + wht (c/w)	27-29	250	400
61/4710/0	1927 'Duke of York'	crimson	*LMS*, lined blk + yellow (c/w)	27-29	250	400
61/4710/0	1927 'Duke of York'	light green	LNER, lined black + white (elec)	27-29	250	600
61/4710/0	1927 'Duke of York'	dark green	SR & GWR, lined blk + wht (elec)	27-29	250	600
61/4710/0	1927 'Duke of York'	crimson	*LMS*, lined blk + yellow (elec)	27-29	250	600
3301/0	1930 'Duke of York'	light green	LNER, lined black + white (c/w)	30	300	500
3301/0	1930 'Duke of York'	dark green	SR & GWR, lined blk + wht (c/w)	30	300	500
3301/0	1930 'Duke of York'	crimson	*LMS*, lined blk + yellow (c/w)	30	300	500
4301/0	1930 'Duke of York'	light green	LNER, lined black + white (elec)	30	350	600
4301/0	1930 'Duke of York'	dark green	SR & GWR, lined blk + wht (elec)	30	350	600
4301/0	1930 'Duke of York'	crimson	*LMS*, lined blk + yellow (elec)	30	350	600
3301/0	1931 'Duke of York'	light green	LNER, lined black + white (c/w)	31-32	250	400
3301/0	1931 'Duke of York'	dark green	SR & GWR, lined blk + wht (c/w)	31-32	250	400
3301/0	1931 'Duke of York'	crimson	*LMS*, lined blk + yellow (c/w)	31-32	250	400
4301/0	1931 'Duke of York'	light green	LNER, lined black + white (elec)	31-32	250	600
4301/0	1931 'Duke of York'	dark green	SR & GWR, lined blk + wht (elec)	31-32	250	600
4301/0	1931 'Duke of York'	crimson	*LMS*, lined blk + yellow (elec)	31-32	250	600

Bassett-Lowke electric 'Duke of York' 4-4-0 (61/4710/0)
[table 31].   (Barry Potter Auctions)

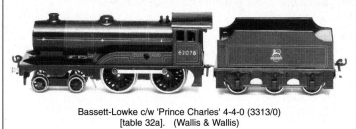

Bassett-Lowke c/w 'Prince Charles' 4-4-0 (3313/0)
[table 32a].   (Wallis & Wallis)

32. Princess Elizabeth 4-4-0 (Freelance)

The alloy wheels on this model were prone to metal fatigue and disintegration with the result that many have been re-wheeled. In such a case, if original period Bassett-Lowke iron replacement wheels have been fitted, add £50 to the value. Electric models with a key hole have been converted to electric operation after purchase. All models are lithographed.

Cat.No.	Name / Number	Colour	Details	Years	£	£
3301/0	2265 'Princess Elizabeth'	crimson	LMS, crest in cabsides, (c/w)	32-35	200	300
3301/0	2265 'Princess Elizabeth'	green	LNER, (c/w)	32-35	200	300
4301/0	2265 'Princess Elizabeth'	crimson	LMS, crest in cabsides, (elec)	32-35	250	500
4301/0	2265 'Princess Elizabeth'	green	LNER, (elec)	32-35	250	500

32a. Prince Charles 4-4-0 (Freelance)

All models were lithographed and all had a key hole whether clockwork or electric.

Cat.No.	Name / Number	Colour	Details	Years	£	£
3313/0	62078 'Prince Charles'	blue	BRb, (c/w)	51-53	200	350
3313/0	62136 'Prince Charles'	dark green	BRb, black + white lining, (c/w)	52-54	200	350
3313/0	62453 'Prince Charles'	dark green	BRb, black + white lining, (c/w)	51-55	200	350
3313/0	62453 'Prince Charles'	dark green	BRb, Brunswick green, black + orange lining, (c/w)	54-64	200	350
4313/0	62078 'Prince Charles'	blue	BRb, (elec)	51-53	250	500
4311/0	62136 'Prince Charles'	dark green	BRb, black + white lining, (elec)	52-54	250	500
4311/0	62453 'Prince Charles'	dark green	BRb, black + white lining, (elec)	51-55	250	450
4311/0	62453 'Prince Charles'	dark green	BRb, Brunswick green, black + orange lining, (elec 3r)	54-64	250	400
2311/0	62453 'Prince Charles'	dark green	BRb, Brunswick green, black + orange lining, (elec 2r)	57-64	250	500

33. Black Prince 4-4-0 (Bing for Bassett-Lowke)

Cat.No.	Name / Number	Colour	Details	Years	£	£
26/0	1902 'Black Prince'	black	L&NWR, (steam)	10-24	NPG	NPG

34. Precursor 4-4-0 (Märklin for Bassett-Lowke)

Cat.No.	Name / Number	Colour	Details	Years	£	£
	513 'Precursor'	black	L&NWR, 4-4-0 (c/w)	07-?	400	500

35. Precursor 4-4-0 (Bing and Carette for Bassett-Lowke)

Cat.No.	Name / Number	Colour	Details	Years	£	£
	513 'George the Fifth'	crimson	LMS, (c/w)	?	NPG	NPG
	513 'George the Fifth'	crimson	LMS, (elec)	?	NPG	NPG
11/0	2663 'George the Fifth'	black	L&NWR, (B) (c/w)	11-19	250	300
2663/0	2663 'George the Fifth'	black	L&NWR, litho (B) (c/w)	19-23	200	250
	2663 'George the Fifth'	black	L&NWR, litho (C) (c/w)	11-?	NPG	NPG
11/0	2663 'George the Fifth'	black	L&NWR, (B) (elec)	11-19	250	300
2663/0	2663 'George the Fifth'	black	L&NWR, litho (B) (elec)	19-23	200	250
	2663 'George the Fifth'	black	L&NWR, litho (C) (elec)	11-?	NPG	NPG
	2664 'Queen Mary'	black	L&NWR, (B) (c/w)	11	NPG	NPG
	2664 'Queen Mary'	black	L&NWR, litho (B) (c/w)	19-?	750	900
	2664 'Queen Mary'	black	L&NWR, (B) (elec)	11	NPG	NPG
	2664 'Queen Mary'	black	L&NWR, litho (B) (elec)	19-?	750	900
61/4710/0	5320 'George the Fifth'	crimson	LMS, litho (B) (c/w)	24-26?	250	350
61/BL/0	5320 'George the Fifth'	crimson	LMS, litho (B) (elec)	24-26-?	300	400

36. Caledonian Dunalastair 4-4-0

This model had an 8-wheel tender.

Cat.No.	Name / Number	Colour	Details	Years	£	£
142/0	142 'Dunalastair'	blue	CR, (c/w)	25-35	1400	1600
	142 'Dunalastair IV'	blue	CR, (B) (c/w)	11-16	1500	1850
142E/0	142 'Dunalastair'	blue	CR, (elec)	25-35	1500	1750

37. Class 3P 4-4-0 (Leeds for Bassett-Lowke)

This model had a 6-wheel tender.

Cat.No.	Name / Number	Colour	Details	Years	£	£
77/0	77 'Pickersgill'	blue	CR, (c/w)	22-?	NPG	NPG
77E/0	77 'Pickersgill'	blue	CR, (elec)	22-?	NPG	NPG

38. Deeley Class 4P Compound 4-4-0 (Bing for Bassett-Lowke)

Cat.No.	Name / Number	Colour	Details	Years	£	£
	1000	crimson	MR, (steam)	12-23	NPG	NPG
	1000	crimson	MR, (c/w)	c21-23	NPG	NPG
	1000	crimson	MR, (elec)	c21-23	NPG	NPG

Bassett-Lowke LMS crimson standard Compound 4-4-0 (4302/0)
[table 39].

Bing for Bassett-Lowke GWR 4-4-0 Atbara Class 'Sydney'
[table 44].   (Barry Potter Auctions)

39. LMS Standard Compound 4-4-0
Pre-war electric models did not have key holes but, after the war, all Compounds had key holes whether clockwork or electric.

3302/0	1190	crimson	*LMS*, litho, small Bing type tender, (c/w)	28-35	250	400
4302/0	1190	crimson	*LMS*, litho, small Bing type tender, (elec)	28-35	250	600
3302/0	1108	crimson	*LMS*, litho, Bassett-Lowke standard tender , (c/w)	46-47	250	400
4302/0	1108	crimson	*LMS*, litho, Bassett-Lowke standard tender , (elec)	46-47	250	600
3302/0	1036	brown	*LMS*, litho, coal rail tender, (c/w)	48-50	250	400
4302/0	1036	brown	*LMS*, litho, coal rail tender, (elec)	48-50	250	600
3302/0	1063	brown	*LMS*, litho, coal rail tender, (c/w)	48-50	250	400
4302/0	1063	brown	*LMS*, litho, coal rail tender, (elec)	48-50	250	600
3302/0	1063	crimson	*LMS*, litho, coal rail tender, (c/w)	48-50	250	400
4302/0	1063	crimson	*LMS*, litho, coal rail tender, (elec)	48-50	250	600
3302/0	1082	crimson	*LMS*, litho, coal rail tender, (c/w)	48-50	250	400
4302/0	1082	crimson	*LMS*, litho, coal rail tender, (elec)	48-50	250	600
3302/0	1082	black	*LMS*, painted over 1082 litho, red lined, (c/w)	48-50	250	400
4302/0	1082	black	*LMS*, painted over 1082 litho, red lined, (elec)	48-50	250	600
3302/0	41109	black	BRb, litho, lined red + grey, (c/w)	51-65	250	400
4302/0	41109	black	BRb, litho, lined red + grey, (elec 3r)	51-65	250	600
2302/0	41109	black	BRb, litho, lined red + grey, (elec 2r)	57-68	300	700
3302/0	41125	black	BRb, litho, lined red + grey, (c/w)	5?-5?	250	400
2302/0	41125	black	BRb, litho, lined red + grey, (elec)	5?-5?	250	600
3302/0	3400	dk.green	GWR, painted over 1108 litho, (c/w)	36-39	400	800
4302/0	3400	dk.green	GWR, painted over 1108 litho, (elec)	36-39	400	800
-	1067**	crimson	super detailed hand built (c/w)	33-37	400	800
-	1067**	crimson	super detailed hand built (elec)	33-37	400	800

** Super detailed models could be had with what ever number the customer required. This is a known example.Other post-war Compounds could also be had with the customer's choice of number applied at the factory and 41107 and 41108 are known to exist.

40. Class 2P 4-4-0

17/0	483	crimson	*LMS*, (c/w)	26?-28-?	NPG	NPG
66/0E	483	crimson	*LMS*, (elec)	c26-28-?	NPG	NPG

41. LMS Class 2P 4-4-0 (altered Compound)
These were former 1108 Compound models that were overpainted. They have had their outside cylinders removed and plated over, and steam chest fairings on each side of the smokebox mounting also removed (the tin tab slots for the fairings can still be seen). The electric models were often fitted with lamp brackets not found on the Compounds.

3306/0		601	black	*LMS*, litho (c/w)	36-40	250	400
4306/0 5506/0		601	black	*LMS*, litho (elec) (also listed as 4306/0AC and 4306/0P) 36-40	350	550

42. Ex-GNR Ivatt Express 4-4-0 (Bing for Bassett-Lowke)

L2103/0	504	green	*LNER*, litho (c/w)	24-25	500	800
LE2103/0	504	green	*LNER*, litho (elec)	24-25	500	800
L2103/0	4390	green	*LNER*, litho (c/w)	27-30	280	340
LE2103/0	4390	green	*LNER*, litho (elec)	c26-28-?	280	340

43. GWR 4-4-0 (Bing for Bassett-Lowke)

	504 'Mercury'	green	*Great* (crest) *Western*, (c/w)	?	NPG	NPG
	504 'Mercury'	green	*Great* (crest) *Western*, (elec)	?	NPG	NPG

44. Atbara Class 4-4-0 (Bing for Bassett-Lowke)

	3410 'Sydney'	green	*GWR*, (c/w)	04-10	700	1000

44a. City Class 4-4-0 (Bing for Bassett-Lowke)

Cat.No.	Name / Number	Colour	Details	Years	£	£
	3433 'City of Bath'	green	GWR, (c/w)	13-16	1200	1500
	3433 'City of Bath'	green	GWR, litho (c/w)	?	1200	1500
	3433 'City of Bath'	green	GWR, (elec)	14-16	1200	1500
	3433 'City of Bath'	green	GWR, litho (B) (elec)	?	1200	1500

45. Churchward County 4-4-0 (Leeds for Bassett-Lowke)   Other names exist.

Cat.No.	Name / Number	Colour	Details	Years	£	£
3800/0	3800 'County of Middlesex'	green	GWR, (c/w)	22-25	NPG	NPG
3800E/0	3800 'County of Middlesex'	green	GWR, (elec)	22-25	NPG	NPG
3800/0	3801 'County of Carlow'	green	GWR, (c/w)	22-25	350	500

46. Wainwright Class D 4-4-0 (Bing for Bassett-Lowke)

Cat.No.	Name / Number	Colour	Details	Years	£	£
		green	SE&CR, (c/w)	14-?	1800	2500

47. Schools Class 4-4-0 (Märklin for Bassett-Lowke)

Cat.No.	Name / Number	Colour	Details	Years	£	£
910/0/C	910 'Merchant Taylors'	green	Southern, (c/w)	34-37-?	1000	1500
910/0/D 910/0/A	910 'Merchant Taylors'	green	Southern, (elec AC and DC versions)	34-36-?	1000	1500

48. NYC Vauclain Compound 4-4-0 (Carette for Bassett-Lowke)

Cat.No.	Name / Number	Colour	Details	Years	£	£
	2350	?	NYC, (c/w)	05-?	NPG	NPG

49. GNR Atlantic 4-4-2 (Carette or Bing for Bassett-Lowke)

Cat.No.	Name / Number	Colour	Details	Years	£	£
	251	green	GNR, (C) (c/w)	07-09	750	1000
	251	green	GNR, (C) (elec)	07-?	NPG	NPG
9/0	1425	green	GNR, (B) (c/w)	13-22	450	600
	1425	green	GNR, (B) (elec)	12-20	450	600
	1442	green	GNR, litho (C) (c/w)	11-?	600	800
	1442	green	GNR, litho (C) (elec)	11-?	600	800

50. Ex-NBR Class C1 Atlantic 4-4-2

Cat.No.	Name / Number	Colour	Details	Years	£	£
	8872 'Auld Reekie'	green	LNER, (elec)	c55	NPG	NPG

51. Goods Loco 0-6-0 (Bing for Bassett-Lowke)

Cat.No.	Name / Number	Colour	Details	Years	£	£
4736/0	773	?	Southern, litho (c/w)	28-?	NPG	NPG
4736/0	4460	green	GWR, litho (c/w)	28-?	NPG	NPG
	4472	green	LNER, litho (c/w)	27-?	NPG	NPG
4736/0	6508	?	LMS, litho (c/w)	28-?	NPG	NPG
4736/0	8851	green?	LNER, (c/w)	28-?	NPG	NPG

52. Cauliflower 0-6-0 (Bing for Bassett-Lowke)

Cat.No.	Name / Number	Colour	Details	Years	£	£
	930	black	L&NWR, (c/w)	12-14	NPG	NPG

Märklin for Bassett-Lowke electric SR Schools Class
'Merchant Taylors' (910/0/D) [table 47]. (Christie's)

Bassett-Lowke c/w LMS Fowler 4F 0-6-0 (3204/0)
[table 53]. (Barry Potter Auctions)

Bassett-Lowke electric LNER Gresley Mogul (4602/0)
[table 57].

Bassett-Lowke electric GWR Class 43XX Mogul (4603/0)
[table 59].   (Barry Potter Auctions)

53. Fowler 4F 0-6-0   This model was of soldered construction with a paint finish.

3204/0	4072	black	*LMS*, lined red (c/w)	27-33	300	600
4204/0	4072	black	*LMS*, lined red (elec)	27-33	350	700

53a. J39 0-6-0   This model was of soldered construction with a paint finish.

3205/0	1448	black	*LNER*, lined red (c/w)	27-35	300	600
4205/0	1448	black	*LNER*, lined red (elec)	27-35	350	700

54. Standard Goods Locomotive 0-6-0   This model was of tab construction and lithographed. The LMS version had a capuchon on the chimney. The non-BR locos had a Bing type tender without the horizontal fluting found on passenger locomotives. The BR model has the later standard Bassett-Lowke tender.

3307/0	4256	black	*LMS*, lined red (c/w)	36-40	250	450
4307/0	4256	black	*LMS*, lined red (elec)	36-40	300	500
A4307/0	4256	black	*LMS*, lined red (20V AC)	36-40	300	500
5307/0	4256	black	*LMS*, lined red (elec spur drive)	36-40	300	500
3308/0	1456	black	*LNER*, lined red (c/w)	36-40	250	450
4308/0	1456	black	*LNER*, lined red (elec)	36-40	300	500
A4308/0	1456	black	*LNER*, lined red (20V AC)	36-40	300	500
5308/0	1456	black	*LNER*, lined red (elec spur drive)	36-40	300	500
3308/0	63871	black	BRb, unlined (c/w)	55-67	200	400
3308/0	64193	black	BRb, unlined (c/w)	55-67	200	400
5308/0	63871	black	BRb, unlined (elec 3r)	55-67	250	450
5308/0	64193	black	BRb, unlined (elec 3r)	55-67	250	450
2308/0	64193	black	BRb, unlined (elec 2r)	57-67	250	450

55. Ex-L&Y Crab Mogul 2-6-0

	2700	crimson	*LMS*, (steam)	25-?	NPG	NPG
	2700	black	*LMS*, (steam)	25-?	NPG	NPG
	2700	crimson	*LMS*, (c/w)	25-?	NPG	NPG
	2700	black	*LMS*, (c/w)	25-?	NPG	NPG
	2700	crimson	*LMS*, (elec)	25-?	NPG	NPG
	2700	black	*LMS*, (elec)	25-?	NPG	NPG
6660/0 6670/0	13000	crimson	*LMS*, (steam)	25-39	550	700
6660/0 6670/0	13000	black	*LMS*, (steam)	25-39	600	850
3601/0	13000	crimson	*LMS*, (c/w)	25-33	500	650
3601/0	13000	black	*LMS*, (c/w)	25-33	550	750
4601/0 4602/0	13000	crimson	*LMS*, (elec)	25-33	650	850
4601/0 4602/0	13000	crimson	LMS, number on cabsides and tender (3 rail 12V DC)	25-33	650	850
4601/0 4602/0	13000	black	*LMS*, (elec)	25-33	750	1000

56. Stanier Mogul 2-6-0

-			kit (steam)	?	NPG	NPG
-			kit (c/w)	?	NPG	NPG
-			kit (elec)	?	NPG	NPG
6660/0	2945	crimson	*LMS*, (steam)	34-c41	300	500
6660/0	2945	black	*LMS*, (steam)	34-c41	300	500
	2945	crimson	*LMS*, kit (steam)	c39-c49	600	750
	2945	black	*LMS*, kit (steam)	c39-c49	600	750
	2945	crimson	*LMS*, (c/w)	34-c41	250	350
	2945	black	*LMS*, (c/w)	34-c41	250	350
	2945	crimson	*LMS*, kit (c/w)	c39-c49	350	450
	2945	black	*LMS*, kit (c/w)	c39-c49	350	450
4601/0	2945	crimson	*LMS*, (elec)	34-c41	250	350
4601/0	2945	black	*LMS*, (elec)	34-c41	250	350
	2945	crimson	*LMS*, kit (elec)	c39-c49	350	450
	2945	black	*LMS*, kit (elec)	c39-c49	350	450
	13007	crimson	*LMS*, (steam)	68-69	NPG	NPG
6661/0	42980	black	BRb, lined grey and red (steam)	c52-64	500	750
	42980	?	BRb, (c/w)	?	NPG	NPG
	42980	?	BRb, (elec)	?	NPG	NPG

57. Gresley Class K3 Mogul 2-6-0

6670/0	33	green	*LNER*, (steam)	25-41	1000	1300
6670/0	33	black	*LNER*, (steam)	25-41	1500	1800
3602/0	33	green	*LNER*, (c/w)	25-41	800	1300
3602/0	33	black	*LNER*, (c/w)	25-41	1200	1600
4602/0	33	green	*LNER*, (elec)	25-41	800	1300
4602/0	33	black	*LNER*, (elec)	25-41	1000	1400

Cat.No.	Name / Number	Colour	Details	Years	£	£
6670/0	982	green	*LNER*, (steam)	26-c38	NPG	NPG
6670/0	982	black	*LNER*, (steam)	26-c38	NPG	NPG
3602/0	982	green	*LNER*, (c/w)	26-28-?	NPG	NPG
3602/0	982	black	*LNER*, (c/w)	26-28-?	NPG	NPG
4602/0	982	green	*LNER*, (elec)	26-28-?	NPG	NPG
4602/0	982	black	*LNER*, (elec)	26-28-?	NPG	NPG
	1864	green	*LNER*, (steam)	46-?	350	500
	1864	green	*LNER*, (c/w)	46-?	400	500
	1864	green	*LNER*, (elec)	46-?	400	500

58. Class K4 Mogul 2-6-0

	2066 'Deer Stalker'	green	*LNER*, (elec)	c69	400	500

59. GWR Class 43XX Mogul 2-6-0

6680/0	4431	green	GWR, (steam)	25-28-?	NPG	NPG
6680/0	4431	black	GWR, (steam)	25-28-?	NPG	NPG
3603/0	4431 or 4331	green	GWR, (c/w)	25-36?	450	500
3603/0	4431	black	GWR, (c/w)	25-28?	NPG	NPG
4603/0	4431 or 4331	green	GWR, (elec)	25-36?	450	500
4603/0	4431	black	GWR, (elec)	25-28?	NPG	NPG

60. Maunsell Class N Mogul 2-6-0

6685/0	864	green	*Southern*, (steam)	26-c38	NPG	NPG
6685/0	864	black	*Southern*, (steam)	26-c38	NPG	NPG
3644/0	864	green	*Southern*, (c/w)	26-28-?	NPG	NPG
3644/0	864	black	*Southern*, (c/w)	26-28-?	NPG	NPG
4644/0	864	green	*Southern*, (elec)	26-28-?	NPG	NPG
4644/0	864	black	*Southern*, (elec)	26-28-?	NPG	NPG
6685/0	866	green	*Southern*, (steam)	26-c38	NPG	NPG
3644/0	866	green	*Southern*, (c/w)	26-c38	NPG	NPG
4644/0	866	green	*Southern*, (elec)	26-c38	NPG	NPG

61. Cardean 4-6-0 (floor model) (Carette for Bassett-Lowke)

	903 'Cardean'	blue	*CR*, litho (c/w)	09-?	NPG	NPG

62. Super Enterprise 4-6-0 (Freelance)

6655/0	851	green	*Southern*, (steam)	37-?	NPG	NPG
6655/0	2495	black	(steam)	37-40	NPG	NPG
6655/0	2871	green	*LNER*, (steam)	37-40	NPG	NPG
6655/0	5524	red	*LMS*, (steam)	37-40	NPG	NPG
	45295	green	BRb, (steam)	37-?	NPG	NPG

Bassett-Lowke early c/w 'Royal Scot' (3303/0)
[table 67]. (Barry Potter Auctions)

Bassett-Lowke electric black 'Royal Scot' (5622/0)
[table 67].

Bassett-Lowke post-war Rebuilt 'Royal Scot' (5622/0)
[table 68]. (Christie's)

Bassett-Lowke electric Jubilee 'Conqueror' (911/0/D)
[table 69]. (Barry Potter Auctions)

63. Castle 4-6-0 (Freelance) (Bing for Bassett-Lowke)

4737/0	4460 'Windsor Castle'	green	GWR, litho (c/w)	28****	NPG	NPG

64. A1 4-6-0 (Freelance) (Bing for Bassett-Lowke)

4737/0	4472? 'Flying Fox'	green	LNER, litho (c/w)	28-?	NPG	NPG

65. Royal Scot 4-6-0 (Freelance) (Bing for Bassett-Lowke)

4737/0	6508 'Royal Scot'	crimson	LMS, litho (c/w)	28-?	NPG	NPG

66. Prince of Wales 4-6-0 (Bing for Bassett-Lowke)

49/0	5600 'Prince of Wales'	crimson	LMS, (c/w)	24-25	NPG	NPG

67. Royal Scot Class 4-6-0

3303/0	6100 'Royal Scot'	crimson	LMS, litho, Fowler tender (c/w)	29-37	800	1350
3611/0	6100 'Royal Scot'	crimson	LMS, Stanier tender (c/w)	37-52	800	1350
3622/0	6100 'Royal Scot'	black	LMS, Stanier tender (c/w)	c48-52	1200	1800
4303/0 A4303/0	6100 'Royal Scot'	crimson	LMS, litho, Fowler tender, (AC and DC versions)	29-37	500	650
5611/0 5711/0	6100 'Royal Scot'	crimson	LMS, Stanier tender and smoke deflectors, (AC and DC versions)	37-52	700	900
5622/0	6100 'Royal Scot'	black	LMS, 4-6-0, Stanier tender and smoke deflectors (3 rail 12v DC)	c48-52	1200	1500

68. Rebuilt Royal Scot 4-6-0

	46100 'Royal Scot'	green	BRb, (c/w)	53-?	1200	1700
5622/0	46100 'Royal Scot'	green	BRb, (3 rail 12 V DC)	53-56-?	2500	3500

69. Jubilee Class 4-6-0

911/0	5552 'Silver Jubilee'	black + silver	LMS, (M) (c/w)	35	3000	4000
911/0/D 911/0/A	5552 'Silver Jubilee'	black + silver	LMS, (M) (elec AC and DC versions)	35	3000	4000
911/0	5573 'Newfoundland'	crimson	LMS, (M) (c/w)	35-?	2750	3500
911/0/D 911/0/A	5573 'Newfoundland'	crimson	LMS, (M) (elec AC and DC versions)	35-?	2750	3500
911/0/C 3607/0	5701 'Conqueror'	crimson	LMS, (c/w)	36-?	3750	5000
911/0/D 911/0/A	5701 'Conqueror'	crimson	LMS, (elec DC and AC versions)	36-?	4000	6500
911/0/C 3607/0	5712 'Victory'	crimson	LMS, (c/w)	36-?	3750	5000
5607/0	5712 'Victory'	crimson	LMS, (elec DC)	36-?	4000	5500

70. LMS Black 5 4-6-0 (rebuilt from Märklin Jubilee)

	4853?	black	LMS, (c/w)	35-c40	750	1000
	5294	black	LMS, (elec 3r DC)	35-c40	750	1000

71. Class 5MT 4-6-0

	45126	black	BR, (elec 2/3 rail)	59-63	NPG	NPG

72. Class B17 4-6-0

	2838 'Melton Hall'	green	LNER, (c/w)	36-c39	2000	2500
	2838 'Melton Hall'	green	LNER, (elec)	36-c39	2000	2500
3608/0	2848 'Arsenal'	green	LNER, (c/w)	36-c39	3500	4500
5608/0 A4608/0	2848 'Arsenal'	green	LNER, (elec DC and AC versions)	36-c39	3500	4500

73. Castle Class 4-6-0

	4079 'Pendennis Castle'	green	GWR, (using Mogul parts)(c/w)	30-?	1250	1500
	4079 'Pendennis Castle'	green	GWR, (c/w)	39-51	1500	2000
	4079 'Pendennis Castle'	green	GWR, (elec)	39-51	1500	2000
	5071 'Spitfire'	green	GWR, (elec 2/3 rail)	55-63	2000	2500
	5015 'Kingswear Castle'**	green	Great Western, (elec 3 rail 12V DC)	50s?	3000	3500

** Special order

Bassett-Lowke electric Black 5 built from a Märklin Jubilee
[table 70]. (Barry Potter Auctions)

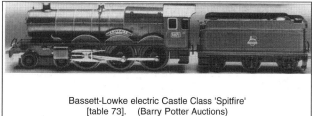

Bassett-Lowke electric Castle Class 'Spitfire'
[table 73]. (Barry Potter Auctions)

74. King Class 4-6-0

Cat.No.	Name / Number	Colour	Details	Years	£	£
912/0/C	6000 'King George V'	green	*Great* (crest) *Western*, (M) (c/w)	35-37-?	3500	4500
912/0/D 612/0/A	6000 'King George V'	green	*Great* (crest) *Western*, (elec DC and AC versions) (M)	35-37-?	4500	5250
	6027 'King Richard'	green	GWR, (elec 2/3 rail) hand built	c60-63	2500	3000

75. Lord Nelson 4-6-0 (rebuilt from litho Royal Scot)

Cat.No.	Name / Number	Colour	Details	Years	£	£
	850 'Lord Nelson'	green	*Southern*, (c/w)	35-?	1200	1500
	850 'Lord Nelson'	green	*Southern*, (elec)	35-?	1200	1500

76. King Arthur 4-6-0 (Bing for Bassett-Lowke)

Cat.No.	Name / Number	Colour	Details	Years	£	£
4737/0	773 'King Arthur'	green	*Southern*, litho (c/w)	28-?	1000	1200

77. Princess Royal Class 4-6-2

Cat.No.	Name / Number	Colour	Details	Years	£	£
3605/0/C	6200 'Princess Royal'	crimson	*LMS*, (c/w)	35-?	4000	5000
3605/0/D 3605/0/A	6200 'Princess Royal'	crimson	*LMS*, (elec AC and DC versions)	35-?	4000	5000
3605/0	6201 'Princess Elizabeth'	crimson	*LMS*, (c/w)	36-39-?	4000	5000
5605/0 A4605/0	6201 'Princess Elizabeth'	crimson	*LMS*, (elec AC and DC versions)	36-39-?	3500	4500
	6202	crimson	*LMS*, Turbomotive (c/w)	36-c50	3000	4000
	6202	crimson	*LMS*, Turbomotive 4-6-2 (elec)	36-c50	3000	4000

78. Princess Coronation Class 4-6-2 Streamlined

Cat.No.	Name / Number	Colour	Details	Years	£	£
	6220 'Coronation'	blue	*LMS*, (c/w)	37-c48	4000	5000
	6220 'Coronation'	blue	*LMS*, (elec)	37-c48	4000	5000
3606/0	6225 'Duchess of Gloucester'	crimson	*LMS*, (c/w)	38?-c48	4000	5000
4606/0 5606/0	6225 'Duchess of Gloucester'	crimson	*LMS*, (elec AC and DC versions)	38?-c48	4000	5000

Bassett-Lowke electric LMS 'Princess Elizabeth' (5605/0) [table 77]. (Wallis & Wallis)

Bassett-Lowke electric BR 'Duchess of Montrose' (5613/0) [table 79]. (Barry Potter Auctions)

Bassett-Lowke electric LNER 'Flying Scotsman' (4304/0) [table 80]. (Barry Potter Auctions)

79. Princess Coronation Class 4-6-2

3613/0	6232 'Duchess of Montrose'	crimson	*LMS*, (c/w)	39-49	2500	3000
5613/0	6232 'Duchess of Montrose'	crimson	*LMS*, (elec DC)	39-49	2750	3500
3613/0	46232 'Duchess of Montrose'	blue	BRb, smoke deflectors (c/w)	c52	3500	5000
3613/0	46232 'Duchess of Montrose'	green	BRb, smoke deflectors (c/w)	c54-c58	2500	3000
	46232 'Duchess of Montrose'	blue	BRb, smoke deflectors (elec)	c52	4000	5000
5613/0 3r, 2613/0 2r	46232 'Duchess of Montrose'	green	BRb, smoke deflectors, (elec 2/3 rail)	c54-c58	3000	4500
-	46245 'City of London'**	black	BRb, smoke deflectors, (3 rail 12 V DC)	50s	3000	3500

** Special order

80. A1/A3 Pacific 4-6-2

	103 'Flying Scotsman'	green	*LNER*, A3, litho (c/w)	c47-c50	1200	1500
	103 'Flying Scotsman'	green	*LNER*, A3, litho (elec)	c47-c50	1200	1500
3304/0	4472 'Flying Scotsman'	green	*LNER*, A1, litho (c/w)	33-c41	1000	1300
4304/0 8vDC	4472 'Flying Scotsman'	green	*LNER*, A1, litho, (elec)			
5304/0 8vAC			(also 5504/0 20vAC, 6304/0 20vAC)	33-c41	1000	1300
3310/0	60103 'Flying Scotsman'	blue	BRb, A3 litho (c/w)	50-52	1200	1500
3310/0	60103 'Flying Scotsman'	green	BRb, A3 litho (c/w)	c53-c58	750	1200
	60103 'Flying Scotsman'	blue	BRb, A3 litho (elec)	50-52	1200	1500
5310/0 3r 2310/0 2r	60103 'Flying Scotsman'	green	BRb, A3 litho, (elec 2/3 rail)	c53-c58	1200	1600

81. A4 Pacific 4-6-2

2507/0	2509 'Silver Link'	silver	*LNER*, (c/w)	36-c40	4000	5000
5606/0 dc 4606/0 ac	2509 'Silver Link'	silver	*LNER*, (elec AC and DC versions)	36-c40	4000	5000
2507/0	2510 'Quicksilver'	silver	*LNER*, (c/w)	36-c40	4500	5500
5606/0 dc 4606/0 ac	2510 'Quicksilver'	silver	*LNER*, (elec AC and DC versions)	36-c40	4500	5500
2507/0	2511 'Silver King'	silver	*LNER*, (c/w)	36-c40	4500	5500
5606/0 dc 4606/0 ac	2511 'Silver King'	silver	*LNER*, (elec AC and DC versions)	36-c40	4500	5500
2507/0	2512 'Silver Fox'	silver	*LNER*, (c/w)	36-c40	4500	5500
5606/0 dc 4606/0 ac	2512 'Silver Fox'	silver	*LNER*, (elec AC and DC versions)	36-c40	4500	5500
2507/0	4489 'Dominion of Canada'	blue	*LNER*, (c/w)	c38-c40	4500	5500
5606/0 dc 4606/0 ac	4489 'Dominion of Canada'	blue	*LNER*, (elec AC and DC versions)	c38-c40	4500	5500
2507/0	4490 'Empire of India'	blue	*LNER*, (c/w)	c38-c40	4500	5500
5606/0 dc 4606/0 ac	4490 'Empire of India'	blue	*LNER*, (elec AC and DC versions)	c38-c40	4500	5500
2507/0	4498 'Sir Nigel Gresley'	blue	*LNER*, (c/w)	c38-c40	4500	5500
5606/0 dc 4606/0 ac	4498 'Sir Nigel Gresley'	blue	*LNER*, (elec AC and DC versions)	c38-c40	4500	5500

82. Britannia Class Pacific 4-6-2 (Hunt for Bassett-Lowke)

	70000 'Britannia'	green	BRc, hand built (elec 2/3 rail)	58-?	2000	3000

83. German State Railways 4-6-2 (Märklin for Bassett-Lowke)

MG/0	?		German State Railways (elec)	34-36-?	NPG	NPG

84. New York Central 4-6-4 (Märklin for Bassett-Lowke)

AK/0	'Commodore Vanderbilt'	black	*New York Central*, (elec)	34-36-?	NPG	NPG

85. Class 8F 2-8-0

	48209	black	BRc, (elec 2/3 rail)	60-63	NPG	NPG

86. French Mountain 4-8-2 (Märklin for Bassett-Lowke)

MF/0	?		*ETAT*, (elec)	34-36-?	NPG	NPG

87. Class 9F 2-10-0 (Hunt for Bassett-Lowke)

	92220 'Evening Star'	green	BRc,(elec 2/3 rail)	61-63	2200	3000
	?	black	BRc, (elec)	61-63	NPG	NPG

88. SECR Steam Railmotor (Carette for Bassett-Lowke)

	1	brown	litho (steam)	07-09-?	1500	1800

89. Deltic Diesel Co-Co

	'Deltic'	blue	(elec) twin electric motor bogies	59-63	2000	3375
	'Deltic'	green	BRc	?	NPG	NPG

90. Steeplecab Electric 0-4-0 (Bing and Märklin for Bassett-Lowke)

	23	blue	*CLR*, (M) (elec)	03-?	1500	1800
	23	blue	*CLR*, (B) (elec)	04-?	450	600

Cat.No.	Name / Number	Colour	Details	Years	£	£

91. Swiss Pantograph Electrics (Märklin for Bassett-Lowke)

	?		*SBB*, 4-6-2 (elec)	35-?	NPG	NPG
	?		*SBB*, 4-4-2 (elec)	35-?	NPG	NPG
	?		*SBB*, 0-4-0 (elec)	35-?	NPG	NPG

92. London Underground Standard Stock EMU

	7083? + ?	red+crm	*London Transport*, 3-car (elec)	37-38	2500	5000

93. Southern EMU

1457/0		green	*Southern*, 3-car set (elec)	c28	1300	1500

94. Euston-Watford 1927 Stock EMU

104/0	1652/****/6560?	crimson	3-car, litho (elec)	30-35	1000	1850

95. Southern EMU (Exley for Bassett-Lowke)

These were 3-car sets with 12V DC Bassett-Lowke motor bogies and B-L coach bogies.

?	?	green	Southern Portsmouth 3-car set	?	1200	1500
	3064	green	*Southern*, 4RES 3-car suburban set	53-57	1200	1500
	?	crimson	*LMS*, ex-Southern 4RES 3-car EMU	c55	1500	2100

Bassett-Lowke electric model of the 'Deltic' prototype   [table 89].   (Wallis & Wallis)

Bassett-Lowke electric Euston-Watford 1927 stock (104/0)   [table 94].   (Barry Potter Auctions)

Bassett-Lowke Southern coach.

Coaches

As with the locomotives, many of the early coaches were imported from Germany where they were made by Bing, Märklin or Carette but, by the 1930s, Bassett-Lowke were manufacturing their own coaching stock. Carette coaches were in pre-grouping liveries, some of which were toy-like but so-called scale model coaches arrived in 1910.

Carette produced nothing after the First World War but some of their tools were acquired to produce the travelling post office and 12-wheeled diner in the 1920s.

Bing lithographed coaches dominated the '20s and are known as the 1921 Series. These were in steel and produced in the new company liveries following the grouping in 1923, when they became the 1924 series, fitted with corridor connections. They were also available in GNR, LNWR and MR livery as well as in GWR lake.

The first Bassett-Lowke coach appeared in 1930 and was part of the Watford EMU set. First class corridor and brake thirds were made in the liveries of all four railway companies but the LMS and SR EMUs also received a pair of suburban coaches. These were available separately and there was a travelling post office.

The 1921, 1924 and 1930 series coaches sell for £120-150 each and the travelling post office with lineside apparatus fetches around £150-£200.

A new design of coach was available after the Second World War in BR crimson and cream which were made alongside Trix by Precision Models in Northampton. These in good condition sell for between £120 and £200. Exley also made coaches for Bassett-Lowke after the war. These had the Exley trade mark carefully removed and were packed in Bassett-Lowke boxes.

The BR coaches sell for between £120 and £200 while Exley for Bassett-Lowke coaches usually cost between £150 and £250. The rarer special restaurant car and LNER tourist green and cream coaches are likely to cost as much as £600 each.

Wagons

Up until the First World War, Carette produced many wagons for Bassett-Lowke, others were made at Winteringham's. Both wooden and tinplate wagons were made and available side by side. The latter were mostly post-grouping examples. In wood you could buy a range of scale handmade wagons at a price four times that of a tinplate equivalent. Even the standard wooden wagons could be twice the price of tinplate ones. After the Second World War, some wooden wagons were available in kit form.

Today, the value of wagons has reversed with tinplate ones selling for twice the price of wooden ones. Tinplate open wagons are usually £10-£15 and vans £15-£25 depending on condition and subject. Look particularly for the 2-rail versions fitted with synthetic wheels and the 3-rail ones which have top quality Bassett-Lowke iron spoked wagon wheel sets.

Some wagons are rare and sought after. Examples are a 'Colman's Mustard' van which sold for £340 in 1998, a 'Bassett-Lowke' open wagon which reached £210 in 1997 and a GWR 'United Dairies' milk tank which sold for £330 at a sale in 1996.

N.B. Work on listing Bassett-Lowke gauges 1, 2 and 3 is underway and we hope to include these in our next edition.

Bassett-Lowke wagons.   (Barry Potter Auctions)

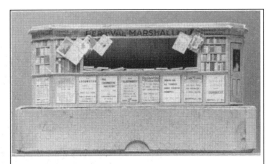

Bassett-Lowke station bookstall.   (Barry Potter Auctions)

Bond's dockland 0-6-0 tank 'Bonzone'.
[table 1]

Bond's Hunslet diesel shunter
[table 2]

Bond's LNER 2-6-2 tank
[table 5]

Bond's LMS Bowen-Cooke 4-6-2 tank.
[table 5]

Bond's LMS Black Five 4-6-0.
[table 5]

Bond's Jinty type LMS 0-6-0 tank.
[table 3]

Bond's LMS 6200
'The Princess Royal'

[table 5]

(Roy Chambers)

Bonds

History

Bond's are primarily known as a manufacturer of mechanisms, locomotives, rolling stock and track parts as well as being agents for other manufacturer's products. They were established in 1887 as Bond's Ltd but in April 1926 took the name Bond's O'Euston Road Ltd; their address being 254 Euston Road. The Company still exists at Midhurst, Sussex, having moved there some 30 years ago.

They catered principally for the 0 gauge and larger scales until manufacturing in 00 scale started in 1925. The pre-war catalogues show a wide selection of model railway items by both British and Continental manufacturers. Materials, castings, tools, lathes, milling machines and boilers were also offered for those keen and skilled enough to build their own models.

Bond's electric motors are highly regarded; in fact, they are sometimes fitted to other makers' locomotives. Some will have been changed during the life of the engine but others may have been installed when new, as some business-minded manufacturers were quite pleased to fulfill extra requirements, such as a Bond's motor, for extra cash.

Following the Second World War, things did not get back to normal until late in 1946. The Company, by then, had changed direction and during the 1950s their catalogues listed the Hornby Dublo, Tri-ang, Trix ranges as well as a wide selection of parts for not only model railways but also aircraft and boats.

Locomotives (O Gauge)

Bond's own locomotives were offered in gauges 00, 0, 1, 2½ " and 3½ " and many were made to special order. Indeed, their catalogues offered to quote for building any type "from the tiny 4mm 00 gauge electric model to a 1½" scale garden steam locomotive".

Prices – It is difficult to assess the value of Bond's locomotives as they are not often found for sale. The two prices shown represent the likely range for one in good condition.

Other Gauges – The locomotives listed below were also available in gauge 1 electric and in live steam in gauges 1, 2½" and 3½".

New information – We would welcome information on other locomotives by this manufacturer and further information about those listed above.

Cat.No.	Name / Number	Colour	Details	Years	£	£

1.   Peckett Type Dockland Saddle Tank 0-6-0ST (Freelance) The model was based on Peckett lines and had six counter-balanced, all flanged, wheels. It also had a toolbox with a lid that opened to reveal the key winder. It had a copper top chimney and brass dome. Post-war mechanisms were 12V.

-	2, 3, 4 'Bonzone'	green	Brunswick green, c/w	27-56?	200	300
-	2, 3, 4 'Bonzone'	black	c/w	27-56?	200	300
-	2, 3, 4 'Bonzone'	dp yell	c/w	27-56?	200	300
-	2, 3, 4 'Bonzone'	green	Brunswick green, 6-8V DC	29-56?	200	300
-	2, 3, 4 'Bonzone'	black	6-8V DC	29-56?	200	300
-	2, 3, 4 'Bonzone'	dp yell	6-8V DC	29-56?	200	300

2.   Hunslet Diesel Shunter 0-6-0DS

-	3	black	electric	32-40?	200	250
-	3	green	electric	32-40?	200	250

3.   Jinty Type Tank Locomotive 0-6-0T   Post-war mechanisms were 12V.

-	7118	black	*LMS*, electric 6-8V DC	38-60	250	300

4.   J39 Goods Locomotive 0-6-0 (Vulcan of Kendal for Bond's)   This model was made by Harry D'Arcy of Vulcan of Kendal.

-	4811	black	*LNER* electric 12V DC	64-69	150	250

5.   Bond's Special Order Locomotives   Post-war mechanisms were 12V.

-	2900	black	*LNER*, 2-6-2T, electric 6-8V DC	35-55?	500	600
-	6798	black	*LMS*, Bowen-Cooke 4-6-2T, 6-8V	35-55?	250	350
-	6798	red	*LMS*, Bowen-Cooke 4-6-2T, 6-8V	35-55?	250	350
-	4472 'Flying Scotsman'	green	*LNER*, Class A3 4-6-2, 6-8V DC	35-55?	NPG	NPG
-	5020	black	*LMS*, Stanier 4-6-0 Class 5MT 6-8V DC	35-55?	500	600

-	6200 'Princess Royal'	red	*LMS,* Princess Royal Class, 6-8V	35-55?	1500	2000
-	6200 'Princess Royal'	black	*LMS,* Princess Royal Class, 6-8V	35-55?	1500	2000
-	6000 'King George V'	green	*Great* (crest) *Western,* King Class 4-6-0, 6-8V DC	35-55?	800	1200
-	1384	black	*LMS,* ex-L&Y 2-4-2T, 6-8V DC	35-55?	150	250
-	?	red	LMS, Stanier 2-6-0, 6-8V DC	35-55?	NPG	NPG
-	?	black	LMS, Stanier 2-6-0, 6-8V DC	35-55?	NPG	NPG
-	850 'Lord Nelson'	green	*Southern,* Lord Nelson Class 4-6-0, 6-8V DC	35-65?	NPG	NPG
-	?	black	LNER, Class N10 0-6-2	35-65?	NPG	NPG
-	A767 'Sir Valence'	green	*Southern,* King Arthur Class 4-6-0, 6-8V DC	35-65?	NPG	NPG
-	3440 'City of Truro'	green	*Great Western,* City Class 4-4-0, 6-8V DC	35-65?	NPG	NPG
-	?	?	LMS ex-CR 0-4-4T	?	NPG	NPG
-	?	?	Southern Class E1 0-6-0T	?	NPG	NPG

Bond's continued to build models to order in gauges 0 and 1 and, in their catalogues during the 1970s, illustrated an LMS 6247 'City of Liverpool' they had built for a Mr Liverpool.

Coaches

A full range of corridor and suburban coaches was offered for the big four companies and were very well costructed in wood with glazing. They were not quite so heavy in proportion as the Milbro coaches and. at present, sell at around £50-£90 each.

Wagons

These were listed as 'True Scale Model Wagons' and described as 'models of lesser known types of goods stock'. The majority were made of wood and fitted with sprung 3-link couplings and buffers. Some had metal chassis; the LMS 20 ton coke hopper was all metal. Unusual types include an LNER trestle wagon, LNER pulley wagon, Harwich ferry wagon, NE 40 ton hopper (also all metal) and a bogie well wagon with a length of 15½" (390mm).

Present day prices are in the region of £10 for common 4-wheel wagons up to £50 for special use vehicles.

Bond's LMS Jinty 0-6-0T   [table 3]   (Roy Chambers)

Bowman

History

Although they built locomotives for only 10 years, this firm's products had a major impact on the live steam locomotive market and many enthusiasts are continuing to run these engines.

Geoffrey Bowman Jenkins had patented a number of ideas for toy steam boats, which he was successfully making in London. In 1923 he was invited to join forces with the well established firm of Hobbies Ltd at Dereham in Norfolk, who traded in materials and tools for keen amateur woodworkers. With Jenkins' ideas and Hobbies machinery and marketing the firm Bowman Models was established.

The powerful single-acting oscillating-cylinder engines were first placed in a series of successful steamboats and then developed onto horizontal stationary engines. In 1925, the first of three non-reversing model railway locomotives was placed on the market, most being powered by two oscillating cylinders.

The scale of these locomotives was really gauge 1 which allowed for the use of a large boiler and burner (meths fired) but the wheels were built to gauge 0. At this stage, gauge 1 was on the decline so it was advantageous to have models which would run on the more popular 0 gauge track.

Bowman items used to be very cheap but the market has risen over the last two years.

Collecting Club
Bowman collectors are catered for by the Bowman Circle and anyone interested in joining should contact Colin Wilson, telephone 01444 232647.

Locomotives

The largest locomotive was a 4-4-0 tender engine whilst the other three were 0-4-0 tanks, one being smaller in size and a bit nearer 0 scale. Strictly speaking the wheel arrangements were not as just described as the locomotives had no coupling rods, only connecting rods to the rear set of wheels.

The word 'ugly' comes to mind for the description but that is perhaps a bit unkind. Let us say you will go a long way before you will find a real locomotive looking like a Bowman with its long thin cylinders and distinctive safety valve! But, one thing is for sure, they really do perform and you need plenty of stock behind to hold them on the track as there is no speed control mechanism.

Prices – The two prices shown represent the likely range for one in good condition.

Cat.No.	Name / Number	Colour	Details	Years	£	£
1.	**4-4-0 Tender Locomotive** (Freelance)					
The model carried the number on the tender and a crest on cabside.						
234	234, 4472 (and others)	green	*LNER*	25-35	175	250
234	234, 4472 (and others)	black	*LMS*	25-35	175	250
234	234, 4472 (and others)	green	*GWR*	25-35	175	250
234	234, 4472 (and others)	green	*Southern*	25-35	175	250
2.	**Large 0-4-0 Tank Engine** (Freelance)					
265	265	green	*LNER*	26-35	120	160
265	265	red	*LMS*	26-35	120	160
265	265	black	*LMS*	26-35	120	160
3.	**Small 0-4-0 Tank Engine** (Freelance)					
300	300	green	*LNER*	26-35	120	160
300	300	red	*LMS*	26-35	120	160
300	300	black	*LMS*	26-35	120	160
4.	**Small 0-4-0 Tank Engine (Baby Bowman)** (Freelance)					
Single oscillating cylinder on the cab floor driving the rear axle by gearing						
410	410	yell brn	?	?	175	250

Coaches

Passenger stock, made between 1926 and 1935, consisted of a bogie coach with a heavy wooden base and ends but with nicely lithographed tin sides with opening doors. The coach was built to gauge 1 proportions but for 0 gauge track. They are not common and can be more expensive than the locomotives to buy (£200-£260).

Wagons

Between 1926 and 1933, Bowman produced some gauge 1 size rolling stock to go with the locomotives. The four wooden goods wagons consist of a timber wagon (£25-£30), Shell petrol tank wagon (£50-£60), box van (£30-£40) and a guard's van (£35-£45); the last two having tin roofs. Again, the wagons, although 0 gauge, were built to gauge 1 proportions. In June 1933 retailers were informed that the wagons were no longer available.

Bowman 4-4-0 express steam engine
[table 1]

Bowman small 0-4-0 tank
[table 3]

Exley

History

This firm is primarily known for its coaching stock in 00 and 0 gauge and was founded at Bradford by Edward Exley about 1922. Initially the products were locomotives, in live steam, clockwork and electrically powered, in gauges 0 and 1, which were made to order.

By the 1930s, 0 gauge coaches had joined the range of products, and both locos and coaches were available 'off the shelf' as well as to order. During this period the company started supplying Bassett-Lowke with models, including the range of 0 gauge coaches which the latter company sold as their 'scale range'! It should be remembered that this was in the days before current consumer legislation, and as we have seen elsewhere in this catalogue, Bassett-Lowke bought in much of their range of products from other manufacturers and sold them through their catalogues under their own name. At the same time a business relationship was formed with J S Beeson, Mills Bros., Leeds Model Company and others, with much cross fertilisation of products between the parties involved.

In the later 1930s, partly as a result of Vivien Boyd-Carpenter having joined the company, high quality 00 coaching stock was added to feed a growing market in this new scale.

During the Second World War, work turned to the war effort and scale model ships for naval recognition use were made. With the return of peace, the Company retooled in 1945 to produce their railway models again. The underframes and bogies of the early post war coaches were improved from those of the pre-war era, and around 1950 the tooling for the coach bodies was also upgraded to the style most commonly found today.

Edward Exley Ltd also produced industrial models to commissioned orders, which included charabancs, industrial installations, large diesel engines, etc., and continued to supply Bassett-Lowke with 'scale' coaches.

In the early post war years the sales department was in Worksop, Nottinghamshire, with Boyd-Carpenter running this part of the business, although the works were still in Bradford. By 1952, however, Edward Exley (Sales) Ltd had moved to Baslow in Derbyshire and Edward Exley had resigned as a Director of the Sales Company in July 1955 after a disagreement. However, Edward continued to manage the works in Bradford. Furthermore, the catalogue carried the statement 'This Company is not now a manufacturing undertaking'. Lists of coaches in 00 and 0 scale were issued by the factory but these were headed 'Exley of Bradford'.

Locomotives had continued to be available after the war, mainly to order, but in the late 1950s Edward Exley sold the loco construction part of the business to Stanley Beeson, who had made locos for a number of Exley clients. Coaches were listed until 1962 when there was a terrible fire which destroyed the Bradford premises and most of the tools. At this point Edward Exley decided to retire.

The company at Baslow continued to offer coaches but discontinued the 00 gauge range as the manufacturing facility was lost in the fire. The 7mm models were listed as available until the death of Boyd-Carpenter in January 1995, but were in fact being made by outside workers to order. It has to be said that quality of the coaches made after 1962, once a hallmark of the company name, was variable, and to the purist no true Exleys were made after the destruction of the Bradford factory.

After the death of Boyd-Carpenter in 1995, Edward Exley Ltd ceased trading at Baslow, and all the shares and remnants of the company were purchased by Quentin and Tricia Lucas from Fife. In the latter half of the 1990s they rebuilt the company, trading in original Exley models, carrying out restorations, and selling modern finescale 0 gauge kits, models and components. Quentin specialises in the 0 gauge Exley market, and Tricia in 00. They are a familiar sight at model railway exhibitions with an 0 gauge presence, and at selected Train Fairs and Auctions, and operate a mail order service too. In January 1999 they moved the business to near Berwick-upon-Tweed, from where it still operates.

Locomotives (O Gauge)

The majority of the Exley locomotives were hand-built, true to prototype and made to order. In the early days of the company many of them were built by Edward himself, this was his first love in the business, but by the 1930s many were built by employees in the factory, and by other contemporary builders such as Mills Bros. and even Stanley Beeson. As a result of almost no records being kept, exact production details are impossible to obtain.

Pre-war, the Exley catalogue listed the following locos as available in both 0 gauge and gauge 1: Royal Scot, LNER A3, LMS Compound, LNWR Hardwicke, LNER N2, LMS Prince of Wales, LNER 10000, LMS Princess Royal, GNR Single, GWR King, Caledonian 4-6-0, SR Lord Nelson, GWR 2-6-2T, GWR Castle, and a freelance steam 0-4-0 Saddle Tank. All of these were listed as stock items, and others were advertised as built to order.

Post-war catalogues show an LNER 'Flying Scotsman', a Southern 4-6-0 'Lord Nelson', a Southern Schools Class, a 36XX Class GWR 2-4-2T and a number of overseas locomotives for special purposes. Further known products were a NBR J35 and an LMS 2-6-4T. Catalogue illustrations post war were usually of locos that had been supplied to customers, rather than an indication of what may be available from stock. As mentioned above, the locomotive building part of the Bradford business was sold to Stanley Beeson in the late 1950s.

Prices – It is difficult to assess the value of Exley locomotives as they are not often found for sale, nor are they easy to identify. They are very well crafted models with nicely finished detail but they rarely carry the makers mark and when buying, one relies more on the provenance. The price for an Exley locomotive model is entirely dependent upon this as well as originality, condition, and the price the buyer and seller are prepared to negotiate. Naturally locos identified positively as 'Beeson for Exley' attract premium prices. The two prices shown represent the likely range for one in good condition.

Both the editor of this catalogue and the proprietors of Edward Exley Ltd. would welcome information on other locomotives by this manufacturer and further information about those listed here.

Cat.No.	Name / Number	Colour	Details	Years	£	£
1.	**0-6-0DS** (Freelance)	This model had a square bonnet and radiator.				
?	?	green	*LNER*	?	100	150
?	?	black	*LMS*	?	100	150
?	?	various	private owner livery	?	100	150

2. Southern EMU (Exley for Bassett-Lowke)   These were sold as 2-car sets with 12V DC Bassett-Lowke motor bogies and B-L coach bogies. Although made for Bassett-Lowke, they were also sold by Exley. The motor and trailer cars of the Portsmouth set were 3rd class centre corridor brake ends suitably modified, and many were sold with normal SR corridor coaches in the middle, to create the image of the prototype train. A similar suburban set was made from two suburban coaches in the same way, again often with additional non corridor coaches added. The suburban set is much rarer than the Portsmouth set. Prices quoted should be adjusted where additional coaches have been added to the basic 2 car sets.

?	?	green	*Southern* Portsmouth 2-car set	53-60?	1000	1400
?	?	maroon	LMS**	c55	1500	2100
?	3064	green	*Southern*, 2-car suburban set	53-60?	1200	1600

** A very small number of the corridor EMUs were turned out to special order in LMS livery (thought to be less than 10 sets). This was entirely a fictional subject and did not represent any known LMS prototype EMU but, nevertheless, makes a fine looking set.

3.   Miscellaneous Locomotives

?	?	various	private owner 0-6-0ST (freelance)	?	100	150
?	?	green	GWR 4-6-0 King Class	?	800	1200
?	1126	red	*LMS* 4-4-0 Compound	?	350	550
?	?	brown	*NBR* 0-6-0 Class J35	?	350	550
?	?	black	*LMS* 2-6-4T	?	450	650
?	5012, 5412	black	GCR/LNER Class 04/05 ROD 2-8-0	30-50	620	700

Exley LMS Compound

[table 3]

(Model Railway News)

Coaches

Exley coaches were made from aluminium using a wrap-round technique so that roof, sides and solebars were one. This was attached to a wooden floor which pre and early post-war sat high inside the coach body, but from about 1950 sat just above solebar level. Pre-war the ends were an alloy casting showing the end planking detail; bowed if the prototype was. They incorporated a cast lug which screwed to the underside of the floor. From around 1950, using a heavier alloy, the end castings were changed to a more modern pattern which was based on the LMS Stanier coach end. These were retained by copper wires cast into the end at solebar level. The heavier cast ends, with integral buffers also became plastic in the late 1950s.

The windows were glass, held in place by spring clips and should not be taken apart - unless by someone experienced in doing so.

Before the war, battery boxes were usually blocks of wood with little or no underframe detail. Post-war, pressed metal battery boxes were introduced, initially with an open bottom and an indication of truss rodding. Bogies were mounted on a central spigot bolted through the wooden floor.

These construction methods were modified with the introduction of the K5 and K6 series of the '50s. There has been much speculation about the significance of K5 and K6 but, suffice to say, the principal difference between them is that K5 and earlier coaches have painted on the glass window ventilators whereas K6, and the plastic range, have window ventilators stamped out from the metal of the coach side. However, this is not an infallible rule as many K5 coaches have stamped metal vents! K6 coaches, and K5 metal vents, do attract a price premium over those with painted vents.

Apart from modified bogie fittings with the advent of the split pin, the underframes became more detailed and were an all metal construction. The bodies were lowered on the bogies so that no daylight showed underneath and material for the interiors changed in the late 1950s so that they now had coloured seats in metal. The final modification to the coaches themselves was the utilisation of plastic for coach ends, bogies and parts of the underframe, and they now carried the 'BFD EXLEY MODDEX' trade mark.

A variety of bogies have been used with Exley coaches over the years. Pre-war the Exley bogie had pressed steel and cast side frames. They had a central spigot socket and wire bracing and the axle ends were suspended on spring steel wire. Exley coaches sold by Bassett-Lowke were fitted with their range of bogies.

Post-war, Exley bogies developed to the familiar 'V' shaped central stretcher for split pin attachment. These had cast side frames and wire end stretchers, but still with spring steel wire support to the axle ends. Again, coaches sold by Bassett-Lowke were fitted with their post-war compensated bogie. Today, post-war coaches appearing on the market are about evenly divided between the 2 bogie types, and this has no effect upon value.

Quite a variety of coaches were made in the liveries of the big four railway companies and latterly in the crimson & cream and maroon BR colour schemes; although BR coaches generally are far less common. Available to special order were coaches for the pre-grouping companies and freelance concerns. The rare availability on the market of these specials makes it impossible to provide a realistic price guide for them, however, good to excellent examples have changed hands recently at prices between £500 and £1200 each, depending upon the livery they carried and their rarity.

The coaches made before 1940 tend to be more accurate to the prototype whereas after the introduction of the K5 series, which were largely based upon the LMS Stanier profile, it became a matter of changing livery, rainstrips and window positions.

Exley coaches are always impressive, run well and, in their day, were the leaders in their field. More recently, handbuilt scale coaches have overtaken Exleys for the finescale enthusiast, but they still have a major following amongst operators, as well as among collectors.

Prices – At this stage we cannot give a price guide to all the types of coach made but we have given an indication of value, of coaches manufactured after the 2nd World War. A price range for coaches in good to excellent condition is given, poor, altered and well used coaches are worth much less.

Coach details	Colour	£	£
1. Suburban 6-Wheel Coaches 31'			
LMS all 3rd	maroon	175	250
LMS 3rd brake end	maroon	175	250
LMS 1st/3rd	maroon	175	250
LMS Brake Stove R	maroon	200	275
LNER all 3rd	teak	175	250
LNER 3rd brake end	teak	175	250
LNER 1st/3rd	teak	175	250
SR all 3rd	green	175	250
SR 3rd brake end	green	175	250
SR 1st/3rd	green	175	250
GWR all 3rd	chocolate+cream	175	250
GWR 3rd brake end	chocolate+cream	175	250
GWR 1st/3rd	chocolate+cream	175	250
2. Suburban 3rd Brake End 50'			
GWR	chocolate+cream	175	250
LMS	maroon	175	250
LNER	teak	200	275
SR	green	300	350
BR	maroon	NPG	NPG
3. Suburban 1st/3rd 50'			
GWR	chocolate+cream	175	250
LMS	maroon	175	250
LNER	teak	200	275
SR	green	300	350
BR	maroon	NPG	NPG
4. Suburban Full 3rd 50'			
GWR	chocolate+cream	175	250
LMS	maroon	175	250
LNER	teak	200	275
SR	green	300	350
BR	maroon	NPG	NPG
5. Restaurant Car Kitchen 1st 57' & 69'			
LMS 57'	maroon	250	300
LMS 69'	maroon	NPG	NPG
SR 57'	green	350	450
BR 57'	crimson+cream	400	500
6. Restaurant Car 1st/3rd Kitchen 57'			
GWR	chocolate+cream	200	275
7. Kitchen Car 50'			
LMS	maroon	225	300
8. Buffet Car (with bar and pantry)			
LMS	maroon	200	300
SR	green	350	400
LNER	cream+green	300	350
BR	maroon	NPG	NPG
9. Travelling Post Office 57'			
GWR	chocolate+cream	350	425
LMS	maroon	250	325
LNER	teak	400	475
BR	crimson+cream	400	475
BR	maroon	NPG	NPG
10. Ocean Mails Van 57'			
GWR	chocolate+cream	300	375
BR	maroon	NPG	NPG
11. Parcels Train Brake Van 57'			
GWR	chocolate+cream	200	250
BR	maroon	NPG	NPG
12. Non-Gangwayed Full Brake 50'			
GWR	chocolate+cream	175	225
LMS	maroon	150	200
LNER	teak	175	250
SR	green	250	300
BR	crimson+cream	250	300
BR	maroon	NPG	NPG
13. Parcels Train Non-Gangwayed 50'			
GWR	chocolate+cream	200	250
LMS	maroon	150	200
LNER	teak	175	250
SR	green	250	300
14. Corridor Full Brake 57'			
GWR	chocolate+cream	225	250
BR	maroon	NPG	NPG
15. Corridor Full Brake 50'			
LMS	maroon	150	200
LNER	teak	200	250
SR	green	250	300
BR	crimson+cream	275	350
BR	maroon	NPG	NPG
16. Side Corridor 3rd Brake End 57'			
GWR	chocolate+cream	150	200
LMS	maroon	150	200
LNER	teak	250	300
SR	green	275	350
BR	crimson+cream	325	400
BR	maroon	250	300
17. Side Corridor Full 3rd 57'			
GWR	chocolate+cream	150	200
LMS	maroon	150	200
LNER	teak	250	300
SR	green	275	350
BR	crimson+cream	325	400
BR	maroon	250	300
18. Side Corridor Full 1st 57'			
GWR	chocolate+cream	150	200
LMS	maroon	150	200
LNER	teak	250	300
SR	green	275	350
BR	crimson+cream	375	450
BR	maroon	250	300
19. Centre Corridor 3rd Brake End 57'			
LMS	maroon	175	250
LNER	cream+green	375	450
SR	green	300	375
BR	crimson+cream	425	500
BR	maroon	250	300
20. Centre Corridor Full 3rd 57'			
GWR	chocolate+cream	200	250
LMS	maroon	175	250
LNER	green+cream	375	450
SR	green	300	375
BR	crimson+cream	425	500
BR	maroon	250	300
21. Centre Corridor Full 1st 57'			
LMS	maroon	175	250
BR	maroon	NPG	NPG

22.	Sleeping Car 1st/3rd 57' & 69'			
LMS 57'	maroon	175	250
LMS 69'	maroon	275	350

23.	Sleeping Car Full 1st			
GWR	chocolate+cream	275	350
LNER	teak	250	325
BR	maroon	NPG	NPG

24.	Sleeping Car Full 3rd			
GWR	chocolate+cream	275	350
LNER	teak	250	325
BR	maroon	NPG	NPG

25.	Engineer's Inspection Saloon 50'			
LMS	maroon	300	350
BR	maroon	NPG	NPG

Other coaches in pre-grouping and private liveries were available to order.

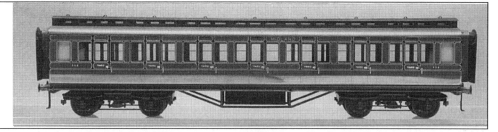

Exley Midland maroon clerestory coach.

(Barry Potter Auctions)

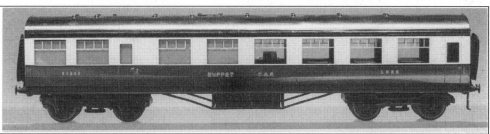

Exley LNER green and cream tourist stock buffet car

[table 8]

(Barry Potter Auctions)

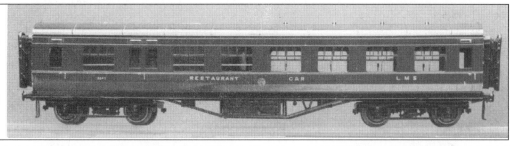

Exley LMS maroon 69' restaurant kitchen car

[table 5]

(Barry Potter Auctions)

Exley GWR travelling post office

[table 9]

(Barry Potter Auctions)

Exley LMS travelling post office

[table 9]

(Barry Potter Auctions)

Hornby M3 LNER tank (EM36) [table 6], SR No.1 special tank (E120) [table 11] and M3 LMS tank (EM36) [table 6]. (Barry Potter Auctions)

Hornby GWR
No.1 tank loco

[table 9]

(Barry Potter Auctions)

Hornby post-war LNER (E502) loco and tender [table 10a] and LMS post-war (101) tank [table 7]. (Barry Potter Auctions)

Hornby No.1 Passenger Set in Midland Railway maroon [table 10]. (Barry Potter Auctions)

Hornby GWR No.1 tank loco (E120) [table 9a] and GWR No.1 Special tender loco [table 12]. (Barry Potter Auctions)

Hornby GWR No.2 tank loco [table 13] and LMS No.1 tender loco [table 10a]. (Barry Potter Auctions)

Hornby 0 Gauge

These models were made by Meccano Ltd at Binns Road, Liverpool, between 1920 and 1962.

History

Hornby Series was started by Frank Hornby, the inventor of Meccano, in 1920 and during a time, following the First World War, when there was strong anti-German feeling. Hitherto, toy trains had been principally imported from Germany by companies like Bassett-Lowke. Although marked 'made in England', the first cheap tinplate LNWR 0-4-0 tender locomotive and coaches, sold under the Hornby name, were based on German designs. However, the backbone of the new Hornby range was the more expensive, better made, nut and bolt constructed series of 0-4-0s in LNWR, GNR and MR company colours. These set a quality standard which was to remain until the demise of Hornby 0 gauge in the early 1960s'.

In 1910, Hornby had taken on two very competent men in key positions within the company. Beardsley was in charge of production and Jones dealt with sales. This proved to be a powerful combination.

Most of the locomotives were freelance in design and although all were beautifully made and finished, some, like the No.3s and the 4-4-2s, were peculiar in character. The products of more prototypical appearance were the No.2 special tender locomotive 4-4-0, the No.4 Schools Class 'Eton' and the top of the range 4-6-2 'Princess Elizabeth'. The latter was introduced in 1937, packed in a very attractive wooden box and cost £5.5.0 at a time when the average weekly wage was about £2.

At the other end of the scale, the market was catered for by the 'M' series, still very nicely made but much more basic.

The locomotives were supported by a large and colourful range of rolling stock, buildings and other accessories; the private owner wagons being particularly attractive. There was also a good range of colourful catalogues (including The Hornby Book of Trains series) and sales leaflets to whet the appetite.

On the death of Frank Hornby, in 1936, his son Roland replaced him as Chairman and George Jones was appointed Managing Director. With a marketing man in charge, Hornby continued to expand its base particularly with the 00 scale Hornby Dublo range

introduced in 1938. On the death of Jones after the war, Beardsley became Managing Director and George Jones marketing skills were very much missed during the 1950s.

After the Second World War the product name had changed from 'Hornby Series' to 'Hornby Trains'. The large locomotives did not return and only 0-4-0 locomotives were made. Bogie rolling stock was scarcer and the range of accessories more limited. The reason was not a shrinkage in the market, indeed, in the first few years after the war the Hornby 0 gauge system was selling quite well. However, trains were no longer the toys of the better-off but had become the toy that every boy wanted. To feed this fast expanding market, and to be more suitable for the typical suburban home, the smaller 00 gauge held preference. Thus British 00 gauge quickly displaced 0 gauge as the country's most popular scale and as the demand for 00 increased, that for Hornby 0 gauge waned.

At the Meccano factory in Liverpool, special attention was now being given to expanding the Hornby-Dublo

Milestones

1901	Frank Hornby invented Meccano.
1908	Meccano Ltd founded.
1914	Meccano Ltd moves to Binns Rd, Liverpool.
1915	Frank Hornby announces he is to make steam engines.
1920	Toy train production starts at Binns Road.
1922	Zulu trains first appear.
1923	Post-grouping liveries.
1924	'Hornby Series' name adopted.
1924	First tab and slot models appear.
1925	Metropolitan electric model introduced.
1926	M Series arrives.
1927	No.3 Pullman sets.
1927	'Hornby Lines' produced in Meccano's American factory.
1928	Meccano Ltd sell their American factory to A.C.Gilbert.
1928	First Southern Railway liveries.
1929	No.2 Special locomotives.
1930	Meccano make a bid for the Canadian market.
1931	Automatic couplings.
1932	Electrically lit accessories.
1932	Countryside sections.
1933	Colour changes on many models.
1934	Automatic reversing in electric locos.
1936	Death of Frank Hornby and Roland Hornby becomes Chairman and George Jones becomes Managing Director.
1937	'Princess Elizabeth' and 'Eton' released.
1938	Arrival of Hornby Dublo points to the future.
1939	First year with no new 0 gauge models.
1941	Toy production closes down.
1946	post-war products reach the shops and are now called 'Hornby Trains' or just 'Hornby'.
1951	Plastic wheels introduced to rolling stock.
1952	M Series models reappeared.
1954	BR liveries begin to appear.
1957	No.50 series wagons arrive as a last ditch attempt to retain interest in Hornby 0 gauge.
1962	Possibly last year of 0 gauge tinplate production.
1964	Lines Bros. invited to take over Meccano Ltd.
1965	Hornby name transferred to Tri-ang Railways to give Tri-ang Hornby.
1965	Meccano Ltd release a plastic Percy Play Train.

range which, for a while in the early 1950s, enjoyed its place as the market leader in Britain. Hornby 0 gauge limped on into the 1960s but production had already ceased when, in 1964, Meccano Ltd invited the toy manufacturing giant, Lines Bros. Ltd, to take them over.

After several months studying the problems at the Meccano factory, Lines Bros. decided to develop the Dinky Toy and Meccano ranges but to not restart the loss-making railway production lines. Instead they set about disposing of the large unsold stocks that had built up in the factory and, until the late 1960s, Hornby 0 Gauge wagons and accessories could be bought for very attractive prices.

Further Reading

For further reading on this subject, the most complete study will be found in 'The Hornby 0 Gauge System' by Chris and Julie Graebe and published by New Cavendish Books (ISBN 0 904568 35 0). By the same authors and publishers there is also the 'Gauge 0 Compendium' (ISBN 0 904568 90 3) which lists model variations and is an excellent guide to dating variations. Both books contain many more variations than we have been able to include here and are strongly recommended for an in-depth study of Hornby 0 Gauge.

Advertisement for Hornby tank engines.

Collectors Club

You may also wish to join the Hornby Railway Collectors Association (HRCA) who publish, for their members, an excellent monthly magazine, called The Hornby Railway Collector, devoted to the toy train and model railway products of Meccano Ltd. Details of this organisation may be obtained from the membership secretary, Bob Field, on Tel: 0115 962 5693.

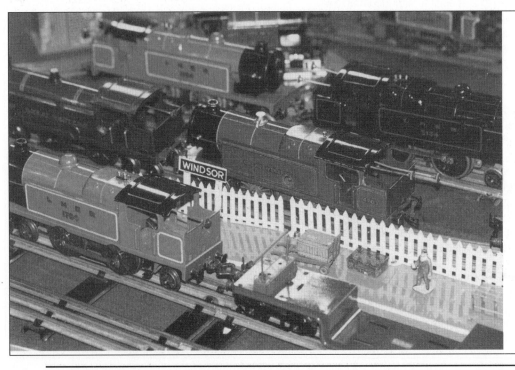

Hornby
No.2 Special tanks

[table 15]

and a No.2 wagon,
platform and
platform accessories.

Loco Search by Type

If you know the *type* of Hornby 0 gauge locomotive you are looking for, the following table will tell you in which table you should look.

Type	Wheels	Table	Type	Wheels	Table	Type	Wheels	Table
'George V' Tender Loco	0-4-0	4	No.2 Tender Loco	4-4-0	14	Metropolitan	0-4-0	20
No.1 Special Tank	0-4-0T	11	LE2	0-4-0	22	No.40 Tank	0-4-0T	7
'Princess Elizabeth'	4-6-2	19	No.2 Special Tender Loco	4-4-0	16	No.0 Tender Loco	0-4-0	8
No.1 Special Tender Loco	0-4-0	12	M0 Tender Loco	0-4-0	1	No.50 Tender Loco	0-4-0	10
'Silver Link', Tender Loco	0-4-0	5	No.20 Tender Loco	0-4-0	1	No.00 Tender Loco	0-4-0	4
No.101 Tank	0-4-0T	7	M1 Tender Loco	0-4-0	2	No.501 Tender Loco	0-4-0	10
'Zulu' Tender Loco	0-4-0T	8	No.30 Tender Loco	0-4-0	3	No.1 Tank	0-4-0T	9
No.2 Tank	4-4-4T	13	M3 Tender Loco	0-4-0	4	No.51 Tender Loco	0-4-0	10
'Zulu' Tank	0-4-0	9	No.3C Tender Loco	4-4-2	17	No.1 Tender Loco	0-4-0	10
No.2 Special Tank	4-4-2T	15	M3 Tank	0-4-0T	6	Streamlined Tender Locos	0-4-0	5
LE1	0-4-0	21	No.4 'Eton' Tender Loco	4-4-0	18			

Loco Search by Number

To help you find your Hornby 0 Gauge locomotive, we have listed below, in the left column, the running numbers that appear on the sides of models and, in the right column, the number of the table(s) in which you will find the model.

Loco No.	Table	Loco No.	Table	Loco No.	Table	Loco No.	Table	Loco No.	Table	Loco No.	Table
0-4-0	9	1000	10a	2301	12	3580	11	6201	19	50153	10a
2	20	1019	13	2323	15	3821	16	6380	8	60199	10a
6	15	1179	12	2329	15	3917	5	6418	11	60985	1
29	9a	1185	16	2449	8+10	4073	17	6600	6+7	82011	7
70	11	1368	12	2509	5	4300	10a	6781	15	A129	11
111	9a	1452	4	2526	2+4	4312	12	6954	15	A179	12
201	16	1504	8	2527	4	4472	1+17	7140	9a	A504	8+10a
234	16	1534	13	2586	11	4525	12	7202	13	A600	9
326	9+9a	1759	16	2595	1	4560	9a	7283	14	A759	8,10+16
4-4-4	13	1784	15	2663	4	4700	12	7391	5	A760	14
460	6,7+13	1842	10a	2691	12	4703	15	8108	11	A950	11
463	9	2051	13	2694	12	4797	8	8123	11	B28	11
483	4	2052	13	2700	12	5096	8+10	8324	8+10	B343	12
492	15	2091	15	2710	4,8+10	5097	8	8327	8+10	B604	13
500	8	2107	13	2711	14	5097	10	8329	15	B667	9
516	11	2115	9a	2728	2+4	5154	15	8712	12	E29	9a
551	8	2120	11	2810	8+10a	5165	13	9319	10a	E111	9a
600	8	2162	11	2900	9a	5399	8	10655	21+22	E126	6+7
623	9+9a	2180	15	2930	2	5500	11	15500	11	E492	13+15
700	16	2221	15	3031	2	5508	8	16045	11	E509	8+10
793	8+10	2243	13	3132	2	5600	8+10a	31240	17	E510	14
826	9a	2251	8	3133	2	6097	10a	31290	17	E793	8+10a
850	17	2270	6+7	3233	1	6100	1+17	31801	17	E850	17
900	18	2290	10a	3435	2	6161	1	45746	3		

Hornby LMS No.2 tender loco [table 14] and early bogie Pullman car [table 3a].

(Barry Potter Auctions)

M Series

These form the bottom end of the range being cheaper, smaller and more toy-like than their relatives and were introduced to compete with the cheaper tin trains of Wells, Brimtoy, etc. The series was colourful and a complete system in its own right with locomotives, rolling-stock, buildings and other accessories. Today the series is probably more admired by toy-collectors than model railway collectors.

No one is sure what the 'M' referred to but it has been suggested that it was derived from 'mechanical', which was used when selling the products abroad instead of the term 'clockwork'.

The 'British Express' was an unusual variation within this series as it was especially made for chain stores and shops which were not normal Hornby outlets. In order to perpetuate this price cutting, these MO products had special tin printings and were devoid of maker's marks. M0 and M1 are the only product series names carried through to the post-war locomotives at the recommencing of manufacture in 1946.

Locomotives

Prices – The chance of finding mint boxed Hornby 0 gauge is so small that the use of the 'mint/boxed' column (right hand one) for this purpose would have no meaning. We have therefore used both price columns to indicate the price range one may expect for examples in very good condition (except for Princess Elizabeth models which had a much higher rate of box survival).

Cat.No.	Name / Number	Colour	Details	Years	£	£

1.   M0 and No.20 Type Tender Locomotives 0-4-0   These were tinprinted, without cylinders and rods but having a fixed key until 1936. From then on it had fitted cylinders, connecting (not coupling) rods and a removable key. The tenders carried numbers only, with no railway companies decals. The British Express trains were produced for sale to non-Hornby agents and so carried no Meccano Ltd identification.

Cat.No.	Name / Number	Colour	Details	Years	£	£
M0	4472	green	black base, cut-out cab windows, c/w	30-32	20	30
M0	2595	green	red or green base, c/w	33-36	25	35
M0, 35	2595	green	cylinders fitted, round printed splashers (1938-41), c/w	36-41	25	
M0	6100	red	black base, cut-out cab windows c/w	30-32	20	30
M0	6161	red	red or green base, c/w	33-36	25	35
M0	6161	red	cylinders fitted, round printed splashers (1938-41), c/w	36-41	25	35
M0	6161, 2595	red or green	wheels unpainted, c/w	46-54	20	30
-	3233	red	British Express Locomotive, black base, no cylinders, no trademark, c/w	32-36	300	350
20	60985	green	BRb black chassis, lined out in orange and black, c/w	54-68	20	30

2.   M1 Tender Locomotives 0-4-0   These tin-printed models were sturdier than the M0, the early examples being copied from a Bing design. The engines had a non-reversible clockwork mechanism, without rods and there were no cylinders or company decals - only numbers. They were almost all green with black chassis and lined out in black and white. The M1 was revised from 1930 with a more modern shaped body (with single piece forming boiler and cab) and a new reversing mechanism. In 1934 two inexpensive electric motors were introduced, EM120 (20 volt) and EM16 (6 volt), both AC.

Cat.No.	Name / Number	Colour	Details	Years	£	£
M1	2526	green	black base, cast chimney, number on tender and cab side, unpainted wheels, c/w	26-32	40	50
M1	2728	green	as above	27-29	40	50
M1, M2930	2930	green	as above but tin chimney	29-32	40	50
M1	3031	green or red	new shape, black base, number on tender only, red wheels, c/w	30	30	40
M1	3132	green or red	as above but tin printed windows	31-33	30	40
M1	3132	dark red	as above	31-33	40	50
M1	3132	green or red	as above but green base	33-34	30	40
M1	3132	dark red	as above	33-34	40	60
M1	3133	green	as above but new number	33-34	30	40
M1	3435	green or red	green, red and black bases, c/w	34-41	30	40
EM120	3435	various	20v motor	34-38	70	80
EM16	3435	various	6v motor	34-38	50	60
M1	3435	green or red	black base, *Hornby* on cabsides, red wheels, c/w	46-58	30	40

3.   No.30 Type Tender Locomotives 0-4-0   Initially designed in 1954 to replace the one-piece pressing M1, it was late being issued and failed to stop the Hornby decline. The No 30 had a larger, squarer, separate cab, an improved tender and was finished in BR green with lion and wheel emblem on the tender. However, the mechanism was the same as the M1 but had very crudely cast con-rods.

Cat.No.	Name / Number	Colour	Details	Years	£	£
30	45746	green	lined orange and black with black chassis and wheels, c/w	56-65	30	40

4. No.00 and M3 (George V) Tender Locomotives 0-4-0

This was an 0-4-0 locomotive with outside cylinders. It was a very early tin-printed design and was based on a Bing original. It was finished in early company colours and had an under-scale tender. A clockwork reversing mechanism was fitted until 1924 after which a larger non-reversing mechanism was fitted. It was referred to as the No.00 engine in 1925 (nothing to do with '00' scale), becoming the M3 tender locomotive in 1926 and finally being paired with the larger M1 style tender with modified open coal rail. Coupling rods were fitted in 1927. No railway company markings were used on the engines in the last two years of the model, when the colour was enamelled instead of tin-printed. There were many sub-variations, especially in the last two years of production, and below we have listed only the main ones.

00, M3	1452	green	GNR on tender, number on cabside, c/w	20-26	60	80
00, M3	483	red	Midland (MR) crest on cabside and number on tender, c/w	20-26	60	80
00, M3	2663 'George the Fifth'	black	LNWR on tender, number on cabside, c/w	20-26	60	80
M3	2526, 2728	green	number on an M1 style tender with cut-out coal rails, c/w	26-28	50	60
M3	2527, 2710	red	number on an M1 style tender with cut-out coal rails, c/w, Midland crest on cabside	26-28	50	60
M3	2710, 2527, 2663 'George the Fifth'	black	number on an M1 style tender with cut-out coal rails, c/w	26-28	50	60
M3	2728, 2710	green, red or black	number on tender, c/w, No.0 style body	28-29	50	70

5. 'Silver Link' and other Streamlined Locomotives 0-4-0

The streamlined 0-4-0 tender locomotives were clockwork and belonged to the 'M' series. It was an 'M' sheep in wolf's clothing! It was heart breaking when you think of the real A4's.

0	2509 'Silver Link'	silver	LNER, number on loco, c/w	36-41	90	100
0	7391	2 green	number on loco and tender, c/w	37-40	100	120
0	3917	mrn+crm	number on loco and tender, c/w	37-40	100	120

6. M3 Tank Locomotives 0-4-0T

This was an 0-4-0 locomotive without cylinders and connecting rods until 1936. Earlier locos that were repaired at factory were often fitted with rods. It had a tin-printed body and no handrail knobs. The engine was fitted with 8-spoke red wheels except between 1932 and 1936 when they were 12-spoke. From 1936, cylinders and rods were fitted.

M3	2270	red	LMS, c/w	31-41	50	70
EM320	2270	red	LMS, 20v motor	32-34	140	180
EM36	2270	red	LMS, 6v motor	34-41	120	140
M3	460	green	LNER, c/w	31-41	50	70
EM320	460	green	LNER, 20v motor	32-34	160	180
EM36	460	green	LNER, 6v motor	34-41	120	140
M3	6600	green	Great Western, c/w	31-41	60	80
EM320	6600	green	Great Western, 20v motor	32-34	180	190
EM36	6600	green	Great Western, 6v motor	34-41	140	160
M3	E126	dk green	Southern, c/w	31-41	70	90
EM320	E126	dk green	Southern, 20v motor	32-34	200	210
EM36	E126	dk green	Southern, 6v motor	34-41	160	180

7. No 101 and No.40 Tank Locomotives 0-4-0T

A post-war 0-4-0 tank locomotive with cylinders, connecting rods and coupling rods, this was a continuation of the pre-war M3 with the same mechanism and body with minor changes in the tinprinting.

101	2270	red	LMS, c/w	47-54	40	60
101	460	green	LNER, c/w	47-54	40	60
101	6600	green	GW, c/w	47-54	60	80
101	E126	green	SR, c/w	47-54	70	90
40	82011	black	BRb, lined, c/w	54-60	40	50
40	82011	black	BRc, lined, c/w	60-65	50	60

Note: Red lining sometimes has pinkish metallic finish.

8. Zulu and No.0 Tender Locomotives 0-4-0

Early examples of this 0-4-0, with outside cylinders and a coal rail tender, had 'Zulu' on the smokebox door but this was later replaced with 'Hornby'. Up until 1928 the wheel splashers were over the rear wheels only but from then on they stretched to cover both sets. In 1931 the whole locomotive was redesigned (rdb) and from now on the tender coal rails were not cut out. All locos were lined out but were made without cylinders until 1937 when outside cylinders were reintroduced to the range. There were many variations of this model, only some of which are listed below. **Note**: In most production runs of Hornby models that were fewer black locomotives and so they normally sell for 30% to 50% more than the coloured ones. Rare numbers such as 1504, add further value.

	'Zulu'	black	Name on splashers in red/gold, c/w	23-24	120	140
0	2710	black or red	LMS on splashers, number on tender, c/w	24-29	80	110
0	2710	black or green	LNER, lined from 1925, red wheels from 1928, c/w	24-29	90	120
0	2710	green	GW on splasher, diecast GWR type safety valve, c/w	26-29	110	140
0	E509	black	Southern + number on tender, red wheels, c/w	28-31	150	200
0	A759	green	Southern + number on tender, red wheels, c/w	28-31	140	180
0	8327, 8324, 600	black or red	LMS on tender, c/w	29-31	120	140
0	5097, 5096,	black or green	LNER and number on tender, c/w	29-31	120	140
0	2449	green	Great (crest) Western on tender, no. on cabside, c/w	29-31	120	140
0	600, 8324, 500, 551, 5600	black or red	LMS, rdb, c/w	31-41	75	100

Cat.No.	Name / Number	Colour	Details	Years	£	£
E06	600, 8324, 500, 551, 5600	blk or red	*LMS*, rdb, 6v motor	34-35	150	160
E020	600, 8324, 500, 551, 5600	blk or red	*LMS*, rdb, 20v motor	34-41	180	200
0	6380, 2810, 5508, 4797	blk or grn	*LNER*, rdb, c/w	31-41	75	100
E06	6380, 2810, 5508, 4797	blk or grn	*LNER*, rdb, 6v motor	34-35	150	160
E020	6380, 2810, 5508, 4797	blk or grn	*LNER*, rdb, 20v motor	34-41	180	200
0	2251, 5399	green	*Great* (crest) *Western*, rdb, c/w	31-41	85	110
E06	2251, 5399	green	*Great* (crest) *Western*, rdb, 6v motor	34-35	160	180
E020	2251, 5399	green	*Great* (crest) *Western*, rdb, 20v motor	34-41	260	280
0	A504, 1504, E793, 793	blk or grn	*Southern*, rdb, c/w	31-41	110	130
E06	A504, 1504, E793, 793	blk or grn	*Southern*, rdb, 6v motor	34-35	180	210
E020	A504, 1504, E793, 793	blk or grn	*Southern*, rdb, 20v motor	34-41	300	350

9. No.1 Tank Locomotives 0-4-0T (original body)

These were 0-4-0 tank locomotives with cylinders and connecting rods. A brass dome was carried until 1928 (except Zulu) after which it was painted. There were wire handrails on the smokebox with brass knob each side and the body was enamelled. In 1931 it received a revised body (see 9a below). **Mechanisms: Clockwork 1922-41, 6 volt DC 1929-31.**

1	'Zulu'	black	red edge to spectacles, name on tank in red/gold, c/w	22-23	130	160
1	-	black	*LMS*, 'Zulu' on front of smokebox, c/w	23-24	130	160
1	0-4-0	red or blk	*LMS* on tank, c/w	24-26	70	90
1	623, 326	black	*LMS*, wheels now black or red, c/w	26-31	70	90
E16	623, 326	black	*LMS*, wheels now black or red, 6v DC motor	29-34	200	250
1	0-4-0	blk or grn	*LNER*, c/w	24-26	70	90
1	623, 326, 463	blk or grn	*LNER*, c/w	26-31	70	90
E16	463	blk or grn	*LNER*, 6v DC motor	29-34	200	250
1	-	green	*Great Western*, crest on some between 1930-31, c/w	26-31	90	110
E16	-	green	*Great Western*, crest on some between 1930-31, 6v DC	29-34	220	280
1	A600, B667	blk or grn	*Southern* and number on tank, c/w	28-31	100	120
E16	A600, B667	blk or grn	*Southern* and number on tank, 6v DC motor	29-34	260	300

9a. No.1 Tank Locomotives 0-4-0T (revised body)

In 1931 a revised body design was adopted for the No.1 tank which was heavier looking with lower chimney, dome, cab and flared bunker. Control rods were now above the bunker (not through its bunker plate as previously). No black body versions were made after 1936.
Mechanisms: Clockwork 1931-41, 6 volt DC. 1931-34, E16 (6 volt). 1934-36, LST1/20 (20 volt). 1932-34, E120 (20 volt) 1934-41.

1	7140, 623, 326, 2115	red or blk	*LMS*, c/w	31-41	80	100
EPM16	7140, 623, 326, 2115	red or blk	*LMS*, 6v motor	34-35	130	150
LTS1/20, E120	7140, 623, 326, 2115	red or blk	*LMS*, 20v motor	32-41	180	200
1	826, 2900	blk or grn	*LNER*, darker green 1936-41, cw	31-41	80	100
EPM16	826, 2900	blk or grn	*LNER*, 6v motor	34-35	130	150
LTS1/20, E120	826, 2900	blk or grn	*LNER*, darker green 1936-41, 20v motor	32-41	180	200
1	4560	green	*Great Western*, c/w	31-34	90	110
EPM16	4560	green	*Great Western*, 6v motor	34-35	130	150
LTS1/20	4560	green	*Great Western*, 20v motor	32-34	180	240
1	4560	green	*GWR* button, c/w	35-41	90	110
E120	4560	green	*GWR* button, 20v motor	35-41	180	240
1	E111, 111, E29, 29	blk or grn	*Southern*, c/w	31-41	100	120
EPM16	E111, 111, E29, 29	blk or grn	*Southern*, 6v motor	34-35	180	220
LST1/20, E120	E111, 111, E29, 29	blk or grn	*Southern*, 20v motor	32-41	250	280

10. No.1 Tender Locomotives 0-4-0 (original body)

The No.1 0-4-0 locomotive had cylinders and connecting rods and was similar to No.0 locomotive but with brass handrail knobs instead of diecast ones. They had cylinders on all variations and the bodies were enamelled. Some early examples had nickel base plates. In 1931, a completely revised and modernised body was fitted (see 10a). **Mechanism: Clockwork 1920-31. N&B = nut and bolt construction**

1	2710	black	LNWR style, N&B, *ML Ltd*, c/w	20-23	100	150
1	2710	green	GN style, N&B, some had red sides to running plate, *ML Ltd*, c/w	20-23	100	150
1	2710	maroon	MR style, N&B, *ML Ltd*, c/w	20-23	100	150
1	2710	blue	CR style, N&B, *ML Ltd*, c/w	20-23	200	250
1	2710	red or black	*LMS* on RH splasher, number on cabsides, c/w	23-24	100	150
1	2710	red or black	*LMS* on both splashers, number on tender, c/w	25-29	100	150
1	2710	green	*LNER* on RH splasher, number on cabsides, red side plates, c/w	23-24	100	150
1	2710	green	*LNER* on both splashers, number on tender, red sides till '26, c/w	25-29	100	150
1	2710	black	*LNER* on both splashers, number on tender, c/w	24-29	150	180
1	8324	red	*LMS* on coal-rail tender, c/w, long splashers, number on cabside	29-31	100	150
1	8327	black	*LMS* on coal-rail tender, c/w, long splashers, number on cabside	29-31	150	180
1	5096	green	*LNER* + number on tender, c/w, long splashers, 232 on cabside	29-31	100	150
1	5097	black	*LNER* + number on tender, long splashers, 232 on cabside, c/w	29-31	150	180
1	8324	green	*LNER* + number on tender, long splashers, 232 on cabside, c/w	30-31	200	240
1	2710	green	*GW* on splasher, crest on cab, number on coal rail tender, c/w	26-29	150	180
1	8327	black	*Great* (crest) *Western*, number on coal rail tender, c/w	26-29	150	180

1	2449	green	*Great* (crest) *Western*, number on cabside, coal rail tender, c/w, long splashers	29-31	150	180
1	A759	green	*Southern* + number on tender, c/w	28-29	200	240
1	E509	black	*Southern* green lining + number on tender, c/w	28-29	250	300
1	A759	green	*Southern* + number on coal rail tender, c/w, long splashers, 232 on cabside	29-31	200	240
1	E509	black	*Southern* + number on coal rail tender, c/w, long splashers, 232 on cabside	29-31	250	300

Note: There were numerous detailed variations on the No.1 tender locomotives.

10a. No.1, No.501, No.50 and No.51 Tender Locomotives 0-4-0

The new body for the No1 tender locomotive, introduced in 1931, had a larger diameter boiler, long splashers, low chimney and dome and a cab with two windows each side. Driving wheels were normally red and a heavier type tender with solid top rails was used.

Mechanism: Clockwork 1931-41, E16 (6 volt) 1934-35, E120 (20 volt) 1934-41. N&B = nut and bolt construction.

The No.501 was a post WWII continuation of the No.1. The enamel was finished with a matt varnish (as were the very late No.1's from 1939). Electric 20 volt versions, numbered E502, are quite rare, having all been sent for export. No black liveries were made in the 501 series and wheels were black except for the LNER c/w locomotive which was produced with green wheels. New details were: a centre lamp bracket above the front coupling and lamp brackets on the rear of the tender.

The No 50 and 51 were basically the same as the No.501 but updated with the introduction of BR liveries, emblems and numbers, being smartly lined out and finished in gloss. They were made only in clockwork.

1	1000	red	*LMS* on tender, number on cabside, c/w	31-41	100	150
1	2290	black	*LMS* on tender, number on cabside, c/w	31-36	100	150
1	5600	red	*LMS* on tender, number on cabside, c/w	36-41	100	150
E16	1000, 2290	red or black	*LMS* on tender, number on cabside, 6v motor	34-35	180	240
E120	1000, 2290, 5600	red or black	*LMS* on tender, number on cabside, 20v motor	34-41	240	280
1	2810	green	*LNER* on tender, number on cabside, darker from '36, c/w	31-41	100	150
1	6097	black	*LNER* on tender, number on cabside, c/w	31-36	100	150
1	1842	green	*LNER* on tender, number on cabside, darker from '36, c/w	39-41	100	150
E16	2810, 6097	green or black	*LNER* on tender, number on cabside, 6v motor	34-35	180	240
E120	2810, 6097, 1842	green or black	*LNER* on tender, number on cabside, 20v motor	34-41	240	280
1	4300	green	*Great* (crest) *Western* on tender, number on cabside, c/w	31-34	140	180
E120	4300	green	*Great* (crest) *Western* on tender, number on cabside, 20v AC	31-34	250	300
1	4300	green	*GWR* button on tender, number on cabside, c/w	35-38	140	180
E16	4300	green	*Great* (crest) *Western* on tender, number on cabside, 6v motor	34-35	200	250
E120	4300	green	*GWR* button on tender, number on cabside, 20v motor	34-38	250	300
1	9319	green	*GWR* button on tender, number on cabside, c/w	38-41	140	180
E120	9319	green	*GWR* button on tender, number on cabside, 20v motor	38-41	250	300
1	E793	green	*Southern* and number on tender, c/w	31-33	250	300
1	793	green	*Southern* and number on tender, c/w	33-41	200	250
E16	793	green	*Southern* and number on tender, 6v motor	34-35	280	320
E120	793	green	*Southern* and number on tender, 20v motor	34-41	300	350
1	A504	black	*Southern* and number on tender, c/w	31-36	300	320
E16	A504	black	*Southern* and number on tender, 6v motor	34-35	320	360
E120	A504	black	*Southern* and number on tender, 20v motor	34-36	350	400
501	5600	red	*LMS*, cabside number was sans-serif after 1 year, c/w	48-54	60	80
E502	5600	red	*LMS*, cabside number was sans-serif after 1 year, 20v	48-54	200	250
501	1842	green	*LNER*, cabside number was sans-serif after 1 year, c/w	48-54	60	80
E502	1842	green	*LNER*, cabside number was sans-serif after 1 year, 20v	48-54	200	250
501	9319	green	*G* (crest) *W*, cabside number, c/w	48-49	300	350
E502	9319	green	*G* (crest) *W*, cabside number, 20v motor	48-49	400	450
50	60199	black	BRb, lined red and grey, c/w	54-61	65	95
51	50153	green	BRb, lined orange and black, c/w	54-61	65	95

Note: There were numerous detailed variations on the No.1 tender locomotives.

11. No.1 Special Tank Locomotives 0-4-0T

These were heavy 0-4-0 locomotives with cylinders and connecting rods. They were larger than other 0-4-0 tanks and had more powerful mechanisms. They were finished in the four railway company colours, and in black liveries (except for the GWR version). Red and black engines had red wheels while green engines had green wheels.

Mechanisms: Clockwork 1929-41, EPM16 (6 volt) 1934-39, and E120 special (20 volt) 1934-41.

1	6418	red	*LMS*, sans-serif letters and numbers, shadowed, c/w	29-30	140	150
1	2120	red	*LMS*, serif letters and numbers, shadowed, c/w	30-34	120	150
1	15500	red	*LMS*, serif letters and numbers, shadowed, c/w	34-36	180	200
EPM16	15500	red	*LMS*, serif letters and numbers, shadowed, 6v motor	34-36	220	280
E120	15500	red	*LMS*, serif letters and numbers, shadowed, 20v motor	34-36	300	350
1	70	red	*LMS*, sans-serif figures '37-'39, c/w	36-41	120	150
EPM16	70	red	*LMS*, sans-serif figures '37-'39, 6v motor	36-39	200	250
E120	70	red	*LMS*, sans-serif figures '37-'39, 20v motor	36-41	250	320
1	16045	black	*LMS*, sans-serif letters for first two years, then with serifs, c/w	29-36	180	240
EPM16	16045	black	*LMS*, sans-serif letters for first two years, then with serifs, 6v	34-36	250	280
E120	16045	black	*LMS*, sans-serif letters for first two years, then with serifs, 20v	34-36	340	380

Cat.No.	Name / Number	Colour	Details	Years	£	£
1	8123	green	*LNER*, seven painted bands on boiler in first year then eight, c/w	29-35	120	150
EPM16	8123	green	*LNER*, seven painted bands on boiler, later eight, 6v motor	34-35	200	250
E120	8123	green	*LNER*, seven painted bands on boiler, later eight, 20v motor	34-35	250	320
1	2162	green	*LNER*, darker green from 1936, c/w	35-41	180	220
EPM16	2162	green	*LNER*, darker green from 1936, 6v motor	35-39	250	280
E120	2162	green	*LNER*, darker green from 1936, 20v motor	35-41	280	340
1	8108	black	*LNER*, c/w	29-30	150	200
1	2586	black	*LNER*, c/w	30-36	200	240
EPM16	2586	black	*LNER*, 6v motor	34-36	250	280
E120	2586	black	*LNER*, 20v motor	34-36	340	380
1	3580	green	*Great Western*, 7 boiler bands 1st year and 8 in 2nd, c/w	29-30	150	200
1	5500	green	*Great Western*, number not on plate for 1st 2 years, c/w	30-35	180	220
EPM16	5500	green	*Great Western*, number not on plate for 1st 2 years, 6v motor	30-35	250	280
E120	5500	green	*Great Western*, number not on plate for 1st 2 years, 20v motor	30-35	340	380
1	5500	green	*GWR* button, number on plate, c/w	36-41	180	220
EPM16	5500	green	*GWR* button, number on plate, 6v motor	36-39	250	280
E120	5500	green	*GWR* button, number on plate, 20v motor	36-41	340	380
1	A950	green	*Southern*, sans-serif letters, white/black lining, c/w	29-30	350	400
1	B28	green	*Southern*, serif lettering, white/black lining, c/w	30-35	350	400
EPM16	B28	green	*Southern*, serif lettering, white/black lining, 6v motor	34-35	400	500
E120	B28	green	*Southern*, serif lettering, white/black lining, 20v motor	34-35	800	900
1	516	green	*Southern*, white/black lining, c/w	35-41	200	250
EPM16	516	green	*Southern*, white/black lining, 6v	35-39	250	300
E120	516	green	*Southern*, white/black lining, 20v	35-41	350	400
1	A129	black	*Southern*, green lining, c/w	29-30	500	600
1	A950	black	*Southern*, now with serif letters, c/w	30-36	400	450
EPM16	A950	black	*Southern*, now with serif letters, 6v motor	34-36	550	600
E120	A950	black	*Southern*, now with serif letters, 20v motor	34-36	600	700

12. No.1 Special Tender Locomotives 0-4-0 These were similar to the previous models but with splashers over the wheels instead of side tanks. They were paired with a four-wheeled tender that was larger than that used with other 0-4-0 models. Other details were those already described for the No.1 Special Tank Loco except that 6 volt mechanisms were not fitted to this model.

1	4312, 4525	red	*LMS* shadowed serif on unlined tender, plain gold numbers on cabside, c/w	29-30	280	320
1	4312	red	*LMS* (serif), lined tender, c/w	30-31	280	320
1	8712	red	*LMS* (serif), lined tender, numbers on cabside, c/w	31-35	280	320
E120	8712	red	*LMS* (serif), lined tender, numbers on cabside, 20v motor	34-35	500	550
1	2700	red	*LMS* letters on lined tender, c/w	35-41	250	300
E120	2700	red	*LMS* letters on lined tender, 20v motor	35-41	300	350
1	4525	black	*LMS* in gold on tender but shadowed after 1st year, c/w	29-36	320	360
E120	4525	black	*LMS* in gold shadowed on tender, 20v motor	34-36	500	550
1	2694	green	*LNER* + large no. on tender, small no. on cabside, black boiler bands 1st year then white, c/w	29-31	200	240
1	1368	green	*LNER*, on tender, large number on cabside, darker '36>, c/w	31-41	200	240
E120	1368	green	*LNER*, on tender, large number on cabside, darker '36>, 20v	34-41	350	380
1	2691	black	*LNER* + number in gold on tender, oval on cabsides, c/w	29-36	320	360
E120	2691	black	*LNER* + number in gold on tender, oval on cabsides, 20v	34-36	500	550
1	2301	green	*Great* (crest) *Western* on tender, c/w	29-34	300	350
1	4700, 2301	green	*Great O Western* on tender, c/w	34-35	250	300
E120	4700	green	*Great Western* on tender, 20v	34-35	350	400
1	4700	green	*GWR* button on tender, c/w	36-41	250	300
E120	4700	green	*GWR* button on tender, 20v	36-41	350	400
1	A179	green	*Southern*, small number on cabside oval, c/w	29-35	350	400
E120	A179	green	*Southern*, small number on cabside oval, 20v motor	34-35	550	600
1	1179	green	*Southern* + large number on tender, c/w	35-41	350	400
E120	1179	green	*Southern* + large number on tender, 20v motor	35-41	650	700
1	B343	black	*Southern* + large number on tender, green lining, c/w	29-36	500	600
E120	B343	black	*Southern* + large number on tender, green lining, 20v motor	34-36	650	700

13. No.2 Tank Locomotives 4-4-4T This was the only 4-4-4 locomotive made by Hornby and had the character of tank engines of the early years of the 20th century, especially on the LNWR. Produced from 1923-29 in clockwork only, there were many detail variations including 24 on LMS locos alone! We have not been able to deal with all of them here. Two lamps were fixed on front of the locomotive from 1924 onwards.

2	1019	red	*LM&SR*, part lined, c/w	23	220	250
2	-	red or blk	*LM&S*, part lined, c/w	23	220	250
2	4-4-4	red or blk	*LMS*, fully lined, c/w	24-26	150	200
2	2052	red or blk	LMS, crest on bunker, c/w	26-28	150	200
2	2107, 2051, 2052	red or blk	*LMS* sometimes on bunker plate and later on tank side, c/w	28-29	150	200
2	-	green	*L&NER*, red side plates, lined bunker, c/w	23	180	220

2	1534	green	L&NER, red side plates, lined tanks, c/w	23	180	220
2	4-4-4	grn or blk	L&NER, red side plates, full lining, c/w	24-25	180	220
2	4-4-4	grn or blk	LNER, full lining, c/w	25-26	180	220
2	460	grn or blk	LNER, crest on cabsides, c/w	26	180	220
2	460, 5165	grn or blk	LNER, crest on bunker, c/w	27-29	180	220
2	-	green	Great Western, crest on cab, c/w	26	200	250
2	7202, 2243	green	Great (crest) Western, c/w	27-29	200	250
2	B604	green	Southern, c/w	28-29	300	350
2	E492	black	Southern, c/w	28-29	350	400

14. No.2 Tender Locomotives 4-4-0 These were elegant 4-4-0 locomotives of early 20th century character. They were powered by clockwork only, except for a very special orders. Produced between 1921 and 1929, they had a six-wheeled coal rail tender which usually carryied the number '2711'; although there are other variations. For the first two years, the locos were made in pre-grouping colours (GN - green, MR - red, CR - blue, LNWR - black) but, after this, the colours of the four grouped companies were introduced. Black engines were again available for all companies except the GWR. The driving wheels were covered by long splashers and the domes were mainly brass. The model was of nut and bolt construction, using Meccano nuts and bolts. The locos had two fixed front lamps from late 1924 onwards.

Electric Models : These exceptionally rare examples were Hornby's first venture into electric mechanisms. No sound price guide is available on the electric versions as they are very rare and usually in poor condition when found. £1300 is a very broad guide.

2	2711	red	MR style, number on brass cab plate, Meccano transfers, c/w	21-23	180	300
2	2711	green	GNR style, number on brass cab plate, Meccano transfers, red valances, c/w	21-23	180	300
2	2711	black	LNWR style, number on brass cab plate, Meccano t'fers, c/w	21-23	180	300
2	2711	blue	CR style, number on brass cab plate, Meccano transfers, c/w	21-23	250	300
2	2711	red or blk	LM&S on splashers, metal cabside number, pre-grouping tender, c/w	23	250	300
2	2711	red or blk	LMS on LH splasher, trademark transfer on other splasher, metal cabside number, pre-grouping tender, c/w	23	250	300
2	2711	red or blk	LMS on both splashers and tender, metal cabside number, c/w	24	180	230
2	2711	red or blk	LMS on both splashers, number on tender, crest on cabside, c/w	24-29	180	230
2	2711	green	GN crests on splashers, metal cabside number, c/w	23	250	300
2	2711	green	L&NER on LH splasher, GN crest on other splasher, metal cabside number, c/w	23	250	300
2	2711	green	L&NER on both splashers and tender, metal cabside number, c/w	23	180	230
2	2711	green	LNER on both splashers and number on tender, c/w	24-29	180	230
2	2711	black	LNER on splashers, crest on cabsides, c/w	24-27	200	250
2	2711	black	LNER crest on cabsides, no lettering on splashers, c/w	28-29	200	250
2	2711	green	GW on splashers, number on tender, GWR crest on cab, c/w	26	250	280
2	2711/7283	green	Great (crest) Western on splashers, 7283 on cab and 2711 on tender, c/w	27-28	250	280
2	7283	green	Great (crest) Western, on tender and number on cabsides, c/w	29	400	500
2	A760	green	Southern and number on tender, c/w	28-29	400	450
2	E510	black	Southern and number on tender, c/w	28-29	450	500

15. No.2 Special Tank Locomotives 4-4-2T This was a 4-4-2 updated replacement for the No.2 tank and was produced from 1929 until 1941. Larger driving wheels were fitted to the later improved mechanisms and smokebox bulbs were used from 1933 onwards. It was a heavier looking engine than the No.2 with higher boiler and lower chimney, dome and cab. It had no outside cylinders but there were two fixed front lamps until 1930 when they were replaced by four brackets front and rear.

Mechanisms: powered by clockwork, 6V 30-34, 6V E26 34-41, 20V LST2/20 33-34, 20V E220 34-41. The early electric motors had protruding brushes.

2	2323	red	LMS and number sans-serif, c/w	29-30	150	190
2	2180	red	LMS and number serif, c/w	30-36	130	170
2, E26	2180	red	LMS and number serif, 6v motor	30-36	240	280
LST 2/20, E220	2180	red	LMS and number serif, 20v motor	33-36	280	340
2	6954	red	LMS and number serif (except 37-39), matt '39>, c/w	36-41	120	160
E26	6954	red	LMS and number serif (except 37-39), matt '39>, 6v motor	36-41	220	270
E220	6954	red	LMS and number serif (except 37-39), matt '39>, 20v motor	36-41	260	320
2	6781	black	LMS sans-serif, c/w	29-30	220	260
2	6781	black	LMS serif, c/w	31-36	200	240
2, E26	6781	black	LMS serif, 6v motor	30-36	260	290
LST 2/20, E220	6781	black	LMS serif, 20v motor	33-36	325	350
2	6	green	LNER, c/w	29-32	170	220
2	1784	green	LNER, darker green '36>, matt '39>, green wheels, c/w	32-41	130	170
2, E26	1784	green	LNER, darker green '36>, matt '39>, green wheels, 6v motor	32-41	220	270
LST 2/20, E220	1784	green	LNER, darker green '36>, matt '39>, green wheels, 20v motor	33-41	260	320
2	5154	black	LNER + numbers gold on tank, red lining, black wheels, c/w	29-36	220	240
2, E26	5154	black	LNER + numbers gold on tank, red lining, black wheels, 6v	30-36	260	290

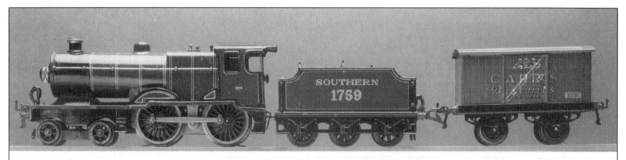

Hornby No.2 Special tender loco Southern L1 [table 16] and Carr's Biscuits van. (Barry Potter Auctions)

Hornby No.2 Special tender loco LMS Compound [table 16] and Crawford's Biscuits van. (Barry Potter Auctions)

Hornby No.2 Special tender loco GWR 'County of Bedford' [table 16] and United Dairies milk tank wagon. (Barry Potter Auctions)

Hornby No.2 Special tender loco LNER 'Yorkshire' [table 16] and Cadbury's van. (Barry Potter Auctions)

Hornby No.2 Special tender loco LNER 'Bramham Moor' [table 16] and Nestles milk tank wagon. (Barry Potter Auctions)

LST 2/20, E220	5154	black	*LNER* + numbers gold on tank, red lining, black wheels, 20v	33-36	325	350
2	4703	green	*Great Western*, c/w	29-30	250	300
2	2221	green	*Great Western*, number plate on cabside '32>, c/w	30-36	200	240
2, E26	2221	green	*Great Western*, number plate on cabside '32>, 6v motor	30-36	250	300
LST 2/20, E220	2221	green	*Great Western*, number plate on cabside '32>, 20v motor	33-36	300	350
2	2221	green	*GWR* button, number plate on cabside, late ones matt, c/w	36-41	200	240
E26	2221	green	*GWR* button, number plate on cabside, late ones matt, 6v motor	36-41	250	300
E220	2221	green	*GWR* button, number plate on cabside, later matt, 20v motor	36-41	300	350
2	8329	green	*Southern* + number (on bunker) sans-serif, c/w	29	300	350
2	8329	green	*Southern* + number on tanks and serif, c/w	30-33	250	300
2	8329	green	*Southern* + number on tanks and serif, 6v motor	30-33	280	320
2	2329	green	*Southern*, c/w	33-35	220	260
2, E26	2329	green	Southern, 6v motor	33-35	240	280
LST 2/20, E220	2329	green	*Southern*, 20v motor	33-35	320	380
2	2091	green	*Southern*, matt finish '39>, c/w	35-41	200	240
E26	2091	green	*Southern*, matt finish '39>, 6v motor	35-41	220	260
E220	2091	green	*Southern*, matt finish '39>, 20v motor	35-41	300	350
2	E492	black	*Southern* sans-serif, number on bunker, red wheels, c/w	29	NPG	NPG
2	E492	black	*Southern* + number on tanks and serif, early whls red late blk, c/w	30-33	300	320
2	E492	black	*Southern* + number on tanks and serif, early whls red late blk, 6v	30-33	320	350
2	492	black	*Southern*, c/w	33-36	320	350
2, E26	492	black	*Southern*, 6v motor	33-36	340	380
LST 2/20, E220	492	black	*Southern*, 20v motor	33-36	500	600

The production of black 'goods' engines was stopped after 1936 but they were obtainable by special order at extra cost.

16. No.2 Special Tender Locomotives 4-4-0 These were 4-4-0 tender locomotives and were Hornby's first real venture into true-to-type models. They were and are a very attractive and popular range embodying the character of the prototypes.
Mechanisms: Clockwork 1929-41, E220 (20 volt) 1934-41, 6V special order.

2	1185	maroon	Compound, *LMS* (sans-serif) red drivers + running plate, unlined tender, c/w	29-30	275	325
2	1185	maroon	Compound, *LMS* (serif) black drivers + running plate, lined tender, c/w	31-36	350	400
E220	1185	maroon	Compound, *LMS* (serif) black drivers + running plate, lined tender, 20v motor	34-37	550	600
2	1185	maroon	Compound, *LMS* (sans-serif) black drivers + running plate, lined tender, c/w	37-38	350	400
E220	1185	maroon	Compound, *LMS* (sans-serif) black drivers + running plate, lined tender, 20v motor	37-38	550	600
2	1185	maroon	Compound, *LMS* (serif) black drivers + running plate, lined tender, matt finish, c/w	39	350	400
E220	1185	maroon	Compound, *LMS* (serif) black drivers + running plate, lined tender, matt finish, 20v motor	39	550	600
2	700	black	Class 2P, *LMS* , no cylinders, special order, beware imitations	38	3000	4000
2	234 'Yorkshire'	green	Shire Class, *LNER* + number on tender, small cab numberplates, c/w	29	550	650
2	234 'Yorkshire'	green	Shire Class, *LNER* on tender, number on cabside, green running plate, c/w	30-31	550	650
2	234 'Yorkshire'	green	Shire Class, *LNER* on tender, number on cabside, black running plate, c/w	31-35	550	650
E220	234 'Yorkshire'	green	Shire Class, *LNER* on tender, number on cabside, black running plate, 20v	34-35	950	1050
2	234 'Yorkshire'	black	Shire Class, *LNER*, white lining, special order	31-32	3000	4000
2	201 'Bramham Moor'	green	Hunt Class, *LNER*, c/w	35-36	550	600
E22	201 'Bramham Moor'	green	Hunt Class, *LNER*, 20v motor	35-36	900	1000
2	201 'Bramham Moor'	green	Hunt Class, *LNER*, darker green, c/w	36-41	550	600
E220	201 'Bramham Moor'	green	Hunt Class, *LNER*, darker green, 20v motor	36-41	900	1000
2	3821 'County of Bedford'	green	County Class, *Great* (crest) *Western*, green running plates, red nameplates, c/w	29-30	1000	1100
2	3821 'County of Bedford'	green	County Class, *Great* (crest) *Western*, black running plates and nameplates, c/w	30-36	550	600
E220	3821 'County of Bedford'	green	County Class, *Great* (crest) *Western*, black running plates and nameplates, 20v motor	34-36	900	1000
2	3821 'County of Bedford'	green	County Class, *GWR* button, black running plates, c/w	36-41	550	600
E220	3821 'County of Bedford'	green	County Class, *GWR* button, black running plates, 20v motor	36-41	900	1000

Cat.No.	Name / Number	Colour	Details	Years	£	£
2	A759	green	Class L1, *Southern*, lined cabside, unlined tender, c/w	29	1100	1500
2	A759	green	Class L1, *Southern*, lined tender, c/w	30-35	900	1200
E220	A759	green	Class L1, *Southern*, lined tender, 20v motor	34-35	1300	1600
2	1759	green	Class L1, *Southern*, lined tender, c/w	35-41	900	1200
E220	1759	green	Class L1, *Southern*, lined tender, 20v motor	35-41	1300	1600

17. Riviera Blue Train and No.3 Tender Locomotives 4-4-2

These 4-4-2 tender engines were of rather odd freelance appearance with their large cylinders and double thickness running plates. They were nothing like the top expresses they are named after. This was almost 'badge engineering', and ironically they were coupled to the excellent No 2 special tenders (except for the 'Nord' which has a bogie tender and was made for the Riviera 'Blue Train' Set).

Mechanisms: Clockwork 26-40, 3E 4 volt 26-29, 3E 6 volt 29-34, E36 6 volt 34-36, E3/20 20 volt 33-34, E320 20 volt 34-40.

Cat.No.	Name / Number	Colour	Details	Years	£	£
3C	31240	brown	*Nord 31801* on tender, black running plate and brass domes, c/w	26-27	200	250
3E	31240	brown	*Nord 31801* on tender, black running plate and brass domes, 4v motor	26-27	220	260
3C	31240	brown	*Nord 31801* on tender, brown running plate and domes, c/w	28-29	220	260
3E	31240	brown	*Nord 31801* on tender, brown running plate and domes, 4v motor	28-29	240	280
3C	31801	brown	*Nord*, black smokebox 1930>,c/w	29-33	220	280
3E	31801	brown	*Nord*, black smokebox 1930>, 6v motor	29-33	280	320
E3/20	31801	brown	*Nord*, black smokebox 1930>, 20v motor	33	320	350
3C	31801	brown	*Nord*, black smoke deflectors, c/w	34-36	250	300
E36	31801	brown	*Nord*, black smoke deflectors, 6v motor	34-36	280	320
E320	31801	brown	*Nord*, black smoke deflectors, 20v motor	34-36	320	350
3C	31801	brown	*Nord*, brown smoke deflectors and smoke box, c/w	36-38	250	300
E320	31801	brown	*Nord*, brown smoke deflectors and smoke box, 20v motor	36-38	320	350
E320	3.1290	brown	*Nord*, brown smoke deflectors and smoke box, cab lined gold only, 20v motor	38-41	380	450
3C	6100 'Royal Scot'	red	LMS, crest on cab and number on coal rail tender, c/w	27-29	200	220
3E	6100 'Royal Scot'	red	LMS, crest on cab and number on coal rail tender, 4v motor	27-29	220	250
3C	6100 'Royal Scot'	red	gold number on cab and number or *LMS* on tender, c/w	29-30	200	220
3E	6100 'Royal Scot'	red	gold number on cab and number or *LMS* on tender, 4v motor	29-30	220	250
3C	6100 'Royal Scot'	red	gold number on cab and number or *LMS* (shaded '33>) on lined tender, c/w	30-36	200	220
3E, E36	6100 'Royal Scot'	red	gold number on cab and number or *LMS* (shaded '33>) on lined tender, 6v motor	30-36	220	250

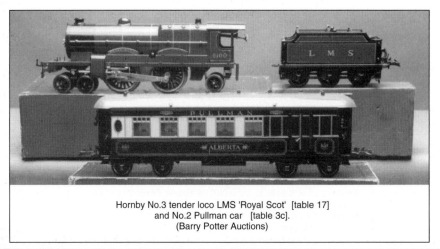

Hornby No.3 tender loco LMS 'Royal Scot' [table 17]
and No.2 Pullman car [table 3c].
(Barry Potter Auctions)

Hornby No.3 tender loco Southern 'Lord Nelson' [table 17] and LMS gunpowder van. (Barry Potter Auctions)

E3/20, E320	6100 'Royal Scot'	red	gold number on cab and number or *LMS* (shaded '33>) on lined tender, 20v motor	33-36	340	380
3C	6100 'Royal Scot'	red	smoke deflectors, gold number on cab and number or *LMS* shaded on lined tender, c/w	36-41	240	290
E320	6100 'Royal Scot'	red	smoke deflectors, gold number on cab and number or *LMS* shaded on lined tender, 20v	36-40	340	380
3C	4472 'Flying Scotsman'	green	*LNER* + number on coal-rail tender, crest on cab, green smokebox, c/w	27	200	250
3E	4472 'Flying Scotsman'	green	*LNER* + number on coal-rail tender, crest on cab, green smokebox, 4v motor	27	220	250
3C	4472 'Flying Scotsman'	green	*LNER* + number on coal-rail tender, crest on cab, black smokebox, c/w	28	200	250
3E	4472 'Flying Scotsman'	green	*LNER* + number on coal-rail tender, crest on cab, black smokebox, 4v motor	28	220	250
3C	4472 'Flying Scotsman'	green	*LNER* + number on coal-rail tender, gold number on cab, black smokebox, c/w	29	200	250
3E	4472 'Flying Scotsman'	green	*LNER* + number on coal-rail tender, gold number on cab, black smokebox, 4v motor	29	220	250
3C	4472 'Flying Scotsman'	green	*LNER* (shadowed '33>) on No2 tender, gold number on cab, black smokebox, c/w	30-36	200	250
3E, E36	4472 'Flying Scotsman'	green	*LNER* (shadowed '33>) on No2 tender, gold number on cab, black smokebox, 6v motor	30-36	220	250
E3/20, E320	4472 'Flying Scotsman'	green	*LNER* (shadowed '33>) on No2 tender, gold number on cab, black smokebox, 20v motor	33-36	300	350
3C	4472 'Flying Scotsman'	green	as above but darker green, c/w	36-41	250	300
E320	4472 'Flying Scotsman'	green	as above but darker green, 20v	36-41	350	400
3C	4472 'Flying Scotsman'	green	*LNER* with smoke deflectors, rare	34-36?	NPG	NPG
E320	4472 'Flying Scotsman'	black	*LNER*, extremely rare, watch out for fakes!	37	2500	3500
3C	4073 'Caerphilly Castle'	green	*Great* (crest) *Western* on coal-rail tender, green smoke box, c/w	27-28	250	350
3E	4073 'Caerphilly Castle'	green	*Great* (crest) *Western* on coal-rail tender, green smoke box, 4v	27-28	240	280
3C	4073 'Caerphilly Castle'	green	*Great* (crest) *Western* on tender, black smoke box, brass whistle, No.2 tender from '30>, c/w	29-36	260	320
3E, E36	4073 'Caerphilly Castle'	green	*Great* (crest) *Western* on tender, black smoke box, brass whistle, No.2 tender from '30>, 6v motor	29-36	240	280
E3/20, E320	4073 'Caerphilly Castle'	green	*Great* (crest) *Western* on tender, black smoke box, brass whistle, No.2 tender from '30>, 20v motor	33-36	400	450
3C E3/20, E320	4073 'Caerphilly Castle'	green	*GWR* button on tender, nameplate black + gold '39>, c/w	36-41	260	320
E320	4073 'Caerphilly Castle'	green	*GWR* button on tender, nameplate black + gold '39>, 20v motor	36-41	400	450
3C	E850 'Lord Nelson'	green	*Southern* + number on coal-rail tender, c/w	28-29	320	350
3E	E850 'Lord Nelson'	green	*Southern* + number on coal-rail tender, 4v motor	28-29	340	380
3C	E850 'Lord Nelson'	green	*Southern* + number on No.2 Special tender, c/w	29-33	260	320
3E	E850 'Lord Nelson'	green	*Southern* + number on No.2 Special tender, 4v motor	29-33	340	380
3C	850 'Lord Nelson'	green	*Southern* as above but new number, c/w	33-36	280	340
3E, E36	850 'Lord Nelson'	green	*Southern* as above but new number, 6v motor	33-36	340	380
E3/20, E320	850 'Lord Nelson'	green	*Southern* as above but new number, 20v motor	33-36	400	500
3C	850 'Lord Nelson'	green	*Southern* as above but smoke deflectors fitted, c/w	36-41	300	350
E320	850 'Lord Nelson'	green	*Southern* as above but smoke deflectors fitted, 20v motor	36-41	450	550

18. No.4 'Eton' Tender Locomotive 4-4-0 This was a 4-4-0 'Schools' Class tender locomotive. A most attractive and popular model, it was Hornby's final engine based on a prototype. The tender (a No.2 special) was incorrect for prototype.
Mechanisms: Clockwork and E240 (20 volt motor).

4	900 'Eton'	green	*Southern* Schools Class, c/w	37-41	750	850
4	900 'Eton'	green	*Southern* Schools Class, 20v motor	37-41	1000	1400
4	900 'Eton'	black	*Southern* Schools Class, mainly for export, lookout for fakes!	37-41	3000	5000

19. 'Princess Elizabeth' Tender Locomotive 4-6-2 The 4-6-2 Princess Royal Class locomotive was Hornby's largest and most impressive piece of motive power. However, incorrect proportions on the locomotive give a distorted appearance to line of boiler and firebox. Early wooden presentation cases were red with blue lining and marked in gold - 'Meccano Ltd. Liverpool Princess Elizabeth'. Boxes from the middle period of production were red with cream lining and late ones were blue with green lining. Both of the latter had a nice printed description and picture inside the lid. **Prices include the wooden presentation case.**
Mechanism: 20 volt electric motor.

	6201 'Princess Elizabeth'	maroon	*LMS* (serif), cab inside sand coloured	37	1800	2300
	6201 'Princess Elizabeth'	maroon	*LMS* (sans-serif), cab inside sand coloured	38	1800	2300
	6201 'Princess Elizabeth'	maroon	*LMS* (sans-serif), cab inside maroon coloured	39-40	1800	2300

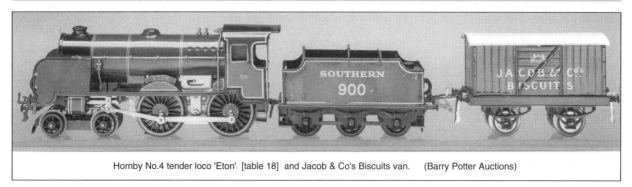

Hornby No.4 tender loco 'Eton' [table 18] and Jacob & Co's Biscuits van.   (Barry Potter Auctions)

20. Metropolitan Locomotive 0-4-0   This was an 0-4-0 with its wheels tucked under its skirt instead of being a double bogied model like the real locomotive. One wonders what could have been achieved if Hornby had developed a motor bogie like Bassett-Lowke and the Leeds Model Company. This was Hornby's first production electric motored model as well as its first prototypical one. It was colourful and attractive but it initially worked on 125 volt AC! Re-railing without the controller turned off could give you an additional thrill! This would appear to be the only Hornby Series locomotive not to be fitted with automatic couplings in later days.
Mechanisms: 1925-29 H.V. (125), 1926-39 clockwork, 1927-29 4V, 1929-39 6V, 1938-39 20V.
In about mid production, clockwork and 6 volt motors were improved.

1, HV	2	maroon	Metropolitan, 125v AC motor	25, 27-29	280	320
2, LV	2	maroon	Metropolitan, 4v motor	27-29	300	350
3, C	2	maroon	Metropolitan, rear windows not punched out, coupling rods, c/w	26-39	240	280
LV, E36	2	maroon	Metropolitan, protruding brush-caps, 6v motor	29-39	300	350
E320	2	maroon	Metropolitan, 20v motor	38-39	400	450

There were numerous mechanical variations of this model but the main ones are listed above.

21. LE1 Swiss Type Locomotives 0-4-0   Here was an 0-4-0 locomotive with a Swiss type body for overhead power collection. Dummy pantographs were fitted and there were coupling rods on the clockwork models but rarely on electric ones. This was a somewhat odd production model which lasted only four years and had five colour changes in this time! These were dark green, light green, red, cream and blue and the roofs were grey, cream, red or yellow. **Mechanisms: 1932-36 LEC1, clockwork. 1932-34 LE1/20, 20V. 1934-36 LE120, 20V.**

LEC1	10655	various	Swiss, pantographs and side vents on roof, double ended, c/w	32-36	200	250
LE1/20, LE120	10655	various	Swiss, pantographs and side vents on roof, double ended, 20v	32-36	300	350

22. LE2 Continental Locomotives 0-4-0   Another 0-4-0 locomotive and a very strange looking object being basically a Metropolitan loco without the skirts. Apart from the 'Princess Elizabeth', it was the sole Hornby model not to have a clockwork version. The body was fitted with overhead pantographs and it carried the same transfers as LE1. Some models had coupling rods and the body colours that may be found are dark green, light green, red or cream. roof colours were grey, cream or blue. **Mechanisms: 1932-34 LE2/20, 20V 1934-36 LE220, 20V.**

LE220	10655	various	Swiss, Metropolitan body, 20v motor	32-36	600	700

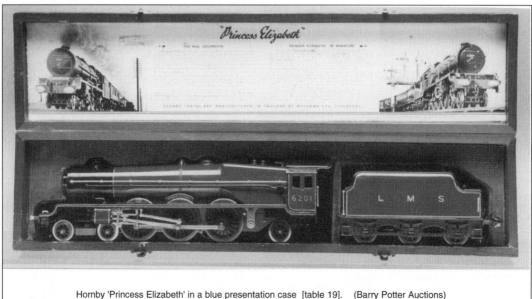

Hornby 'Princess Elizabeth' in a blue presentation case [table 19].   (Barry Potter Auctions)

Hornby 1924 No.1 passenger coach
[table 2b].   (Barry Potter Auctions)

Hornby No.3 tender loco Nord [table 17].   (Barry Potter Auctions)

Hornby 1934 No.1 passenger coach
[table 2c].   (Barry Potter Auctions)

Hornby 1928 No.2 Special Pullman 'Loraine' [table 3c].   (Barry Potter Auctions)

Hornby Metropolitan electric loco [table 20]
and metropolitan coach [table 3b].   (Barry Potter Auctions)

Hornby 1921 No.2 Dining Saloon [table 3a].
(Barry Potter Auctions)

Coaches

Until the middle of the 1920s, rolling stock was of nut and bolt (Meccano type) construction. After that, tabs and slots were used to join pieces together when items were assembled. Below we provide a means of identifying the age of coaches by their structure and finish.

Coach details	Years	£	£

1. M Series Coaches (4-wheel)

1a. M0 Pullman Coaches (also No.0 Pullman and No.21 BR Coach)
This was a small coach with no buffers, tin hook and loop couplings, cream and brown livery and named 'Joan' or 'Zena'.

red or green roof, marked *Hornby Series*	30-41	10	12
same but w' automatic couplings (No.0)	31-41	10	12
grey roof, marked *Hornby*	46-54	8	10
same body but as a BR crimson and cream coach (No.21), no names	54-59	5	8

1b. M1/2 and M1 Pullman Coaches
This was larger than the M0 Pullman coach. All had drop-link couplings, cream and brown livery and were named 'Pullman' (1926-28), 'Marjorie', 'Aurelia' or 'Viking'.

yellow, green, cream, red or brown roofs and bases (M1/2)	26-41	15	20
white or grey roofs and black bases (M1)	46-57	15	20

2. No.1 Coaches (4-wheel)

2a. 1921 No.1 Passenger Coaches
These were of nut and bolt construction, had brass numbers on the doors, grey roofs, coats of arms on the sides, cut-out windows and 4 silver wheels.

CR, orangy brown, ochre doors	21-23	80	100
GN, orangy brown, ochre doors	21-23	60	70
LNWR, brown and white	21-23	60	70
MR, maroon, brownish pink doors	21-23	60	70

2b. 1924 No.1 Passenger Coaches
This had a completely different body of tab and slot construction and a full brake was also made from now onwards. The coaches had grey clerestory roofs (until 1929), three opening doors in each side and printed windows. The wheel base was short for the length of body making them look toy-like.

LMS, red, clerestory roof	24-28	40	50
LNER, brown, clerestory roof	24-28	40	50
GWR, brown and cream, clerestory roof	24-28	55	65
LMS, red	28-34	30	40
LNER, brown	28-34	30	40
GWR, brown and cream	28-34	35	45
SR, green	28-34	55	65

2c. 1934 No.1 Passenger Coaches
These coaches were completely redesigned models which were wider and higher than previous ones, with wheels further apart, non-opening doors and closed axle springs. Roofs were grey (lighter shade after the war) and post-war versions were marked 'Hornby' or 'Hornby Trains'.

LMS, red, yellow and black detail	34-41	25	35
LNER, light brown, printed wood-grain	34-41	30	40
GWR, brown and cream	34-41	50	60
SR, green, yellow printed detail	34-41	80	90
LMS red	47-59	20	30
LNER light brown	47-59	20	30
GWR brown and cream	47-49	70	80
SR green	47-49	90	110
BR crimson with yellow lining, no black lined panels (No.41)	54-58	20	25
BR crimson and cream (No.51)	54-58	30	40

2d. 1928 No.1 Pullman Coach
Both coach and brake end versions were made over a long period so mums and dads must have loved them but to kids they were hideous! They had rounded roof ends and recessed end doors. They had brown and cream tin-printed sides and were named *'Corsair'*, *'Cynthia'*, *'Niobe'*, *'Ansonia'* or *'Aurora'*. Roofs were cream, grey, red, green or blue.

opening doors	28-35	20	25
non-opening doors	35-41	20	25

3. No.2 Bogie Coaches (with compensating bogies)
The passenger coaches were 1st/3rd composites and the brake coaches were all 3rd class. They were similar in style and colour to the 1934 No.1 coaches but twice as long.

3a. 1921 No.2 Pullman and Dining Saloon
These were the first bogie coaches to be made by Hornby and were a light cream and green and had greenish grey roofs. They were of nut and bolt construction and had celluloid windows. Until 1923 the doors were fixed but from then they were hinged.

Pullman crests, green and cream	21-25	100	120
as above but scrolled box around name	25	100	120
same but livery now brown and cream	25-27	100	120

Hornby 1937 No.2 corridor coach [table 3e].
(Barry Potter Auctions)

Dining Saloon, CR crest, green and cream	21-23	100	120
Dining Saloon, GN crest, green and cream	21-23	100	120
Dining Saloon, LNWR crest, green and cream	21-23	100	120
Dining Saloon, MR crest, green and cream	21-23	100	120
Dining Saloon, Pullman crests, green and cream	23-25	100	120

3b. Metropolitan Coaches
This was a suburban bogie coach with a fine wood grain tin-printed finish made specially to go with the Metropolitan electric locomotive. Two versions were made - 1st class and brake/3rd. They had grey roofs, yellow windows, brass buffers, drop-link couplings and were available in both lit and unlit versions.

1st class coach	26-39	120	180
brake 3rd coach	26-39	120	180

3c. 1928 No.2/3 or No.2 Special Pullmans
These replaced the No.2 and No.3 Pullmans in sets. They had a restyled body with smaller, better shaped, windows which had more elegant window frames. They had square accumulator boxes beneath the coach instead of cylinders. They also had snap-on roofs, seven windows in their sides and they had a curved roof with rain gullies and ventilators. All were brown and cream and a brake end (or composite) was now produced. They were called No.2/3 Pullmans until 1930/31 when they were renamed No.2 Special Pullmans.

all cream upper half, cream roof with blue vents, named 'Iolanthe'	28-30	90	120
all cream upper half, cream roof with blue vents, named 'Iolanthe' or 'Zenobia'	29-30	90	120
brake, all cream upper half, cream roof with blue vents, named 'Arcadia'	28-30	90	120
brake, all cream upper half, cream roof, blue vents, named Arcadia' or 'Alberta'	29-30	90	120
brown above windows, grey roof, named 'Iolanthe', 'Zenobia' or 'Grosvenor'	30-35	120	175
as above but named 'Zenobia', 'Grosvenor' or 'Loraine'.	35-41	120	175
brake, brown above windows, grey roof, named Arcadia', 'Alberta' or 'Montana'	30-35	120	175
as above but named 'Alberta', 'Montana' or 'Verona', luggage compartment now all brown	35-41	120	175

3d. 1935 No.2 Passenger Coaches
These were the first Hornby bogie coaches for general passenger stock of the four railway companies despite the fact that Bing and Bassett-Lowke had issued theirs in the early 1920s. The coaches consisted of a 1st/3rd composite and an all 3rd brake end.

LMS, red with black and yellow lining	35-41	125	150

Hornby 1935 No.2 passenger coach [table 3d].   (Barry Potter Auctions)

LNER, light brown teak effect	35-41	150	175
GWR, brown and cream with badge in lower half	35-41	180	220
Southern, green with yellow/black lining	35-41	200	250
LMS, red with black and yellow lining	48-50	155	180
LNER, light brown teak effect	48-50	185	220
GWR, brown and cream with badge in lower half	48-50	225	275
Southern, green with yellow/black lining	48-50	250	300

3e. 1937 No.2 Corridor Coaches

This was a later design to go with the larger express locomotives. They had longer windows and the end panels were cut to take the 'concertina' type corridor connections. All were composites except the Southern coach which was an all-3rd. There were destination board brackets above windows and the roofs white except LMS ones which were grey. The coaches consisted of a 1st/3rd composite and a 1st/3rd brake end.

LMS, red with yellow lining, black chassis (matt after 1939)	37-41	100	140
LNER, light brown teak effect, yellow and black panelling	37-41	125	160
GWR, brown and cream with badge in lower half	37-41	160	200
Southern, green, yellow panelling, brake coach had deep orange around door windows.	37-41	200	250

4. No.3 Bogie Coaches

4a. Riviera Blue Train and Mitropa Coaches

The Riviera Blue Train coaches were the first Hornby coaches to be made with corridor connectors and were for use with the Nord locomotive. Two types, a sleeper and a diner, were available but these were structurally the same but with different celluloid strips at the windows. From 1931 onwards, they were fitted with compensating bogies and a Mitropa version of each was produced in red livery. The latter had white roofs and were a strange choice because Hornby did not have an appropriate locomotive to pull them. They could perhaps have been put behind the Nord as a through train!

CIE *Dining Car*, blue	26-41	150	175
CIE *Sleeping Car*, blue	26-41	150	175
Mitropa *Schlafwagen*, red and gold	31-41	500	600
Mitropa *Speisewagen*, red and gold	31-41	500	600

4b. No.3 (No.2) Pullman and Saloon Coaches

Based on the Riviera Blue body, these Pullmans originally came with the No.3 train sets. They also had corridor connections and brown corridor end plates but used the same transfers as the No.2 Pullmans and carried the same livery with cream roofs. From 1930 the No.3 was renamed the 'No.2 Pullman Coach' and LMS and LNER 1st class end vestibule saloon coaches were made to the same design.

Pullman, large crests, drop-link couplings	27-28	70	90
Pullman, small crests, automatic couplings	30-31	70	90
LMS red saloon coach No.402	30-41	70	90
LNER brown saloon coach No.137	30-41	70	90

Hornby trademark transfers

 1920–22 trademark

 1929–34 trademark (without red outer line)

 1922–23 trademark

 1934–40 trademark (with red outer line)

 1923–25 trademark

 1934–40 trademark (without red outer line)

 1926–29 trademark

 1934–40 trademark (with red outer line and short black line under 'Meccano')

 1929–34 trademark (with red outer line)

 1929–40 footplate trademark

Wagons

In this catalogue it is not possible to give full listing of all the variations of wagons made by Meccano Ltd for their Hornby 0 gauge range as more than 50 basic wagon types were produced, each with its own range of colours and detail differences.

No.0 and M0 Series Wagons

The standard 4-wheel wagons were the No.1 series while the No.0 series were a cost cutting exercise, having non-opening doors or a cheaper chassis, sometimes without buffers. Some of the latter were designated 'M1' and others, for tank goods sets, were labelled 'M3'. The M0 series were small, toy-like, tinplate wagons designed to go with the M0 locomotives. Many special wagons do not have a series number.

No.1 Wagons

Over the years five types of base were fitted to the standard wagons, the main visual difference being the representation of springs and axleboxes.

Type 1: (early 1920s) Solid and plain.
Type 2: (1923-32) An open chassis with pierced springs.
Type 3: (1932-40) Solid with embossed springs and can also be found on some wagons released immediately after the Second World War.
Type 4: (1949-57) Simple embossed spring shapes which did not show leaves as the previous type did.
Type 5: (1957-63) Known as the No.50 chassis, this had cast ends and buffers, no brake rod connecting the axleboxes but had a separate silver coloured brake lever.

Hornby 0 gauge wagons offer variety ranging from dull to fanciful and in colours from sombre to exotic!

Two strange models of the pre-war days were the barrel wagon and wine wagon. Both sold well despite their non-existence on British railways. Today the barrel wagon is unpopular, selling for around £25 whereas a nice wine wagon will command a price of £75.

Wagons to cover most railway operations were manufactured but the real attraction in the Hornby range today is their private owner stock. These come as open wagons, tippers, tankers and vans. Of these the rotary tipping and side tipper of Sir Robert McAlpine & Sons, Trinidad Lake Asphalt and Robert Hudson Ltd are the cheapest, selling at £20-£35. The Meccano rotary tippers are more expensive at £45-£65. Also, the two private owner open (coal) wagons lettered 'Meccano' and 'Hornby Railway Company,' which are finished in red or maroon, are expensive costing around £75-£100.

Twelve different petrol companies were represented on the tank wagons with numerous colour and lettering changes over the years. The cheapest pre-war ones are Shell and Royal Daylight at £20-£30 each. Esso, with a normal price of £12-£20, is the cheapest post-war tanker. Several pre-war variants fetch high prices and the short run (1938-40) of the Power Ethyl has helped to push the price of it up to £85-£120.

Up until now post-war rolling stock has been less sought after but there is currently a renewed interest in the range and the attractive type 50 Manchester Oil refinery Ltd tank wagon has risen to £30-£35 in price. It is worth noting here that, although it is not a tank wagon, the most attractive post-war wagon (type 50), the Saxa Salt, is currently changing hands at £60-£70.

Hornby No.1 wagons.   (Barry Potter Auctions)

There was a more sophisticated tank wagon which was larger and had more detail including ladders. The transfers were United Dairies or Nestles Milk on white tanks and Colas on blue or red tanks. Genuine examples of the latter are quite rare and so beware of reproductions!

There were eight private owner vans, three of them being in the liveries of biscuit manufacturers and all are listed here in a very basic guide to prices. Variations on basic types have not been included, nor have those produced in overseas ranges such as the Huntley & Palmers biscuit van which appeared only in the French range (it was one of only a few private owner wagons produced by the French factory and now sells for £150-£250).

These colourful and attractive wagons were a very effective way for manufacturers to advertise as they were toy versions of real wagons on the railways in the '20s and '30s. Hornby usually encouraged the companies, whose names appeared on the vans, to contribute towards the cost of the transfers.

The following are sought after Hornby private owner rolling stock:

Wagon details	Years	£	£
Colmans Mustard van – black open chassis, pale yellow body, white roof, royal coat-of-arms, bull head logo	23-24	450	650
Seccotine van – black type 2 or 3 chassis, blue body, silver grey lettering, orange or red roof, sliding or hinged doors	23-34	250	350
Carr's Biscuits van – black type 2 or 3 chassis, blue or blue-grey body and roof, gold lettering, royal coat-of-arms, sliding or hinged doors	24-41	100	175
Crawford's Biscuits van – black type 2 or 3 chassis, red body and roof, gold lettering, royal coat-of-arms, sliding or hinged doors	24-41	125	200
Jacob & Co's Biscuits van – black type 2 or 3 chassis, maroon body and roof, gold lettering, royal coat-of-arms, sliding or hinged doors	24-41	125	200
Fyffes Bananas van – green, red or black type 3 chassis, yellow body, red or white roof, blue lettering, sliding or hinged doors	31-41	70	120
Cadbury's Chocolate van – black or green type 3 chassis, blue body, white roof, gold lettering, sliding doors	32-41	150	225
Palethorpe's Sausages van – black type 3 chassis, maroon body and roof, gold lettering, sausages logo, sliding doors	38-41	200	300
United Dairies tank wagon – blue or blue-grey type 2 or 3 chassis, white tank, red lettering	29-37	300	350
Nestlés Milk tank wagon – green, blue or black type 3 chassis, white tank, blue lettering	36-41	200	300
Colas bitumen tank wagon – blue type 2 or 3 chassis, blue tank, yellow logo	29-36	300	500
Colas bitumen tank wagon – blue or black type 3 chassis, red tank, yellow logo	36-41	500	800

More common pre-1940 rolling stock is generally priced around £15-£30, whereas common post 1946 vehicles are in the £8-£20 range. There is, therefore, scope for those who wish to collect and run a few nice examples on a limited budget. Another generalisation is that, in the pre-1940 stock, the standard type 3 chassis examples are more highly regarded than the earlier type 2, open chassis, products.

No.2 Wagons

These are just over twice as long as the four wheeled No.1 wagons and were fitted with bogies. Manufacture commenced in 1924 and continued until 1941. Two No.2 luggage vans, LMS and LNER, were reintroduced between 1948 and 1950 and these today sell for £50-£80 each.

The following bogie models were also made:
breakdown van and crane   cattle truck
high capacity wagon (no SR version made)
luggage van   lumber wagon
timber wagon   trolley wagon

Some carried railway company initials while others did not and colours were frequently changed. Colours were sometimes garish with bright yellows, greens and reds but these ones are usually cheaper to buy (£15-£30). In contrast an SR luggage van could set you back £100-£120 while a high capacity NE brick wagon will probably cost £60-£80.

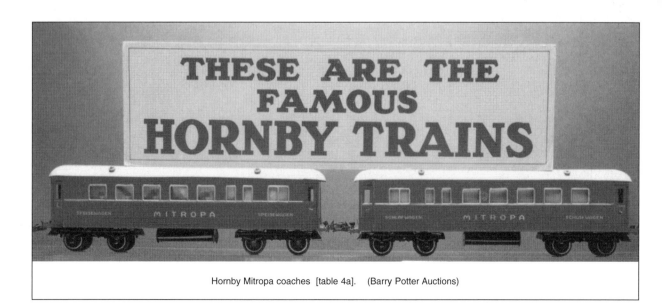

Hornby Mitropa coaches [table 4a]. (Barry Potter Auctions)

Accessories

Hornby 0 Gauge was a very complete system providing scores of lineside features with which to embellish your train and track. Some of these are now quite rare, as they are the items that were thrown away when mothers gave their children's trains to their younger cousins. Many of the accessories continued in production throughout the life of the Company; obviously with many style and colour variations – a fair number during the post-war period. The 'Hornby' (or 'Meccano' on very early examples) trade marks appeared on all but the smallest pieces so identification is fairly easy. In this catalogue we are unable to provide a complete listing (with description and price) of all variations or even all products but the following basic listing gives some idea of what is of interest and roughly what it is worth. With the exception of fields, hedges, trees, tunnels and cuttings which are made of wood and fabric, all of Hornby's accessories were made from printed tinplate.

Buffers

No.1 buffers were the short spring type in various colours (£3-£5) while No.2 buffers were the long hydraulic type as seen in large terminus stations (£15-£20). There were also versions of both types with electric lamps coded No.1E (£25-£30) and No.2E (£40-£60).

Countryside Sections

These were made from thick card and printed paper and came in various shapes to fit around the track (£20-£40 per piece).

Cuttings

There were straight and curved sections of the embankments that formed the cuttings (£30-£50).

Engine Sheds

These were Hornby's finest buildings and were made between 1928 and 1941. They were constructed of printed tinplate and featured a late 19th Century industrial building, the best having a roof ventilator and smoke vents. The No.2 engine shed was twice the length of the No.1 and may be found with either clockwork 2-rail fittings or electric 3-rail with electric interior lighting (£100-£400).

Footbridges and Lattice Girder Bridge

Over the years these were made in blues, creams and white. The No.2 footbridge had two signals on it (£30-£65). The much larger lattice girder bridge was made only between 1921 and 1934 (£90-£150).

Goods Platform

This had a rectangular platform and a simple building shape on which the detail was printed. It had a gabled overhanging roof and came in various colours. The No.2 version had an operating crane and sliding doors while a No.2E also had an electric light (£60-£250).

Hedges and Trees

Hedges were made from dyed loofah fixed to a wooden base to fit around fields. The trees were of similar construction but had lead bases to give them stability (£6-£12).

Island Platform

This had a long platform with ramps at either end and two posts supporting a central canopy. Posts were latticed pre-war but plain post-war. They may be found in various colours and with an assortment of names. There was also an electrically lit version (£80-£300).

Lamp Standards

These had latticed posts and hanging glass globe lamps; two in the case of the No.2 version. Standard models were non-lighting (£60-£90) but No.1E and No.2E were lit versions, with simpler brackets, lampshades and bulbs (£70-£120)

Level Crossings

The No.1 and No.E1 level crossings had single track, one for 2-rail clockwork and the other for 3-rail electric respectively. There was also a 3-rail No.E1E which had lamps on the gates (£10-£30). It is therefore logical that the No.2 level crossing had double track with No.2, No.E2 and No.E2E versions (£30-£100) being available. Over the years there were many variations in the attractive printing on the bases, showing road and verges, while gates were white with red diamonds.

Loading Gauge

Early loading gauges (1920s) had round bases but later ones were square. While the posts were white, the bases were usually blue, but green and black examples may be found (£40-£60).

Platelayers Hut

This was an attractive feature with its red brick finish, chimney, blue roof and green door which opens on some models (£40-£65).

Platform Crane

This was an operating crane on a square base with steps. Some came in bright colours (£15-£30).

Platform Accessories

There were platform machines (ticket and nameplate), pillar box, fire hut, seats and luggage consisting of hampers and trunks - all made in printed tinplate (£8-£35 each). Between 1924 and 1926 the trunk was made with a 'Carlisle' label on it. This version is much sought after and has been valued at £90.

Watchman's Hut

The hut had an open front and was blue with a red roof. It came with a shovel and poker hanging on its sides and a brazier standing in front (£25-£35).

Signal Cabins

All the signal cabins had a gabled roof and a chimney stack. No.1 had printed windows while on the No.2 version they were pierced and the cabin had separate steps. The box was unnamed except for those made between 1924 and 1928 which carried the name 'Windsor'. The No.2E had a lamp inside while the Control Cabin had an opening roof and a base for a lever frame (£25-£85).

Signal Gantries

The No.1 signal gantry was of simple construction consisting of two supporting posts and four signal posts which push-fitted together on the gantry (£30-£50). The No.2 gantry was larger with lattice posts and had railings and a ladder. The signals were worked by a series of

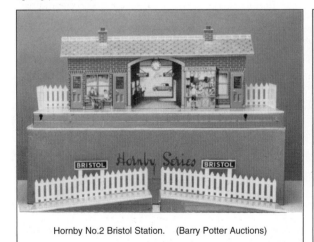

Hornby No.2 Bristol Station.   (Barry Potter Auctions)

Hornby No.2E signal gantry and No.2 double arm signal.
(Barry Potter Auctions)

Hornby No.2E station yard lamp.
(Barry Potter Auctions)

wires (£250-£450). There was also a No.2E which had electric lights behind each signal (£1,000-£2,000).

Signals

There were many colour variations although the main part was always white – single arm, double arm, home, distant and bracket. Most post-war examples have non-latticed posts (£10-£50). There were also electrically lit examples (£30-£90).

Stations

Many variations in stations were made during 1923-41 and 1948-57. These included variations in colour and printing, the latter providing an interesting study of changing clothes fashion and car design etc. Sadly, the long gable ended shape with two chimneys (missing from cheaper stations) is less interesting than stations designed by other manufacturers such as Bing and Märklin.

Fences, an open booking hall concourse and electric lamps may be found on some Hornby stations. Prices vary from £60-£90 for fairly

basic units to £120-£220 for more elaborate ones.

Staff and Passengers

These were cast in lead, the size of them being slightly reduced around 1938. The range included six station staff, six passengers, six engineering staff and five train and hotel staff. There were also sets of farmyard animals, a shepherd and sheep. Single figures in good condition sell for £5-£10 while boxed sets range from £50-£120 depending on the set.

Telegraph Pole

This was over-scale and was fixed to a square tinplate base. Until 1929 the two cross bars were tin after which they were cast in lead (£30-£45 each).

Tunnel

Between 1924 and 1931 the tunnel was printed tin to represent moorland (£70-£90). From then until 1937 the picture represented countryside with hikers (£70-£120), from 1932 up to the Second World War, many were made of wood

and fabric and finished with coloured sawdust. The latter were made in various lengths and available curved or straight (£20-£60).

Viaduct

This was single track and the centre section had grey or green girder sides. There were ramp sections at both ends and they came with either clockwork (£30-£35) or electric (£70-£80) track.

Water Tank

During the 1930s the No.1 water tank was red with a green base, black ladder and yellow or buff column. Post-war it was black and red with a plastic column (£15-£35). The No.2 water tank was more like gauge 1 in scale and came with a blue or green base and column and a red or yellow tank (£75-£85). There was also a No.2E version with a blue electric light fitting on the tank (£800-£1200).

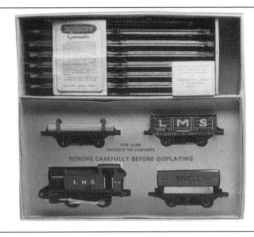
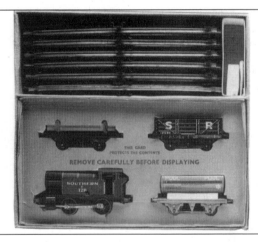

Hornby post war LMS and SR 201 train sets.

(Barry Potter Auctions)

Sets

If one counts the many company and colour variations, Meccano Ltd produced 223 different Hornby 0 gauge train sets before the outbreak of World War 2 and a further 34 after the war.

The Hornby train sets were released in attractive packaging and very early boxes were brown or maroon with pictures of locomotives tastefully embossed in gold on their lids.

From 1921 onwards inspiring coloured pictures of fast-moving prototypical trains appeared on most sets and only from 1925 until 1931 did Hornby show their own products on the lid. These were a 2711 4-4-0 in LMS livery, with smoke coming from the chimney, pulling No.2 Pullman cars at speed through a country scene.

The 'Royal Scot' and 'Flying Scotsman' were the most common images on set boxes and were continued in 1945. In this last period, a No.41 tank passenger set had the picture of a Castle Class locomotive on the box lid while another 0-4-0 locomotive set showed a Britannia Class engine racing along the word 'Hornby'. This was before the Trade Description Act and one thing is for sure - the contents did not match the picture!

Boxes for sets had stoutly made compartments and each contained a circle of clockwork or electric track. There were also a small box of track clips, a locomotive and either coaches or wagons. Clockwork sets also had a key in a packet and some sets had a packet of locomotive lamps

and/or coach connectors. The sets contained a 'tested' label, guarantee slip, instructions and an application form for the Hornby Railway Association which the purchaser was invited to join.

Collecting sets is a specialist's field which is ignored by many who prefer to run their trains. Constant use of the contents of sets can lead to destructive and devaluing wear and tear. Replacement inserts are available for some boxes through the Hornby Railway Collectors Association.

A rough guide to the value of a run-of-the-mill set is the sum of the contents plus a bit extra for the box. A 3C set of the late '30s, containing a 4-4-2 and two coaches has a value of £550-£850 in nice condition; depending on the exact contents. A rare electric set containing a large locomotive will be upwards of £1000. On the other hand, pre-war clockwork sets with No.1 locomotives (either tender or tank) are valued at £150-£250. M series items are generally inexpensive and small attractive sets, with good pictures on their lids, sell for £40-£60.

There are obviously more post-war 0-4-0 sets about in good order and one can expect to pay between £100-£150; unless it is uncommon in which case it could cost as much as £200. Some of the pre-war sets were given impressive names of real named trains. These include 'The Pines Express' on a No.1 0-4-0 passenger set of 1939, 'The Dover Pullman', 'The Golden Arrow' and the 'Cornish Riviera', all of which contained various No.3 4-4-2s with bogie coaches or Pullman cars. From 1945 the romantic names disappeared but the enticing pictures remained.

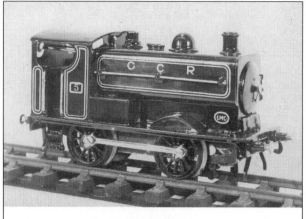

LMC 0-4-0 saddle tank [table 1].
(The Leeds Stedman Trust)

LMC 4-6-0 North Eastern tank [table 4].
(The Leeds Stedman Trust)

LMC ex-GE Class G5 0-4-4T [table 7].

LMC ex-GE Class F4 2-4-2T [table 7].

LMC ex-GC Class N5 0-6-2T [table 7].

LMC ex-LSWR Class T1 0-4-4T [table 7].

LMC ex-L&Y 2-4-2T [table 7].

LMC ex-L&Y 0-6-2T [table 7].

LMC
4-4-0 North Eastern
tank locomotive

[table 2]

(The Leeds Stedman
Trust)

Leeds Model Company

History

The Leeds Model Company was started in 1912 by Rex Stedman, an engineer, whose entry into the model railway world was postponed by work on aircraft design and aerial photography in the First World War. After the war Stedman moved his fledgling company to new premises at Balm Road, Hunslet, in Leeds and tooling up started in 1919. With the financial help of a wealthy model railway enthusiast, G.P.Keen, the Company was incorporated in March 1920 as The Leeds Model Company Limited and Keen became its chairman.

In Britain, the Leeds Model Company ranked third, after Hornby and Bassett-Lowke, during the 1920s and '30s, the emphasis being on reasonably affordable 0 gauge models rather than toy trains. The principles Stedman adopted were that his designs must provide the widest possible product range, at minimum cost to give the customer maximum choice at the lowest possible price. To achieve this he had to produce standard models that shared parts and could look good in a range of liveries. The result was a series of freelance tank engines which were released in the early '20s.

Next, Stedman needed to make an impact in the market to get noticed and his choice was a Great Central Railway 4-4-0 Director Class, 437 'Charles Stuart Wortley'. Using much of the same tooling he went on to make another Great Central locomotive - the 4-6-0 'Sir Sam Fay'. Production went on apace with Stedman doing most of the design work himself. Besides producing their own models to sell LMC also sold a large range of parts for customers to build their own models.

The Company produced a full range of rolling stock, accessories and wooden sleepered track. Today it is especially known for its lithographically printed, paper covered, wooden wagons and coaches and later, as we shall see, they were the first manufacturer to use bakelite for rolling stock construction. Their cast metal wheels are much closer to scale and have finer flanges than either Hornby or Bassett-Lowke products. Some locomotives had smoke units fitted after the Second World War, pre-empting Tri-ang by a number of years.

In 1925 The Leeds Model Company merged with the Bristol Model Co. and Stedman was reduced from Managing Director to Chief Engineer and Designer. The Bristol directors, headed by Hugh Leader, had money to invest in new designs and are largely responsible for the appearance of GWR locomotives in the range including a Churchward County for Bassett-Lowke. This was followed by a CR Pickersgill 4-4-0. Whilst under the agreement with Bassett-Lowke LMC could not sell these two models in their own range, they did use the tooling to produce their own GWR Mogul and Pickersgill 0-6-0. Also, from 1925, an 8V DC mechanism was available as well as the clockwork one.

Things, however, did not continue to run smoothly. Stedman had invested heavily in producing models of the pre-grouping companies but by 1924 the public had been wanting the liveries of the Big Four. During an acute financial crisis in 1928, Rex Stedman left LMC and set up a new company called R.F.Stedman & Co Ltd at Jack Lane, Hunslet, Leeds. At the same time, The Leeds Model Company started cutting its prices by up to 20%. A few months later Stedman purchased the entire stock and plant as well as trade mark of LMC. He continued to manufacture under the new company name and work now went into extending and updating the range of models with the new liveries. The changes included a switch from clockwork to electric mechanisms and the dropping of the expensive to produce hand-built rolling stock.

In 1927 Stedman had visited the Bing factory in Nuremberg and been impressed by the new developments in die casting with alloys. However, in

---

Mansted Foundry

In the mid 1920s, after G.P.Keen had given up the chairmanship of the Leeds Model Company, Rex Stedman built locomotives specifically for Keen's own 0 gauge model railway which he had at home and called 'K Lines'. These unique and mainly freelance models, produced in the mid to late 20s, were supposed to come from a fictitious Mansted Foundry, the first part of the name being an anagram of 'Stedman'.

The name 'Mansted Foundry' was inscribed on the models along with the serial number. A report in the model railway press at the time indicated that some parts were supplied by Winteringhams who were part of the Bassett-Lowke group, and with whom G.P.Keen also had business links.

The bodies of the locomotives were brass instead of tinplate and the 20V DC mechanisms had cobalt steel magnets and 8-pole armatures.

K Lines was broken up a number of years ago, following the death of Keen, but several of the Mansted Foundry models have survived. Probably Stedman's finest work was an LNER Garrett.

A further link with Bassett-Lowke occurred in the early 1920s when LMC made two locomotive models exclusively for the Bassett-Lowke range.

1931, he again relinquished control of the Company (this time for good) and the name reverted to Leeds Model Company or just 'LMC'. George Simpson now took over as Managing Director. As a sign of their success, LMC was the victim of Japanese imitation when Stromlite marketed copies of several models in the 1930s. These included 'Sir Sam Fay', the 0-4-0ST, Brighton Belle set and several of the coaches and wagons.

Bakelite had been considered for wagon production as long ago as 1925 but was not used by the LMC until the late 1930s. Trix, of course, had been using it for their track bases since the mid '30s but LMC were the first company in the UK to produce coach and wagon bodies in the material.

After the Second World War, model parts for scratch builders became available again, followed by the standard locomotive range. Shortage of materials and a shrinking market meant that the large scale models were no longer viable and so did not reappear. Instead, a standard 4-4-0 was designed and tooled up.

In 1954 LMC became Ellemsee Accessories supplying a wide range of parts for 0 gauge scratch builders. Stedman himself had returned to modelling after the war forming a new company in 1949 called S&B Productions ('S' stood for Stedman) who are particularly remembered for their signal parts for the 00 market. The battle to maintain proprietary 0 gauge was finally lost in 1966 and by the late 1960s the Leeds Model Company had vanished.

Buyers Beware!
Sadly the description of a model for sale today as 'possibly Leeds' is often a misnomer and should be described as 'origin unknown'! Beware! LMC models are very well constructed from tinplate and the chief fault is flaking paint due to poor cleaning and priming before they were painted. In consequence of this, professional repaints are relatively common and do not greatly affect the value of Leeds locomotives. However, original paint work can be stabilised by a carefully applied light spray of matt or satin finish varnish. The electric mechanisms of the earlier models had brass side frames but in the 1930s these were replaced by diecast parts some of which, over the years, have suffered from swelling and cracking due to impurities in the alloy. This is sometimes difficult to see, however, so do look carefully for distortion and cracks and ask, when buying, if the locomotive is in good working order.

Further Reading
We are unaware of a book on the Leeds Model Company but there have been several articles written about it. One by Rex Stedman's son, Adrian, was published in the Model Railway Constructor in May 1984. A series of articles by David Peacock of the Leeds Stedman Trust and called 'Leeds Lines' has been running in the magazine of the O Gauge Guild. We are indebted to David Peacock for much of the information provided here.

Collecting Organisation
The Leeds Stedman Trust is an organisation run by David Peacock to look after the Stedman archives and to help collectors and operators of LMC models to keep them running by supplying spare parts. It is not a club but you can be placed on a mailing list for the annual price list of parts. The E-mail address for the Leeds Stedman Trust is dpeacock@btconnect.com

Locomotives
Locomotives were built in heavy gauge soldered tinplate and all were fitted with clockwork mechanisms, only, until 1925 when 6-8V DC mechanisms, with a permanent magnet field which was self reversing, were introduced. 20V AC mechanisms, with a hand reverse switch, were supplied between 1934 and 1939. Wheels were cast iron until 1929/30 and then alloy ones were fitted. They were insulated from 1959. Smoke units were fitted from late 1949.

Catalogue Numbering – The 'LO' prefix was used up until 1937/8 after which 'LA' or 'LD' prefixes were used according to whether an AC or DC mechanism was fitted.

Freelance or 'Standard' Models – As we have seen, LMC produced a series of cost saving tank locomotives which were basically freelance in design and available in a variety of liveries. The character of individual railway companies was established by the changing of chimneys, domes and other detail fittings.

Prices – The prices quoted show the range in which good condition examples usually sell.

1. Standard Saddle Tank 0-4-0ST (Freelance) One of the most distinctive of the freelance models was the 0-4-0 tank which is easy to recognise because of its very square appearance although it was one of the models copied by Stromlite. This was the very basic 'starter' locomotive in the range and its unusual shape was almost certainly chosen to give plenty of room for the clockwork motor. In addition to the liveries listed below, freelance liveries were also supplied to customer's requirements.

LO/150	?	green?	NER		22-24	150	200
LO/151	?	black	L&NWR		22-24	150	200
LO/152	?	black	MR		22-24	150	200
LO/153	5	green?	GCR		22-24	150	200
LO/154	?	green?	GNR		22-24	150	200
LO/155	?	blue?	GER		22-24	150	200
LO/156	No3	blue	CR		22-24	100	150
LO/157	6	brown?	LB&SCR		22-24	150	200
LO/158	60	green?	*SE&CR*		22-24	150	200
LO/159	4	green?	GWR		22-24	100	150
LO/160	78	green	LNER		25-?	100	150
LO/161	93	black	*LMS*		25-?	100	150
LO/162	?	green	GWR		25-?	150	200
LO/163	?	green	Southern		25-?	150	200
LD/10	68116	?	BR, also supplied in train sets with a smoke generator		c50-66	150	200
LD/10	68113	?	BR, shorter and with outside cylinders fitted and smoke		c50-66	150	200
L/10	?	?	loco kit		?	150	200
-	'Leeds Model Company'	green	-		c50-66	NPG	NPG

The freelance, or 'Standard' range, included several wheel combinations, the largest being 4-6-0. There were two distinct series of these. The first, starting in 1920, had high mounted boilers (to take a tall and powerful clockwork mechanism), high side tanks and squat cabs with ribbed roofs. The original plan was to top wind these locos through the cab roof (the very earliest 4-4-0s have a key hole covered with a ventilator plate) but the idea was dropped. Electric drive was available from 1925 and all models had standard 1½" driving wheels. It is possible that some of the pre-grouping liveries listed in the catalogue, and therefore included in our tables, were never made unless hand painted. Archive material includes NE, LNWR and GCR examples.

2. Standard Tank 4-4-0T (Freelance)

LO/100	723	green	*North* (crest) *Eastern*	20-23?	200	225
LO/101	3268	black	*L&NWR*	20-23?	250	275
LO/102	2908	red	*MR*	20-23?	325	350
LO/103	276	green?	*GCR*	20-23?	325	350
LO/103	?	green?	*GNR*	20-23?	325	350
LO/105	52	blue?	*GER*	20-23?	325	350
LO/106	?	blue	*CR*	20-23?	325	350
LO/107	910	brown	*LB&SCR*	20-23?	325	350
LO/108	695	green?	*SE&CR*	20-23?	325	350
LO/109	6412	green	*LNER*	25-32	200	225
LO/109	6412	black	*LNER*	25-32	200	225
LO/110	?	maroon	*LMS*	25-32	275	300
LO/110	?	black	*LMS*	25-32	275	300
LO/111	?	green	*GWR*	25-32	325	350
LO/112	2664	green?	*Southern*	25-32	250	275

3. Standard Tank 4-4-2T (Freelance) This was said to look like an L&NWR Precurser tank or one of the LB&SCR tanks used on express duties.

LO/120	3495	black	*L&NWR*	20-23?	300	325
LO/121	?	brown	*LB&SCR*	20-23?	325	350
LO/122	?	green?	*GCR*	20-23?	325	350
LO/123	3754	maroon	*LMS*	25-32	325	350
LO/124	?	green	*Southern*	25-32	325	350
LO/125	?	green	*LNER*	25-32	325	350
LO/126	?	green	*GWR*	25-32	325	350

4. Standard Tank 4-6-0T (Freelance)

LO/130	690	green	*North* (crest) *Eastern*	20-23?	300	325
LO/131	?	black	*L&NWR*	20-23?	325	350
LO/132	271	green	*GCR*	20-23?	325	350
LO/133	386, 396	green	*LNER*	25-32	300	325
LO/134	?	maroon	*LMS*	25-32	300	325
LO/134	?	black	*LMS*	25-32	300	325

5. Standard Tank 0-4-4T (Freelance)

LO/170	314	green?	*L&SWR*	20-23?	325	350
LO/171	?	maroon	*MR*	20-23?	325	350
LO/172	?	green?	*SE&CR*	20-23?	325	350
LO/173	E508, 185	green	*Southern*	25-32	325	350
LO/173	E508	black	*Southern*	25-32	325	350
LO/174	?	maroon	*LMS*	25-32	325	350

Cat.No.	Name / Number	Colour	Details	Years	£	£

6. Standard Tank 0-6-2T (Freelance)

Cat.No.	Name / Number	Colour	Details	Years	£	£
LO/180	510	brown	*LB&SCR*	20-23?	325	350
LO/181	?	green?	*GNR*	20-23?	325	350
LO/182	?	blue?	*GER*	20-23?	325	350
LO/183	E148	green	*Southern*	25-32	325	350
LO/184	5769	green	*LNER*	25-32	325	350

Production of the first series standard tanks ended in 1932 and the second series was delayed until 1935 because of a disastrous factory fire at the Jack Lane Works on 29th June 1932. This second range was nearer to scale in appearance and the wheel arrangements and locomotive numbering related to prototype examples. Company character, however, was still achieved by the changing detail of fittings. They are the product by which LMC is best remembered but, ironically, although designed by Stedman, they were not produced until after he had left the Company. A reduced selection of these tank engines was continued in the late 1940s until the closure of LMC although towards the end only kits were available.

7. Various 'Scale' Tanks (Freelance)   These replaced the models listed in tables 2-6 above. They were described as 'scale' although they relied on detail fittings to give standard bodies prototype character. After 1949 it is likely that the interchangability of parts increased as castings became used up. In later years lining was simplified or left off altogether.

Cat.No.	Name / Number	Colour	Details	Years	£	£
LD/10	8120 (and others)	black	*LNER* ex-GC G5 Class 0-4-4T, red lining	35-39	200	250
LD/11	7102 (and others)	black	*LNER* ex-GE F4 Class 2-4-2T, red lining	35-39	200	250
LD/12	5773 (and others)	black	*LNER* ex-GC N5 Class 0-6-2T, red lining	35-60	275	300
LD/12	5773 (and others)	green	*LNER* ex-GC N5 Class 0-6-2T, black and white lining	48-60	275	300
LD/20	6530 (and others)	red	*LMS* ex-L&Y 0-6-2T, red lining	35-60	250	300
LD/20	6530 (and others)	black	*LMS* ex-L&Y 0-6-2T, red lining	35-60	250	300
LD/21	6720,10763 (and others}	black	*LMS* ex-L&Y 2-4-2T, red lining	35-60	200	250
LD/22	126 (and others)	green	*Southern* ex-LSWR T1 Class 0-4-4T, yellow lining	35-60	250	275

8. Standard Tank 0-6-0T (Freelance)   This model was close to a Jinty in appearance.

Cat.No.	Name / Number	Colour	Details	Years	£	£
LD/15	8418 (and others)	black	*LMS*, posing as a Jinty	48-c60	100	150
LD/16	8305	green	*LNER*, posing as a J72, black and white lining	48-c60	100	150
LD/17	126, 259	green	*Southern*, yellow lining	48-c60	150	200
LD/17	216	black	*Southern*, yellow lining	48-c60	150	200
LD/18	?	black	BRb	c50-60	100	150

A GWR version is known to exist but this was not catalogued.

After the Second World War, the Leeds Model Company introduced a basic inside cylinder 4-4-0 tender locomotive with an affinity to their pre-war Director Class model, however, there was no provision for GWR fans! In fact, the 1948 catalogue carried an apology to these people and a promise to provide some GWR locomotives as well as describing present productions as a 'stop gap' measure. The shape of the model was obviously wrong for the GWR. Within a short time the model was being offered with outside cylinders as an alternative and the model was also available in BR livery. Other names and numbers were available on these late products.

LMC ex-GCR 4-4-0 Improved Director Class 5506 'Butler Henderson' [table 10].   (The Leeds Stedman Trust)

9. 4-4-0 Tender Loco (Freelance)   This post-war standard locomotive model was based roughly on the pre-war Director Class but was also thought to have a close resemblance to an LMS 2P and a Southern L1. From late 1949 the model was offered with a smoke unit fitted.

LD/50	570, 621	black	*LMS*, lined	47-54	100	150
LD/50	570	black	*LMS*, lined, outside cylinders	53-54	100	150
-	570	red	*LMS*	55?-59	100	150
LD/51	2683, 2685	green	*LNER*, lined black and white	47-59	100	150
LD/51	2683, 2685, 2608	green	*LNER*, lined black and white, outside cylinders	53-59	100	150
LD/52	1756	green	*Southern*, lined yellow	47-59	150	200
LD/52	1756, 1783, 1754 (and others)	green	*Southern*, lined yellow, outside cylinders	53-59	150	200
LD/53	-	green	GWR	53-59	150	200
LD/53	-	green	GWR, outside cylinders	53-59	150	200
LD/53	60734	black	BR	53-59	100	150
LD/53/C	60734	black	BR, outside cylinders	53-59	100	150
-	-	-	loco kit	c55-66?	NPG	NPG

Scale Models

The development of the Director and Sir Sam Fay classes has already been described above, and these were certainly the mainstay of the Scale range, but several other scale model locomotives were made by the Leeds Model Company during the years from 1920 to 1939. After the war only few prototypical locomotives were introduced. Most examples were reasonably detailed and could be further enhanced if required. Special models were manufactured to order and you got what you paid for. These included, in 1952, a nice 4-6-0 County Class and enthusiasts of the LMS were also tempted by the introduction of a 'special order' 4-6-0 Jubilee Class.

10. Classes D10 (Director) and D11 (Improved Director) 4-4-0   The LNER cab versions had a Ross pop safety valves replacing the larger GCR twin lever units. From 1930 alloy wheels were fitted and from 1935, diecast frames replaced brass ones. While mass production of the model ceased in 1939, it was available by a special order from the mid 1950s. **DC = Director Class   IDC = Improved Director Class.**

LO/200	429 'Sir Douglas Haig'	green	*Great (crest) Central*, DC	22-24	400	500
LO/200	436 'Sir Berkeley Sheffield'	green	*Great (crest) Central*, DC	22-29	400	500
LO/200	437 'Charles Stuart Wortley'	green	*Great (crest) Central*, DC	22-26	400	500
LO/201	5437 'Sir Berkeley Sheffield'	green	*LNER*, DC, GCR cab	25-29	400	500
LO/201	5437 'Charles Stuart Wortley'	green	*LNER*, DC, GCR cab	25-37	400	500
LO/201	5437 'Prince George'	green	*LNER*, DC, GCR cab, number on cabside	28-31	400	500
LO/201	5437 'Prince George'	green	*LNER*, IDC, LNER cab	31-39	400	500
LO/202	5501 'Mons'	green	*LNER*, IDC, LNER cab	29-60	350	400
LO/202	5503 'Somme'	green	*LNER*, IDC, LNER cab	29-60	350	400
LO/202	5504 'Jutland'	green	*LNER*, IDC, LNER cab	29-60	350	400
LO/202	5505 'Ypres'	green	*LNER*, IDC, LNER cab	29-60	350	400
LO/202	5506 'Butler Henderson'	green	*LNER*, IDC, LNER cab	29-60	350	400

11. Robinson Class B2 (B19) 4-6-0

LO/352	5423 'Sir Sam Fay'	green	*Great (crest) Central*	?	NPG	NPG
LO/352	5423 'Sir Sam Fay'	green	*LNER*	29-60	450	550
LO/352	5427 'City of London'	green	*LNER*	29-60	450	550
LO/352	5423 'City of Lincoln'	green	*LNER*	29-60	450	550
LO/352	5426 'City of Chester'	green	*LNER*	29-60	450	550
LO/352	5425 'City of Manchester'	green	*LNER*	29-60	450	550
LO/352	5428 'City of Liverpool'	green	*LNER*	29-60	450	550

12. Robinson Class B3 4-6-0   Standard Leeds 8-pole 8V motor and engraved brass nameplates.

LO/356	6169 'Lord Faringdon'	green	*LNER*	26-30	450	550
LO/357	6165 'Valour' **	green	*LNER*	26-30	450	550

** Nameplates engraved 'In memory of G.C.R. employees, 1914-1918'.

LMC GCR 4-4-0 Director Class 437 'Charles Stuart Wortley'
[table 10]   (The Leeds Stedman Trust)

LMC ex-GC 5423 'Sir Sam Fay' 4-6-0
[table 11]   (The Leeds Stedman Trust)

13. Claughton Class 4-6-0

Cat.No.	Name / Number	Colour	Details	Years	£	£
LO/351	2222 'Sir Gilbert Claughton'	black	*L&NWR*	22-32	550	650
LO/351	5900 'Sir Gilbert Claughton'	crimson	*LMS*	25-32	550	650
LO/351	5931 'Captain Fryatt'	crimson	*LMS*	25-32	550	650
LO/351	5919 'Lord Kitchener'	crimson	*LMS*	25-32	550	650
LO/351	? (un-named)	crimson	*LMS*	25-32	550	650

14. Miscellaneous Scale Models

Cat.No.	Name / Number	Colour	Details	Years	£	£
-	2402 'City of York'	green	*LNER* Raven A2 Pacific 4-6-2	24-27	800	1200
-	1471 'Sir Fredrick Banbury'	green	*LNER* Raven Pacific 4-6-2	24-27	800	1200
LO/353	1443	green	*LNER* ex-GN Atlantic 4-4-2	25-31	450	550
LO/300	1470	green	*GNR* Pacific 4-6-2 special order	22-28	600	800
LO/300	4472 'Flying Scotsman'	green	*LNER* Pacific 4-6-2 special order	29-39	600	800
-	516	green	LSWR Urie 4-6-2T	?	NPG	NPG
-	E516	green	SR Urie 4-6-2T	?	NPG	NPG
LO/358	17604, 17608	black	*LMS* ex-CR Pickersgill 0-6-0	27-48?	350	400
-	5553 'Canada' (and other names)	crimson	*LMS* Jubilee special order	52-60	500	600
-	5581 'Biha and Orissa'	crimson	*LMS* Jubilee special order	52-60	500	600
-	'Princess Royal'	?	? special order?	59-60	NPG	NPG
LO/348	4362	green	*Great Western* Class 43XX Mogul 2-6-0	27-37	350	400
LO/355	(any name)	green	GWR Castle Class 4-6-0, special order	25-31	500	600
LO/354	(any name)	green	GWR Star or Abbey Class 4-6-0, special order	25-31	500	600
LD/54	1024 'County of Pembroke' (and others)	green	GWR Hawksworth County Class 4-6-0	52-60	500	600
-	?	green	*GWR* Class 57XX Pannier Tank	53-60	120	180
-	?	green	*GWR* Class 51XX Pannier Tank	53-60	120	180
SC/1	233 'Nettle'	green	*LNER* Sentinel-Cammel rail-car	35-60	100	150
CD/153	Car 89 / Car 88	brown + cream	SR Brighton Belle *Pullman* driving car	35-50	80	120

LMC ex-CR Pickersgill 0-6-0   [table 14]

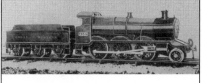

LMC GWR Class 43XX 2-6-0   [table 14]

LMC LNER Sentinel Railcar   [table 14]

LMC LNER Director Class 5437 'Prince George'   [table 10]   (Roy Chambers)

LMC original 1921 NE coach and full brake.   (The Leeds Stedman Trust)

Coaches

The first coaches were made of wood but these were eclipsed by a new technique involving detailed lithograph paper prints pasted on sheets of pine wood and, later, a thinner plywood. This was simple but effective and bogie coaches were produced in the pre-grouping colours - MR, NER and LNWR.

Later the liveries of the Big Four were used and Pullman cars of the Brighton Belle set were added. These provided a full rake consisting of No.89, 'Hazel', 'Doris', No.86 and No.88. There were also a 3rd class Pullman car with no number and a 1st class one with no name, presumably so that you could apply one of your own choice.

Suburban, corridor and brake coaches were made and LNER lithographed articulated coaches were introduced in 1925. Other articulated coach sets were made by cutting and splicing the lithos of full length coaches.

In the late 1930s, Leeds scored another first by using bakelite for their coaches which were of medium length, had glazed windows and were finished in the four regional colours. Lithograph and bakelite coaches now sell for £40-£60.

Wagons

The methods of manufacture were the same as those used for coaches and 'True Scale' stock, made entirely of wood, was also offered. Wagons made after the First World War were initially embossed paper on pine, by 1922 litho printed paper covered wagons were produced; later in great variety. These included the eight private owner coal wagons (including one for R.F.Stedman) which are particularly attractive (£18-£25). Bogie goods vans are another popular product (£30-£35). 4-wheel open wagons and vans sell for £8-£15 and petrol tankers for £40-£50.

Accessories

A full range of brass/steel, wooden-sleepered track was made. The electric type had the centre third rail raised 3mm above the running rails. Wooden stations, goods depots, signal boxes, huts, tunnel mouths and signals provided the enthusiast with a complete railway system.

Milbro SR Schools 901 'Winchester'   [table 2]   (Roy Chambers)

Milbro GCR 4-6-2T   [table 2]   (Roy Chambers)

Milbro (Mills Brothers)

History

Mills Brothers (Engineers) Ltd was founded in 1919 by three brothers - William, Frank and Herbert Mills. They were based at 129 St. Mary's Road, Sheffield, and were later registered as Mills Brothers (Sheffield) Ltd; another address being Ellesmere Road, Sheffield. They used the trade mark 'Milbro' and, at one time, had a London showroom at 2 Victoria Colonnade, Victoria House, Southampton Row. The Company manufactured good quality, true to scale, 0 gauge railway models of prototypical appearance. While 0 gauge was their main output, they also produced some models in gauge 1. Wooden sleepered track was one of their principal products.

During the second half of the 1920s and throughout the 1930s, their locomotives set a standard higher than that of Bassett-Lowke but, being a small firm with low production runs, limited range and higher prices, they made less of a mark in the history of railway modelling. As an example of the higher cost of their quality products, in 1936, the Milbro 6-8 volt DC 'Princess Royal' cost £22.10.0d (£22.50) while the Hornby 0 gauge 20 volt AC 'Princess Elizabeth', when it was released the following year, was priced just £5.5s.0d (£5.25)!

Early catalogues produced by Mills Brothers Ltd suggest that they started off by marketing models produced by the Leeds Model Company (LMC) and then used the LMC motors as the power unit for their own models. However, before long, Mills were producing a mechanism of their own which was built into the chassis side-frames which stretched the length of the locomotive. As many Milbro products did not carry their trade mark, this is a distinctive feature which helps in identifying their locomotives. Like the Leeds Model Company, Mills sold parts for the scratch builder and these can mislead you into thinking that a model was made by Mills. Ultimately, experience is needed for sound identification of a Mills product but a common fault to look for on scratch built models is parts (possibly minor ones) that are fitted out of square.

By the end of the 1940s Mills were selling only their track and parts for scratch builders. After the war this level continued although they also stocked other manufacturers' products such as Romford motors and Bilteezi sheets. The Company disappeared in the 1960s.

Locomotives (O Gauge)

1. Freelance Tank 4-4-2T

Only once were Mills Brothers tempted into producing for the popular market. This was a freelance 4-4-2 tank locomotive which was produced in the 1930s. Called the 'Standard Electric Tank Locomotive', it was LNER in character with a straight footplate, fully enclosed cab with two windows each side and a variety of chimneys and domes according to the railway it represented.

No.	Details
201	LMS
401	Southern
601	GWR
701	LNER

2. 'Scale' Models

The Company normally produced only electrically powered locomotives and built to special order in addition to its catalogue items which were as follows:

Locomotive	Company	£	£
0-6-0 Jinty Tank	LMS	250	300
4-4-0 3P	LMS	NPG	NPG
4-4-0 Compound	LMS	NPG	NPG
2-6-4 Stanier Tank	LMS	NPG	NPG
4-6-0 'Royal Scot'	LMS	NPG	NPG
4-6-2 'Princess Royal'	LMS	1500	2000
0-6-0 J39	LNER	NPG	NPG
4-6-2 GC Robinson Tank	GC or LNER	700	900
4-6-2 'Flying Scotsman'	LNER	NPG	NPG
4-6-2 A4 'Silver Link'	LNER	2000	2500
2-8-2 'Cock of the North'	LNER	NPG	NPG
4-6-4 Hush-Hush Compound	LNER	NPG	NPG
2-4-0 Class 3232	GWR	NPG	NPG
4-6-0 'King George V'	GWR	NPG	NPG
4-4-0 Schools 901 'Winchester'	Southern	800	1200

Coaches

Milbro coaches were particularly attractive, being made of wood with glass windows. They were available in gauges 0 and 1, as corridor or non-corridor stock and in the liveries of the Big Four. One could also buy the wooden parts, in both scales, with which to build your own and this included dining and Pullman cars. Interiors including seating, tables and electric lights could also be supplied. In 1928 they introduced articulated sets with compensating bogies. These were available in twins or triplets.

The LNER teak coaches (teak was actually used in their construction) are everyone's favourites, some of these having nicely detailed interiors with antimacassars on the seats and lamps on the tables. LNER teak bogie coaches today sell for between £200 and £250 each while, in comparison, the LMS corridor bogie coaches normally fetch £90 - £120 and the GWR ones £75 - £100.

Wagons

There was a wide range of wooden wagons available, in both gauges 0 and 1, including the following:

10 ton open wagon
box van
cattle wagon
lime and cement wagon
10 ton brake van
tar or oil wagon
single bolster timber wagon
carriage wagon
bar and rail bogie wagon
high-capacity bogie wagon
bogie tanker
refrigerator van

Nearly all were also available in kit form. Private owner wagons and bogie tankers are particularly sought after. As a result they are expensive with the Esso bogie tanker selling for £100 to £120 while wooden open wagons and vans sell at around £10 - £30.

Accessories

There was an interesting range of buildings and accessories all of which were made of wood including stations, low overbridges, tunnel mouths, signal cabins and platelayers huts. Other accessoeies included buffer stops, level crossings, loading gauges, field sign posts, coal stacks, turntables and gradient posts. These were also made in both scales.

Milbro standard coach in Southern livery

Milbro bar and rail bogie wagon

The Mills Brothers shop in London

'CRACK' TRACK PERFORMANCE

Correct in every detail, MILBRO model locomotives are precision-built to limits of .001 of an inch! Their true-to-scale accuracy, sturdy construction and perfect finish ensures 'crack' track performance.

● Send 6d. for a copy of 100-page catalogue describing the full range of MILBRO models.

This MILBRO L.M.S. Tank Loco is complete in every detail.

MILBRO
TRUE-TO-SCALE
MODELS OF PERFECTION

MILLS BROS. (Model Engineers) LTD., Dept. M.M., ST. MARY'S ROAD, SHEFFIELD
London Showrooms: 2, Victoria Colonnade, Victoria House, Southampton Row, W.C.1

An advert for the Milbro 2-6-4 LMS tank

SYMMETRICAL POINTS

Mills were famous for their wooden sleepered track

Airfix

History

Airfix are best remembered for their comprehensive range of plastic construction kits but in 1971, on the collapse of the Lines Group, they had bought Meccano Ltd who, incidentally, had been stripped of all connection with the model railway industry seven years earlier.

In 1975 Airfix announced their own intention of entering the ready-to-run model railway market. They had recognised a need for ready-to-run models of a finer standard than were available at the time and planned to fill the gap in the market. Unfortunately for them, the American backed Palitoy toy company, had come to the same conclusion and made similar plans.

Airfix had little experience or expertise in model railway production and so had to buy in this from professional designers or overseas companies including Bachmann of America. This resulted in their first venture being a joint project with Bachmann; a Wild West Adventure train set which made use of existing H0 Bachmann products. The Dr. X adventure set followed but this time used 00 models designed specifically for the British market.

In the early 1970s, the Hong Kong Trade Development Commission were looking for business for local factories and this resulted in the Hong Kong company, Sandakan, producing models for Airfix.

Their first samples were displayed at the Harrogate and Brighton Toy Fairs in 1976 where they received a cool reception due to their poor quality. They had been cobbled together in a hurry and bore little resemblance to what was to follow.

Mechanically the locomotives were not exceptional but the mouldings were good and brought much praise. The first locomotive release was the Class 31 in the 'Doctor X' set, which arrived in time for Christmas 1976.

In 1977, Airfix drew up an overall programme that was to give a balanced range. There were to be 5 groups: Midland, Western, Southern, Eastern and BR. Each group was going to have an express passenger, mixed traffic, goods, large tank and small tank engines. In addition, the coaches for each group were to be gangwayed (express mainline) and suburban.

The range of locomotives, coaches and wagons expanded in 1978. Not all the models were made by Sandakan, another Hong Kong company, Cheong Tak, made the 4F, Royal Scot, Stanier and suburban coaches and were to make a Compound followed by a Crab, Black 5 or 8F. Other planned models were the N2, Dean Goods, Schools and B1 but the Company's fortunes were now affecting future plans.

It was becoming more apparent that communication with Hong Kong and control of the finished product was not very good whereas UK production, although more expensive, would deliver as good a product, on time, to Airfix's specifications, without masses of communication and without so many hidden costs. The Company, therefore, produced some wagons themselves in the UK and the success of these proved this point and would have ultimately lead to the phasing out of overseas production.

This change happened in 1979 and, at the same time, the name of the product was altered to GMR which stood for Great Model Railways to better distinguish the product line from the Airfix kits. The GMR assembly line was to be at Charlton (South East London) and the Dean Goods its first product. As this model was about to go into production in mid 1980, the Airfix empire was crumbling. Other parts of the Company were being closed down, moved or sold off. £7M was spent in an attempt to save Meccano and when this failed Airfix went into receivership.

Airfix/GMR exhibited for the last time at the 1981 Toy Fairs but shortly after this they ceased production. The Airfix model railway interests were acquired by its rival - Palitoy - the makers of Mainline Railways. Many models were made by Palitoy from Airfix tooling and later by Dapol and today Hornby - each adding their improvements.

Milestones

1971	Airfix buy Meccano Ltd.
1975	Airfix announce the launch of a ready-to-run railway system.
1976	First samples seen at toy fairs.
1976	Class 31 and Doctor X set released for Christmas.
1977	Airfix draw up their production plan.
1979	GMR name adopted and wagon production starts in the UK.
1980	Airfix empire crumbles.
1981	Production ceases and Palitoy acquires the model railway tools.

Further Reading
A detailed listing of the Airfix and Mainline model railway systems was produced by the late Charles Manship in the 1980s but it is no longer available. However, there has been a series of articles by Graham Smith-Thompson, in Model Railway Enthusiast magazine, profiling the Airfix and Mainline ranges and other systems that later used the tools. There were six parts devoted specifically to Airfix published in the July-December issues in 1998.

Collectors Clubs
The Airfix Collectors Club caters for collectors of any Airfix product including the model railway range and publishes a newsletter called Constant Scale. Further information about this organisation may be obtained from Jeremy Brook at 29 Elley Green, Neston, Nr. Corsham, Wiltshire SN13 9TX or by visiting them at

their Web site which is at:
www.djairfix.freeserve.co.uk

Locomotives
Dates – The dates used in the following tables are based on catalogues and price lists and should not be taken as evidence of availability.

Listing – The models are arranged in the order we believe they were available.

Samples on the Market – Far East manufacturers sent samples to their customers for approval before proceeding with full production. These samples often ended up in collections and today they command a good price. Samples of models that did not reach the production stage are of even greater interest to collectors.

Cat.No.	Name / Number	Colour	Details	Years	£	£
1.	**American 4-4-0**					
54170-5	'Jupiter'	red+silver	Central Pacific (*CPRR*)	77-80	20	25
54171-8	119	red+black	*Union Pacific RR*	77-80	20	25
2.	**Class 31/4 Diesel Co-Co**					
54100-6	31401	blue	BRe, front code IP02	77-81	12	20
54109-9	D5531	green	BRc, front code C	77-81	14	22
3.	**Class 61XX Prairie Tank 2-6-2T**					
54150	6110	green	*Great Western*, solid wheels	77-81	18	25
54151	6167	black	BRb, lined, solid wheels	77-81	20	28

The tools for this model passed to Palitoy, then Dapol, and finally Hornby who now make their own versions of the model.

Cat.No.	Name / Number	Colour	Details	Years	£	£
4.	**Class 6P/7P 'Rebuilt Royal Scot' 4-6-0**					
54120	6103 'Royal Scots Fusilier'	black	*LMS*	78-81	30	45
54121	46100 'Royal Scot'	green	BRb, smoke deflectors, badly positioned decals on tender	78-81	28	35
5.	**Class 14XX 0-4-2T**					
54152	1466	green	*GWR*	78-81	20	25
54153	1466	green	BRa, lined	78-81	22	30

The tools for this model passed to Palitoy, then Dapol, and finally Hornby who now make their own versions of the model.

Cat.No.	Name / Number	Colour	Details	Years	£	£
6.	**Class 4F 0-6-0**					
54122	4454	black	*LMS*	78-81	30	35
54123	44454	black	BRb (small)	78-80	30	40
54123	44454	black	BRb (large)	80-81	35	45

The tools for this model passed to Palitoy, then Dapol, and finally Hornby who now make their own versions of the model.

Cat.No.	Name / Number	Colour	Details	Years	£	£
7.	**Class 4073 'Castle' 4-6-0**					
54124	4073 'Caerphilly Castle'	green	*Great* (crest) *Western*	79-81	32	40
54125	4079 'Pendennis Castle'	green	BRb, incorrectly numbered in cat.	79-81	35	45

'Powderham Castle' and 'Pembroke Castle' were Airfix models renamed and renumbered by Dapol but sold in original Airfix boxes. These will be found listed under Dapol.

Cat.No.	Name / Number	Colour	Details	Years	£	£
8.	**Class 2361 'Dean Goods' 0-6-0** (see Mainline)					
54156	2516	green	*GWR*	**	–	–
54157	2538	black	BRb	**	–	–

** Arrived too late and were sold by Palitoy in Mainline packaging. The tools for this model passed to Palitoy, then Dapol, and finally Hornby who now make their own versions of the model.

9.   Class N2 Tank 0-6-2T (see Mainline)

54154	9522		green	*LNER*	**	–	–
54155	69531		black	BRb	**	–	–

** Arrived too late and were sold by Palitoy in Mainline packaging. The tools for this model passed to Palitoy, then Dapol, and finally Hornby who now make their own versions of the model.

One of the first three test shots of the Airfix Castle, with many errors!   [table 7]

Final production finish with mock-up chassis of the planned Airfix Class N2 tank   [table 9]

Prototype model (from a K's kit) of the proposed Airfix Dean Goods   [table 8]

Prototype model of the proposed Airfix Compound - project abandoned.   (Courtesy of Bachmann Industries Europe Ltd)

Coaches

The first coaches made by Airfix were the Mk 2D stock which are fairly common and inexpensive. The later GWR Autocoach, Centenary stock, B Suburbans and the H and G Siphons were very nice models but also quite easy to find. There were also Stannier type LMS mainline coaches and non-corridor stock. Most of these in mint boxed condition would cost between £10 and £15 but the 2nd class Mk2Ds are scarcer and can fetch as much as £20.

Wagons

The range of wagons was quite large and included 5 and 7-plank wagons, vent van, SR box van, conflat and container, lowmac, large mineral, LMS and GWR brake vans, a long wheelbase tanker, hopper and a bogie bolster wagon. These came out in a range of liveries including a number of non-authentic private owner vans. The latter are interesting as some were re-liveried models, done in batches of 7,000 to use up surplus stocks of BR ventilated vans and some of these were deliberately done in very small quantities of incorrect colours to generate an interest in collecting them. These are very rare and could cost between £20 and £40 to buy. Ones to look out for include a 'Spratt's' van with red printing, a 'Stalybridge Corporation Gas Department' 7-plank in grey, a 'Broadoak' 7-plank and a 'Highley Mining' 5-plank, both in grey, and 'Hales Fuels' in brown. Other Airfix wagons sell for around £5-£10 in mint boxed condition.

Accessories

There were very few accessories for the Airfix range but they included, in 1979, a series of card lineside structures which were both available separately and provided in the train sets. The models released that first year were a signal box (54650-6), tunnel (54651-9) and a station (54652-2).

Track was supplied by Peco and Airfix supplied both battery and mains power units. At the end Airfix launched their own version of Zero 1 which was called 'MTC' which stood for Multiple Train Controller.

Sets

Airfix tried hard to sell their sets and produced a total of 19 before they went into liquidation. Retailers always wanted sets made up of boxed items so that they could break up sets that did not sell and offer the items individually. As the Airfix range is relatively small and so easy to build a complete collection of, there is a growing interest in Airfix train sets. This particularly applies to those of the pre GMR days. Of special interest are the adventure sets - 'Doctor X' and the two Wild West sets which can fetch as much as £80. Another interesting set is the Cornish Rivera without the gold beading on the splashers of the locomotive or with it applied as print splasher labels. The latter were done in an emergency to cover a production mistake.

GMR packaging introduced by Airfix in 1979 to improve their image.

Airfix Class 31/4 diesel BR blue as 31401 (54100-6)
[table 2]
This was the first locomotive released by Airfix.

Airfix Class 14XX 0-4-2 tank in BR green as 1466 (54151)
[table 5]

Airfix Class 4F in BR black as 44454 (54123)
[table 6]

Bachmann BR green Class A4 60022 'Mallard' (pre-production model)   [table 24]

Bachmann LMS black Class 2MT Ivatt tank (pre-production model)   [table 14]

Bachmann

History

The name Bachmann came from a German emigrant to the USA who, in 1835, founded a company in Philadelphia. Amongst other things, the company made tinplate toys and, many years later, was one of the pioneers of plastic goods, including toy trains. Bachmann went on to become the largest distributor of toy trains and model railways in America.

Meanwhile, in 1925, in China, a man named Ting Hsiung-chao bought a battery manufacturing company in Shanghai for US$500. During the civil war between the Nationalist and Communist factions in China he was imprisoned for political reasons by the Communists, and was unable to tend to his business, which ultimately collapsed as a result. He was eventually forced to flee from Communist China, to re-establish what became a thriving business in North Point, Hong Kong.

His company, Kader, was founded in 1948 and went on to become the largest manufacturer of toys in the Far East. In the mid 1950s, the Company started manufacturing for Bachmann and by 1987, Kader had bought Bachmann outright.

Kader Industrial Co. Ltd, one of the Kader group of companies, is now based in Kowloon Bay, very near the old airport, Kai Tak.

One British company it manufactured for was Palitoy, the owners of the Mainline Railways range which was prominent in the 1970s and early 1980s. Palitoy had an arrangement whereby they required the manufacturers to produce their own tools for their products with the tools remaining in the ownership of the manufacturing company. As a result of this, when Palitoy closed down and its model railway assets were acquired by Dapol, the latter did not acquire the Far East tools of Kader origin.

By the late 1980s, Kader were looking at the European market. With their good collection of tools for making locomotives and rolling stock for the British market, they decided to form a European company to develop the local potential. Thus, Bachmann Industries Europe Ltd was formed in June 1989 and the model railway press in Britain announced the newly launched Bachmann Branch-Line range in January 1990. Kader also acquired a number of famous European names including Liliput which is based in Altdorf, near Nuremberg, Germany. A new purpose made block was added to the Zhong Tang factory complex fairly recently, in Guang Dong Province, dedicated solely to the manufacture of railways in various gauges for the UK, Continental Europe, China and US markets.

While the former Mainline tools formed the basis of the Bachmann British range, the last ten years have seen considerable improvements made to the models and, at an early stage, the launch of many new models. This process continues with Bachmann setting the highest standards for ready-to-run 00 scale models in the UK.

Further Reading

There has been a series of articles by Graham Smith-Thompson, in Model Railway Collector magazine (formerly Model Railway Enthusiast), profiling the Airfix and Mainline ranges and other systems that later used the tools. The first part was published before the magazine ceased publication in the summer of 2000.

Collectors Club

For a number of years the Company sponsored an enthusiasts club called Bachmann Times which operated at arms-length. In 2000 the club was reformed in-house under the name: Bachmann Collectors Club. Members receive a quarterly magazine called Bachmann Times. Further information about this may be obtained by writing to the Club at Bachmann Industries Europe Ltd, Moat Way, Barwell, Leicestershire LE9 8EY.

Dates – It is difficult to date Bachmann Branch-Line models by their appearance in catalogues as some models have not been ready for distribution until one or two years after their catalogue launch. As near as possible, in the tables below, we have given the years

---

Milestones

1835	Bachmann founded in Philadelphia.
1925	Ting Hsiung-chao buys a battery company in Shanghai.
1948	Ting founds Kader in Hong Kong.
1975	Kader start producing Mainline models for Palitoy.
1987	Kader buys Bachmann.
1989	Bachmann Industries Europe Ltd formed.
1990	Bachmann Branchlines launched in UK initially using former Mainline tools.
1993	Kader acquires Liliput.
1998	Bachmann Industries Europe Ltd introduce their Blue Riband range.
2000	Bachmann buy Graham Farish.

in which we believe the models first appeared in the shops.

A single date has been given because Bachmann operated a batch production supply system. Generally there was only an initial batch of models which, when sold-out, was not repeated. Instead, the model was either dropped from the catalogue or replaced by a similar model renumbered and generally improved in finish. Some models have been available in the shops for several years from the date of the initial production - the length of time being dependent on the popularity of the model.

Listing – As Bachmann adopted a catalogue numbering system that was designed to keep like models together we have listed the models below in catalogue numerical order. This will make it easy for the searcher to find the model if they have the catalogue number which should be on the box. We have also found that advertisers often list models for sale in this order.

Catalogue Numbers
Generally the addition of a letter suffix to a catalogue number indicates a modification of some kind to the model. This could be a change of number or an alteration to the chassis.

Blue Riband Models
With the ever increasing strive for higher quality in their models, in 1998, Bachmann launched their Blue Riband range. This badge is worn only by those models that Bachmann consider to be to the high standard they have set themselves to achieve and it is expected that all completely new models will fall in this category. The name comes from transatlantic shipping where the Blue Riband was awarded to the fastest liner to ply the route.

Boxes
wpc - wooden presentation case. These have been provided for a number of limited or special editions.

The men behind Bachmann Industries Europe Ltd - Graham Hubbard and Merl Evans

Locomotives

1. Class 165/1 'Network Turbo' and 166 'Network Express Turbo'

31.025	166202	white, red+blue	Network SouthEast 3-car 166 set	99	65	90
31.035	165001	white, red+blue	Chiltern Line 2-car 165 set	99	NPG	70

2. Class J72 0-6-0T (ex-Mainline model)
Similar to the last Mainline J72 but now fitted with an open frame motor driving on centre axle.

31.050	8680	green	*LNER*	90	28	35
31.050A	8680	green	*LNER* lined	99	30	40
31.051	69023	green	BRc/NER	90	25	35
31.052	68680	black	BRb lined	90	28	35
31.053	69012	black	BRc unlined	90	27	35
31.054	2313	black	*LNER* lined**	96	25	35
31.055	68680	green	BRb lined**	96	25	31
31.056	69025	black	BRc unlined**	96	27	35
31.057	8693	black	*LNER* unlined**	98	30	40
(30.100)	68745	black	BRb, NER Ross 'pop' valves, number on tanks, from 30.100 freight set only	94	25	28*

** full length ejector pipe

3. Class 46 'Peak' Diesel Electric 1Co-Co1 (ex-Mainline model)

31.075	46026 'Leicestershire and Derbyshire Yeomanry'	blue	BRe	94	28	35
31.076	46045	blue	BRe	94	20	30
31.076A	-	blue	BRe	95	18	25
31.077	D193	green	BRc	97	20	30
31.078	D181	blue	BRe	97	20	32
31.080	D172 'Ixion'	green	Watermans Railway Ltd Edn 2000, wpc	96	75	100

4. Standard Class 4 4-6-0 (ex-Mainline model)   dc = double chimney

31.100	75014	black	BRb, BR2 tender	96	35	45
31.100A	75015	black	BRb, BR2 tender	98	45	55
31.101	75023	green	BRc, BR2 tender	96	35	45
31.102	75073	black	BRb, BR1B tender	90	35	45
31.102A	75072	black	BRb, BR1B tender	98	45	55
31.103	75020	black	BRc, dc, BR2 tender	90	36	45
31.104	75069	green	BRc, dc, BR1B tender	90	35	45
31.105	75078	black	BRc, dc, BR1B tender	90	36	45
31.105A	75075	black	BRc, dc, BR2 tender	98	45	55
31.106	75029 'The Green Knight'	green	BRc, dc, BR2 tender	90	40	50
31.106A	75003	green	BRc, dc, BR2 tender	98	35	55

5. Jubilee Class 5XP 4-6-0 (ex-Mainline model)
dc = double chimney   ebn = etched nameplate   Ft = Fowler tender with coal rails   St = Stanier 4,000 gallon tender.

31.150	5552 'Silver Jubilee'	black	*LMS*, 1930s livery with chrome** plated fittings, Ltd Edn 500, wpc	90	160	250
31.150A	5699 'Galatea'	crimson	*LMS*, St, Sp Edn 600 (Loco Marketing Services)	96	200	280
(31.150Y)	45679 'Armada'	green	BRc, Ft, ebn, paired with 'Howard of Effingham' (see next item)	00	✦	✦
(31.150Y)	45670 'Howard of Effingham'	green	BRb, St, ebn, paired with 'Armada', Sp Edn 250 (Trafford Model Centre), wpc	00	NPG	175
(31.150Z)	45732 'Sanspareil'	green	BRc, St, ebn, paired with 'Novelty' (see next item)	00	✦	✦
{31.150Z}	45733 'Novelty'	green	BRb, St, ebn, paired with 'Sanspareil', Sp Edn 250 (Trafford Model Centre), wpc	00	NPG	175
31.151	45552 'Silver Jubilee'	green	BRc, ebn, yellow cabside band, St	90	40	56
31.152	45568 'Western Australia'	black	BRb (small), Ft	90	45	55
31.153	45596 'Bahamas'	green	BRc, dc, St	90	48	56
31.154	5721 'Impregnable'	crimson	*LMS*, St	94	40	50
31.155	5699 'Galatea'	crimson	*LMS*, Ft	94	47	55
31.155A	5699 'Galatea'	crimson	*LMS*, Ft	00	35	47
31.156	45715 'Invincible'	green	BRc, Ft	97	40	55
31.156A	45715 'Invincible'	green	BRc, Ft	99	45	55
31.157	5684 'Jutland'	crimson	*LMS*, St, single + dc's supplied with model	00	NPG	66
31.158	45742 'Connaught'	green	BRb, St, single + dc's supplied with model	00	NPG	66

** The chrome plating was applied befor the black paint and the latter tends to peel off.

Cat.No.	Name / Number	Colour	Details	Years	£	£

6. Re-Built Patriot Class 4-6-0 (ex-Mainline model)   St = Stanier 4,000 gallon tender   nsd = no smoke deflectors

Cat.No.	Name / Number	Colour	Details	Years	£	£
31.200	45528	black	BRa, St,	91	38	50
31.201	45545 'Planet'	green	BRc, St,	91	45	54
31.202	5526 'Morecambe and Heysham'	black	*LMS*, St, nsd	96	35	47

7. Rebuilt Royal Scot 4-6-0 (ex-Mainline model)   nsd = no smoke deflectors   St = Stanier 4,000 gallon tender

Cat.No.	Name / Number	Colour	Details	Years	£	£
31.225	46102 'Black Watch'	green	BRb, etched brass military crest	96	45	60
31.226	6133 'Green Howards'	black	*LMS*, nsd	97	45	64
31.227	46162 'Queens Westminster Rifleman'	green	BRc	97	45	64
(31.275Y)	46169 'The Boy Scout'	green	BRb, St, Sp Edn 350 (Trafford MC), paired with 46168 in wpc, Mancunian headboard	99	✦	✦
(31.275Y)	46168 'The Girl Guide'	green	BRc, St, Sp Edn 350 (Trafford MC), paired with 46169 in wpc, Mancunian headboard	99	NPG	175 **
31.277Z	46159 'Royal Air Force' ***	green	BR Sp Edn 500 (Annex Industries), wpc + diecast aircraft	00	NPG	NPG

** Price quoted is for the pair in the presentation box.
*** Sold solely on the Internet, commemorating an RAF Anniversary.

8. Re-Built Jubilee 4-6-0 (larger boiler + double chimney)   nsd = no smoke deflectors   St = Stanier tender

Cat.No.	Name / Number	Colour	Details	Years	£	£
31.250	45735 'Comet'	black	BRa, nsd, St	91	45	54
31.251	45736 'Phoenix'	green	BRc, yellow cabside band, St	91	45	54

9. Parallel Boiler Scot 4-6-0 (ex-Mainline model)
Ft = Fowler tender with coal rails   St = Stanier 4,000 gallon tender   nsd = no smoke deflectors

Cat.No.	Name / Number	Colour	Details	Years	£	£
31.275	6100 'Royal Scot'	crimson	*LMS*, St, brass bell, special nameplates, Ltd Edn 1000	94	85	125
31.275Z	6110 'Grenadier Guardsman'	crimson	LMS, Ft, nsd, LMS crest on cabsides, number on tender, wpc, Sp Edn 500 (Beatties)	98	85	125
31.276	6134 'The Cheshire Regiment'	black	*LMS*, St, new deflectors with curved tops	94	40	50
31.277	6112 'Sherwood Forester'	crimson	*LMS*, Ft, nsd	94	40	50
31.278	46148 'The Manchester Regiment'	green	BRb, St	95	40	52
31.279	6130 'The West Yorkshire Regiment'	crimson	*LMS*, Ft with extensions to coal rail, angled smoke deflectors	96	40	50
31.280	6106 'Gordon Highlander'	crimson	*LMS*, St	98	40	64

10. Manor Class 4-6-0 (ex-Mainline model)

Cat.No.	Name / Number	Colour	Details	Years	£	£
31.300	7802 'Bradley Manor'	green	*GWR*, unlined	91	35	45
31.300Z	7816 'Frilsham Manor'	green	BR, black metalwork, Sp Edn 500 (Brunswick Model Railways)	99	NPG	NPG
31.301	7820 'Dinmore Manor'	green	BRb unlined,	91	35	45
31.302	7823 'Hook Norton Manor'	green	BRc lined	91	35	45
31.303	7829 'Ramsbury Manor'	black	BRb lined, red plates	91	35	45
31.303A	7829 'Ramsbury Manor'	black	BRb lined, red plates, modified chassis	99	35	50
31.304	7800 'Torquay Manor'	green	*GWR* (button)	96	35	60
31.305	7805 'Broome Manor'	green	*GWR*	96	35	60
31.306	7822 'Foxcote Manor'	green	BRc lined	96	35	60
31.2000/1	7828 'Odney Manor'	green	BRc, Ltd Edn 1000 with Class 43XX 31.2000/2 + 6 coaches**	00	NPG	270

** Price shown is for complete Cambrian Coast Express set

11. Class 04 Diesel Shunter 0-6-0DS   nhs = no hazard stripes

Cat.No.	Name / Number	Colour	Details	Years	£	£
31.335	11226	black	BRb, nhs	97	23	28
31.336	D2334	blue	BRe	97	25	38
31.337	D2280	green	BRc	97	25	29
31.338	D2282	green	BRc, nhs	99	25	38

12. Class 03 Diesel Shunter 0-6-0DS (ex-Mainline model)   ats = air tanks supplied   nhs = no hazard stripes

Cat.No.	Name / Number	Colour	Details	Years	£	£
31.350	D2000	green	BRc, conical exhaust, nhs	91	24	35
31.351	D.2012	green	BRc, conical exhaust,	91	24	35
31.352	03371	blue	BRe, conical exhaust, ats	91	24	35
31.353	03197	blue	BRe, cast flared chimney, ats	91	24	35

13. Lord Nelson Class 4-6-0   Final form as rebuilt by Bulleid.

Cat.No.	Name / Number	Colour	Details	Years	£	£
31.400	850 'Lord Nelson'	green	*Southern*, based on the preserved loco, Ltd Edn 1000	92	120	250

31.401	864 'Sir Martin Frobisher'	green	*Southern*	92	45	56
31.402	30851 'Sir Francis Drake'	green	BRb	92	45	56
31.403	30861 'Lord Anson'	green	BRc	92	45	56
31.404	855 'Robert Blake'	green	*Southern*, olive green, original small chimney	96	48	60
31.405	30852 'Sir Walter Raleigh'	green	BRb	96	45	63
31.406	30850 'Lord Nelson'	green	BRc	98	50	82
31.407	856 'Lord St.Vincent'	green	*Southern*	98	50	82

14. Class 2MT Ivatt 2-6-2T   p-p equip = push-pull equipment

31.450	41221	black	BRb, p-p equip	95	30	40
31.450A	41272	black	BRc, p-p equip, plaque as 7000th loco from Crewe	96	35	45
31.450B	41281	black	BRb, lined, p-p equip	98	28	37
31.450C	41224	black	BRc, lined, p-p equip	00	NPG	51
31.451	41241	black	BRb, lined	95	30	40
31.451A	41250	black	BRb	96	28	34
31.451B					NPG	NPG
31.451C	41247	black	BRb	00	NPG	51
31.452	41313	black	BRc	95	30	40
31.452A	41202	black	BRc	96	30	40
31.452B	41233	black	BRc lined	98	28	37
31.453	1206	black	*LMS*	95	30	40
31.453A	1202	black	*LMS*	98	28	38

15. Class 158/159 Express Units

31.500	158860	blu+wht	*Regional Railways*, 2-car 158 set		NPG	NPG
31.500A	158791	blu+wht	*Regional Railways*, 2-car 158 set	97	45	61
31.500B	158868	blu+wht	*Regional Railways*, 2-car 158 set	98	40	52
31.501	158702	blu+wht	*Express/Scotrail*, 2-car 158 set	97	40	52
31.502	158906	red	BRe *West Yorks PTE Metro*, 2-car 158 set	97	40	52
31.503	158757	blu+wht	*Express/Regional Railways*, 2-car 158 set	97	40	52
31.504	158783	green	*Central Trains*, 2-car 158 set	00	NPG	70
31.505	158758	blue	*First North Western*, 2-car 158 set	00	NPG	70
31.506	158745	silver	*Wales & West*, 2-car 158 set	00	NPG	70
31.510	159001 'City of Exeter'	wht+r+b	*Network SouthEast*, 3-car 159 set	98	75	89
31.511	158809	blu+wht	*Express*, 3-car 158 set	98	75	89
31.512	159009		SWT / *A Stagecoach Company*, 3-car 159 set	98	75	89
31.513	158811	pur+gold	*Northern Spirit*, 3-car 158 set	99	75	92

16. Class V2 2-6-2   step = stepped tender   osp = outside steam pipes

31.550	4771 'Green Arrow'	green	*LNER*, Ltd Edn 1000, wpc	92	120	225
31.551	60800 'Green Arrow'	black	BRb	92	45	54
31.552	60964 'The Durham Light Infantry'	green	BRc	92	45	54
31.553	60807	black	BRa	92	40	50
31.553A	60807	black	BRb	97	40	53
31.554	60903	green	BRc, double chimney	92	40	50
31.555	4801	green	*LNER*	92	40	51
31.556	3650	black	*LNER*, unlined wartime livery	92	40	54
31.557	60884	green	BRb, osp	97	40	58
31.558	4844 'Coldstreamer'	green	*LNER*, separate printed nameplates	96	45	58
31.559	60800 'Green Arrow'	green	BRc, as preserved, Ltd Edn 500	00	NPG	NPG
31.560	4806 'The Green Howard'	green	*LNER*, step	99	NPG	80
31.561	60825	green	BRc, step, osp	99	NPG	80

17. Class V1 & V3 2-6-2T   hb = hopper bunker   csp = cranked steam pipes

31.600	7684	green	*LNER*, (V3), hb	92	32	45
31.601	67601	black	BRc, (V1), csp	92	32	45
31.602	67664	black	BRb, (V1), hb	92	32	45
31.603	466	black	*LNER*, (V1), hb, csp	92	34	45
31.604	67666	black	BRc, (V3), hb	96	35	45
31.605	67601	black	BRb, (V3), csp	96	35	45
31.606	448	black	*LNER*, lined, hb	97	35	42
31.606A	2911	black	*LNER*, csp	00	NPG	51
31.607	67684	green	BRa, hb	97	32	42
31.608	7684	green	*LNER*, hb	99	35	51
31.609	67673	black	BRb, lined, Westinghouse pump, hb	99	35	51

Cat.No.	Name / Number	Colour	Details	Years	£	£

18. Class B1 4-6-0 (ex-Replica model)

Cat.No.	Name / Number	Colour	Details	Years	£	£
31.700	1264	green	*LNER*	95	32	40
31.701	61241 'Viscount Ridley'	black	BRb	94	35	45
31.701A	61399	black	BRb	96	32	40
31.702	61354	black	BRc	94	32	40
31.702A	61190	black	BRc	96	32	47
31.703	61010 'Wildebeeste'	black	BRc	96	35	40
31.705	1306 'Mayflower'	green	*LNER* Ltd Edn 2000, 9ct gold plates, wpc	96	50	70
31.706	1041 'Roedeer'	black	*LNER* lined	98	40	58
31.707	61002 'Impala'	green	BRa, Doncaster green	98	40	58

61009 'Hartebeeste' and 61018 'Gnu' may also be found. These, we understand, were finished by Rails of Sheffield, using Fox transfers.

19. Class 6959 Modified Hall 4-6-0 (ex-Replica model)

Cat.No.	Name / Number	Colour	Details	Years	£	£
31.775	6990 'Witherslack Hall'	black	BRb, red plates	96	45	53
31.776	7915 'Mere Hall'	green	BRc	96	45	68
31.777	6962 'Soughton Hall'	green	*G*(crest)*W*	96	45	68
31.778	6969 'Wraysbury Hall'	green	BRb, Hawksworth tender	96	45	68
31.779	6960 'Raveningham Hall'	green	*G*(crest)*W*, Ltd Edn 1000, 9ct gold plates, wpc	97	65	98

20. Class 93XX 2-6-0

Cat.No.	Name / Number	Colour	Details	Years	£	£
31.801	9319	green	*GWR*	92	33	40
31.802	9308	black	BRb	92	33	40
31.803	7332	green	BRc	92	33	40

21. Class 43XX 2-6-0 (ex-Mainline model)

Cat.No.	Name / Number	Colour	Details	Years	£	£
31.825	4318	green	*GWR*	96	30	37
31.826	6384	green	BRc, unlined	96	30	37
31.827	5355	green	*GWR* (button)	96	30	37
31.828	5370	black	BRb lined, red plates	00	NPG	55
31.829	4331	green	*Great* (crest) *Western*	00	NPG	55
31.2000/2	5331	green	BRc lined, Ltd Edn 1000 with Manor 31.2000/1**	00	NPG	270

** Price given is for complete Cambrian Coast Express set.

22. Class J39 0-6-0   step = stepped tender

Cat.No.	Name / Number	Colour	Details	Years	£	£
31.850	1974	black	*LNER* lined	94	32	40
31.851	64964	black	BRb	94	32	40
31.851A	64958	black	BRb	96	35	45
31.852	64967	black	BRc	94	32	40
31.852A	64970	black	BRc	96	35	45
31.853	1996	black	*LNER*	96	35	45
31.855	1856	black	*LNER* lined	00	NPG	51
31.860	1496	black	*LNER*, step	99	NPG	51
31.861	64838	black	BRb, step	99	NPG	51
31.862	64791	black	BRc, step	99	NPG	51

23. Class 57XX Pannier Tank 0-6-0PT (ex-Mainline model)   imp = improved chassis

Cat.No.	Name / Number	Colour	Details	Years	£	£
31.900	7760	green	*Great Western*	93	20	28
31.900A	7702	green	*GWR*, imp	96	25	29
31.901	5796	black	BRb	93	20	28
31.901A	8700	green	*GWR* (button), imp	96	25	27
31.902	7754	black	BRb	93	20	28
31.902A	5775	black	BRc, imp	96	25	27
31.903	L94	maroon	*London Transport*, imp, Sp Edn 500 (London Transport Museum)	99	28	35
(30.200)	L91	maroon	*London Transport* sold in sets	91	80	90*
(30.201)	L99	maroon	*London Transport* sold in sets	93	30	35*

24. Class A4 4-6-2   Based on the former Trix/Liliput model mouldings on a Bachmann split-chassis of standard design principal.
dc = double chimney   sc = single chimney   ct = corridor tender   nct = non-corridor tender
v = valances fitted   nv = no valances   bm = blackened metalwork

Cat.No.	Name / Number	Colour	Details	Years	£	£
31.950	4489 'Dominion of Canada'	blue	*LNER*, v, sc, brass bell, Ltd Edn	95	90	125
31.950A	60011 "Empire of India'	green	Ltd Edn 500 (Rails), wpc	99	90	120
31.951	60009 'Union of South Africa'	green	BRc, etched brass nameplates and plaques	95	NPG	NPG
31.951A	60009 'Union of South Africa'	green	BRb, sc, ct, short run	96	60	70
31.951Z	60009 'Osprey'	green	BRc, Sp Edn (75069 Fund) 350, wpc	98	125	175
31.952	4903 'Peregrine'	blue	*LNER*, v, st	96	50	70
31.952A	2512 'Silver Fox'	silver	*LNER*, v, st	98	55	87
31.953	60008 'Dwight DEisenhower'	green	BRc, dc, nct, USA Ltd Edn 250, wpc	95	350	500

31.953A	60008 'Dwight DEisenhower'	blue	BRb, sc, ct, USA Ltd Edn 500, wpc	96	200	300
31.953B	4496 'Dwight DEisenhower'	blue	LNER, sc, ct, bm, USA Ltd Edn 500, wpc	97	95	125
31.953C	60008 'Dwight DEisenhower'	green	BR , USA Ltd Edn , wpc	99	95	125
31.954	60007 'Sir Nigel Gresley'	blue	BRb, dc	96	50	70
31.954A	60007 'Sir Nigel Gresley'	green	BR, Ltd Edn 1000	00	75	90
31.955	60013 'Dominion of New Zealand'	green	BRb, nct, large chime whistle, sc	96	55	78
31.956	4482 'Golden Eagle'	green	LNER, v, sc	97	45	87
31.957	60033 'Seagull'	green	BRc, dc	97	50	87
31.958	60020 'Guillemot'	green	BRc, dc	98	50	87
31.959	26 'Miles Beevor'	blue	LNER, nv	98	50	87
31.960	60017 'Silver Fox'		BR + 6 coaches Ltd Edn Elizabethan set**	96	NPG	295
31.961/1	4468 'Mallard'	blue	LNER, v, 160th anniv. Ltd Edn 1000 with 31.961/2, wpc	98	♥	♥
31.961/2	60022 'Mallard'	green	BRc, dc, 160th anniv. Ltd Edn 1000 with 31.961/1, wpc	98	N/A	220
31.2001/1	4491 'Commonwealth of Australia'	blue	LNER, v, Ltd Edn 1000 with 31.2001/2 and 31.2001/3**	00	♥	♥
31.2001/2	60012 'Commonwealth of Australia'	blue	BRb, Ltd Edn 1000 with 31.2001/1 and 31.2001/3**	00	♥	♥
31.2001/3	60012 'Commonwealth of Australia'	green	BRc, dc, Ltd Edn 1000 with 31.2001/1 and 31.2001/2**, wpc for all 3	00	N/A	295
	4462 'William Whitelaw'	black	LNER, Sp Edn 300 (Rails)	99	NPG	75
	2510 'Quicksilver'	black	LNER, Sp Edn 300 (Rails)	99	NPG	75
	4496 'Golden Shuttle'	black	LNER, Sp Edn 300 (Rails)	99	NPG	75

** Price given is for complete set

25. Class 42 'Warship' Diesel Hydraulic B-B (Blue Riband model)

32.050	D817 'Foxhound'	maroon	BRc	98	35	46
32.051	D832 'Onslaught'	green	BRc, yellow ends	98	35	35
32.052	D816 'Eclipse'	green	BRc, no yellow half panels	99	35	38
32.053	D804 'Avenger'	blue	BRe	00	NPG	48
32.054	D831 'Monarch'	blue	BRe	99	35	42
32.055	D800 'Sir Brian Robertson'	green	BRc	00	NPG	48

26. Class 08 Diesel Shunter 0-6-0DS (Blue Riband model)

32.100	13365	green	BRc, no hazard stripes	00	NPG	41
32.101	D3729	green	BRc	00	NPG	41
32.102	08623	blue	BRe, without ladders fitted	00	NPG	41

27. Class N 2-6-0 (Blue Riband model)

32.150/1	A863	grey	SE&CR, Ltd Edn 1000 with 32.150/2**, wpc	98	♥	♥
32.150/2	1863	green	Southern, Ltd Edn 1000 with 32.150/1**, wpc	98	NPG	135
32.150W	383	gry+blk	CIE, Sp Edn 640 (Murphy's Models, Dublin)	00	NPG	68
32.150X	376	LNWR black	CIE, Sp Edn 640 (Murphy's Models, Dublin)	00	NPG	68
32.150Y	372, 385, 390	green	CIE, alt. number transfers provided, Sp Edn 500 (Murphy's Models, Dublin)	00	60	68
32.150Z	31874 'Brian Fisk'	black	BRb, Sp Edn 500 (Beatties) wpc	99	55	75
32.151	31860	black	BRb lined	98	40	46
32.151A	31816	black	BRc lined	99	40	63
32.152	31813	black	BRc lined	98	40	50
32.153	1824	green	Southern, olive	98	40	45
32.153A	1821	green	Southern, olive	99	40	63
32.154	31843	black	BRc lined	00	NPG	63
32.155	1854	green	Southern, malachite	00	NPG	63

** Price quoded is for the complete set

28. Class 8750 Pannier Tank 0-6-0PT (Blue Riband model)

32.200	9643	green	GWR	99	35	44
32.201	8763	black	BRb lined	99	35	44
32.202	4672	black	BRc	99	35	44

29. WD 'Austerity' 2-8-0 (Blue Riband model)

32.250	400 'Sir Guy Williams'	blue	LMR Ltd Edn 2000	99	100	150
32.250KCR	21	green	Kowloon & Canton Railway (British Section) HK Millennium Ltd Edn 1000 (only 200 in UK)	00	NPG	170
32.250Y **	NS4310	green	NS, Vulcan Foundry type, Ltd Edn 500 (Tasco Nederland BV)	00	NPG	NPG

Cat.No.	Name / Number	Colour	Details	Years	£	£
32.250Z	NS4329	green	NS, North British type, Ltd Edn 500 (Tasco Nederland BV)	00	NPG	NPG
32.251	90275	black	BRb	99	80	100
32.252	90445	black	BRc	99	80	100
32.253	60312	black	BRb	00	NPG	100
32.254	3085	black	*LNER*	00	NPG	100
32.255	78697	green	*WD 21st Army Transport Group*	00	NPG	100
32.256	90566	black	BRc	00	NPG	100
32.257	90015	black	BRb weathered, Ltd Edn	00	NPG	100

** The Dutch agent allocated his own number of 32.259 to this model.

30. Class 2251 'Collett Goods' 0-6-0 (Blue Riband model)

Cat.No.	Name / Number	Colour	Details	Years	£	£
32.300	3202	green	*GWR*	98	35	54
32.301	2260	black	BRb	98	35	54
32.302	2277	green	BRc lined	98	35	54
32.303	2251	green	BRb	99	35	54

31. Class 4MT Standard Tank 2-6-4T (Blue Riband model)

Cat.No.	Name/Number	Colour	Details	Dates	£	£
32.350	80061	black	BRb	01?	NPG	NPG
32.351	80097	black	BRc	01?	NPG	NPG

32. Class 25/3 Diesel Bo-Bo (Blue Riband model)

Cat.No.	Name/Number	Colour	Details	Dates	£	£
32.400	D7645	green	BRc	01	NPG	47
32.401	25279	blue	BRe	01	NPG	47

33. Class 170 'Turbostar' DMU (Blue Riband model)

Cat.No.	Name/Number	Colour	Details	Dates	£	£
32.450	?	teal blue	*Midland Mainline* 170/1	01	NPG	NPG
32.451	?	green	*Central Trains* 170/5	01	NPG	NPG
32.452	?	?	?	01	NPG	NPG

34. Class 221 Super Voyager DEMU (Blue Riband model)

			01?		
			01?		

Bachmann SE&CR N Class Mogul as 810 (from set 32-150) (pre-production model)   [table 27]

Bachmann B1 Class 61002 'Impala' (31-707) [table 18] still in LNER apple green but with BRa insignia.

Bachmann LMS crimson Jubilee Class 5684 'Jutland' (31-157) [table 5] (pre-production model).

Bachmann BR Standard Class 4 as 75029 'Green Knight' (31-106) [table 4] (without nameplates).

Coaches

The earliest coaches were a number of GWR Colletts and LMS types from the former Mainline range but with different stock numbers. These were followed by LNER coaches of Thompson design and Bulleid Southerns all of which are still available nearly 10 years after introduction but subject to changes in the stock numbers and liveries. The finest development so far is the range of Mk1 coaches in the Blue Riband series which first appeared late in 1999 and is being greatly expanded. For guidance with prices, look at current advertisements in the model railway press.

Wagons

As with the locomotives and coaches, wagons started with Mainline originals reproduced in a selection of new liveries. A new development was the sets of themed coal wagons and petrol tankers which are likely to become more collectable than single wagons in general. Some of the early wagon sets should now be going up in price. The new Blue Riband wagons are the bee's knees of the ready-to-run wagon world and

the range is expanding fast. Again, for prices, consult magazine advertisements as most are still readily available.

Sets

Initially, Bachmann sets came with a circle of track, an inexpensive controller, a standard range locomotive and rolling stock drawn from what was available at the time. None of these are of particular interest to collectors but interest in them will almost certainly grow in future years as they were not sold in very great quantities and many sets were broken up by retailers in order to sell the contents separately.

An exception to the general run were the London Transport sets (30-200 and 30-201) of 1991 which contained the early pannier tank in LT livery and three wagons. Another exception will be the Cambrian Coast Express set (31-2000), which was originally planned by Palitoy for their Mainline range. The Bachmann set will have two locomotives and six coaches along with accessories.

Bachmann WD 2-8-0 in Army livery as 78697 (32-255) (pre-production model)
[table 29]

Bachmann London Transport Class 577XX Pannier tank   [table 23]

Bachmann Rebuilt Royal Scot Class 46169 'The Boy Scout' (from set 31-275Y) – special edition   [table 7]

Bachmann Class 08 diesel shunter in BR blue as 08623 (pre-production model)　　[table 26]

Bachmann M.O.S. tank wagon (33-510)

One of the new Bachmann Blue Riband 8-plank (37-125) wagons showing the fine detail.

Bachmann GWR 57XX Class Pannier tank as 7702 (31-900)
[table 23]

Bachmann Network South East Class 159 as 159001
'City of Exeter' (31-510) [table 15] (pre-production model)

Lower Dee Mill, home of Dapol.

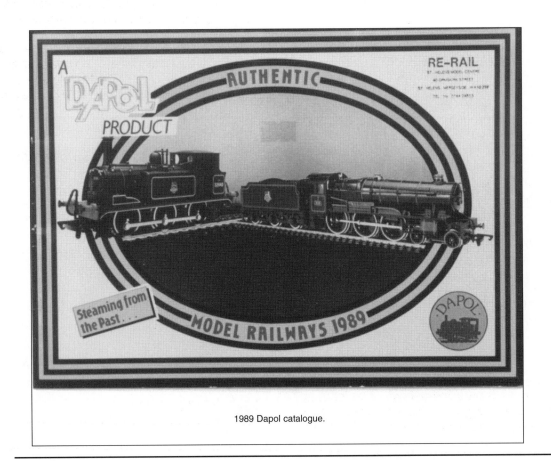

1989 Dapol catalogue.

Dapol

History

David Boyle, of Highfield Birds & Models, who in 1981 had been unsuccessful in a bid to buy the model railway division of Airfix when the Company was being broken up and sold off, founded a company of his own called Dapol. This was established to handle a large amount of Airfix stock and spares that he had been able to acquire. Boyle's ambition, all along, was to produce a range of British outline locomotives and rolling stock of a quality in performance and detail that, previously, had only been found in some Continental ranges.

Research and development had already commenced for a L&Y Pug, a GWR County Class and a J94 tank to the extent that plans had been drawn and the tools manufactured.

When Airfix stocks ran low, Boyle had new moulds made of some of the old Airfix wagons, which went on the market in November 1983. His company also commenced the production of the ex-L&Y 'Pug', which was released the following year, and the Hawksworth `County' which arrived soon after.

When Palitoy closed down in 1985, David Boyle was finally offered the Airfix models as well as the intellectual assets of Palitoy's Mainline Railways range. There followed a merging of Airfix, Mainline and Dapol products under the Dapol name. In fact, very few Mainline designs were used, except as old stock, as the tools for them belonged to the production company in Hong Kong - Kader.

Dapol next took over some of the British Trix/Lilliput range in the late '80s and these included the tooling for the bodies of the E3000 and Trans-Pennine DMU, the chassis remaining with Liliput in Austria and ending up with Bachmann. Dapol also bought the assets of G&R Wrenn in 1992 although, to date, only some wagons from the Wrenn range have been made. Some of these are sold on chassis purchased from Bachmann when the latter turned production over to their Blue Riband range. Dapol's other main production is plastic kits from the former Airfix tools. At one time they also made kits from the ex-Tri-ang Model-Land tools.

Stock was stored in various places including Boyle's own home. From time to time, forgotten boxes of obsolete stock emerged and the contents sold, often through Dapol's shop - especially at their Winsford

addresses. Some of this stock was never advertised making it difficult to record what and when models were released. A severe fire at the Cheshire factory damaged a number of tools. Dapol has also moved from Winsford in Cheshire to Llangollen, in Wales, where it has opened an exhibition which includes some of the Wrenn machines and tools which started life in the Hornby-Dublo production line at the Meccano factory in Liverpool.

Around 1996, some of the Dapol and former Airfix tools were offered to Bachmann but, subsequently, were sold to Hornby. Almost all of these are back in production out in China, having first undergone further improvements. Dapol, however, will continue to produce limited runs of some of these models from their stock of parts.

Further Reading

There has been a series of articles by Graham Smith-Thompson, in Model Railway Enthusiast magazine, profiling the Airfix and Mainline ranges and other systems that later used the tools. There were four parts devoted specifically to Dapol published in the August-November 1999 issues of the magazine.

Dates – we have found little evidence of when models first became available and when they were out of production. Those quoted in the tables below are based on this limited knowledge, coming largely from catalogues and press advertising, and are for guidance only.

Listing – The models are arranged in the order we believe they were available.

Packaging – Items in the following list shown as being 'ex-Airfix stock' or 'ex-Mainline stock' were, as far as we know, sold in their original packaging.

Milestones

1981	Dapol formed by David Boyle to market former Airfix products and spares.
1983	Dapol market their own wagons and renamed Airfix Castles.
1984	Dapol release their first locos, the L&Y Pug and Hawksworth County.
1985	Dapol acquire the intellectual assets of the Mainline system from Palitoy and Airfix tooling.
1988	Dapol acquire residue of British Liliput.
1992	Dapol buy G&R Wrenn.
1995	Dapol move to Llangollen.

Cat.No.	Name / Number	Colour	Details	Years	£	£

1. Class 0F 'L&Y Pug' 0-4-0ST

Cat.No.	Name / Number	Colour	Details	Years	£	£
D1	11217	black	*LMS*	84-94	28	35
D2	51241	black	BR	84-99	25	30
D10	19	black	L&Y lined in red	90-00	20	30

2. Class 1000 'Hawksworth County' 4-6-0

Cat.No.	Name / Number	Colour	Details	Years	£	£
D3	1029 'County of Worcester'	green	*G*(crest)*W*, Hawksworth tender	84-89	35	45
D4	1027 'County of Stafford'	green	BRc lined, Hawksworth tender, double chimney	84-93	40	48
D68	1019 'County of Merioneth'	black	BRb	88-93	35	43
D103	1011 'County of Chester'	green	*G*(crest)*W*, remodeled boiler and firebox, improved finish	90-96	40	50

3. Class 4073 'Castle' 4-6-0 (ex-Airfix model with tender drive)

Some of the stock of Airfix Castles were renamed and renumbered by Dapol. Of these, some were sold in their original Airfix boxes while others were put into new Dapol packaging once the expanded polystyrene tray had been trimmed with a large knife!

Cat.No.	Name / Number	Colour	Details	Years	£	£
D29	4079 'Pendennis Castle'	green	BRb, Airfix stock	85-88	35	45
D30	4073 'Caerphilly Castle'	green	*Great* (crest) *Western*, Airfix stock	83-89	32	40
?	4080 'Powderham Castle'	green	BRb, Airfix stock renamed by Dapol	83-85	75	100
?	4080 'Powderham Castle'	green	*Great* (crest) *Western*, Airfix stock renamed by Dapol	83-85	75	100
?	4078 'Pembroke Castle'	green	BRb, Airfix stock renamed by Dapol	83-85	75	100
?	4078 'Pembroke Castle'	green	*Great* (crest) *Western*, Airfix stock renamed by Dapol	83-85	75	100

4. Class 4073 'Castle' 4-6-0 (with loco drive and Hawksworth tender)

Cat.No.	Name / Number	Colour	Details	Years	£	£
D5	4090 'Dorchester Castle'	green	BRb lined, optional double chimney	85-95	30	40
D6	5090 'Neath Abbey'	green	*GW*	85-93	30	40

5. Class J94 'Austerity' 0-6-0ST

Cat.No.	Name / Number	Colour	Details	Years	£	£
D7	'Warrington'	green	*WD*, under-feeder stoker type chimney, preserved livery	85-98	20	30
D8A	68077	black	BRc, rectangular windows	86-88	25	35
D8B	68034	black	BRc	86-88	25	35
D8C	68068	black	BRc, round windows	86-89	25	35
D9	68080	black	BR, with extended bunker/EM wheel conversion kit	90-96	22	30
?	?	khaki	*LNER* Ltd Edn 125	99	130	145
?	?	black	*LNER* Ltd Edn 125	99	130	145

D9 and D10 – In 1985, these numbers were allocated to two versions of a Beyer Garret locomotive due to be released in 1987 but the model did not reach production and D10 was reallocated.

D11 – In 1985 this number was allocated to a WD 2-8-0, also due for release in 1987 but about which no more was heard.

6. Class 56 Diesel Co-Co (ex-Mainline model)

Cat.No.	Name / Number	Colour	Details	Years	£	£
D12	56079	blue	BRe, ex-Mainline stock	85-98	25	30
D13	56086	blue	BReLL, ex-Mainline stock renumbered	85-93	22	28
D14	56075 'West Yorkshire Enterprise'	grey	Railfreight red stripe	85-88	28	35
D14	56077	blue	BRe	94-95	20	25
D14A	56064	grey	*Railfreight*	89-98	20	30
D14B	56068	grey	*Railfreight*	89-98	20	30
D14C	56098	grey	*Railfreight*	89-96	20	32
D80	56001	grey	BRe Construction Sector	89-98	22	35
D81	-	grey	unpainted	89-93	15	25
D104	56094	grey	BRe Coal Sector livery	91-95	25	35

7. Class 2P 4-4-0 (ex-Mainline model)

Cat.No.	Name / Number	Colour	Details	Years	£	£
D15	635	black	*LMS*, lined red, ex-Mainline stock	85-96	30	40
D16	40568	black	BRb lined, ex-Mainline stock	85-90	30	38
D16A	40567	black	BRb lined	90-93	32	38
D16B	?	black	BRb lined	90-93	NPG	NPG
D16C	40569	black	BRb lined	90-95	35	40
D17	563	crimson	*LMS*, lined	86-96	30	35
D67	45	blue	*SDJR*	88-96	27	35

8. Class 2361 'Dean Goods' 0-6-0 (ex-Airfix model)

Cat.No.	Name / Number	Colour	Details	Years	£	£
D18	2516	green	*GWR*, ex-Mainline stock	85-88	28	36
D18A	2517	green	*Great Western*	86-98	25	32
D18B	2518	green	*GWR*	86-94	25	32
D18C	2519	green	*GWR* (button)	86-94	25	32
D50	2538	black	BRb (large) ex-Mainline stock	85-87	28	35

9. Class 14XX 0-4-2T (ex-Airfix model)

D19	1466	green	GWR, ex-Airfix stock	85-95	20	25
D20	1466	green	BRc lined, ex-Airfix stock	85-95	22	30
D19	1420	green	GWR (button), new chassis	95-00	25	32
D96	1438?	black	BRc (small), new chassis	95-00	25	32
D97	1459	black	GWR, new chassis	95-00	25	32
?	?	green	GWR, Ltd Edn 125	99	100	125

10. Class 61XX Prairie Tank 2-6-2T (ex-Airfix model)

D21	6167	black	BRb lined, ex-Airfix stock	85-94	20	28
D22	6110	green	Great Western, ex-Airfix stock	85-94	18	25
D23	6167	green	BRc lined, ex-Mainline stock	85-89	27	33
D24	6169	green	GWR, ex-Mainline stock	85-88	25	30

11. Class 4F 0-6-0 (ex-Airfix model)

D25	4454	black	LMS, ex-Airfix stock	85-94	30	35
D26	44454	black	BRb (small or large), ex-Airfix stock	85-94	30	40
D25	4312	black	LMS, lined red	not made	-	-
D98	?	maroon	LMS	not made	-	-
D99	?	blue	S&DJR	not made	-	-

12. Rebuilt Royal Scot 4-6-0 (ex-Airfix model)

D27	46100 'Royal Scot'	green	BRb, ex-Airfix stock	85-94	28	35
D28	6103 'Royal Scots Fusilier'	black	LMS, ex-Airfix stock	85-94	30	45

13. Class 31/4 Diesel Electric Co-Co (ex-Airfix model)

D30**	31401	blue	BRe, ex-Airfix stock, new bogie	85	15	20
D30	31226	grey	BReLL Railfreight plain	not made	-	-
D31**	D5531	green	BRc, ex-Airfix stock	85	12	20
D31	31247	grey	BReLL Railfreight red stripe	not made	-	-
D32	31217	grey	BRe Railfreight Distribution livery, panther motifs	not made	-	-
D61	31401	blue	BRe, ex-Airfix stock	88	15	20
D62	D5531	green	BRc, ex-Airfix stock	88	14	25

** Early code numbers used for D61 and D62.

14. American 4-4-0 (ex-Airfix model)

D33	'Jupiter'	red+silv	ex-Airfix stock	85-89	20	25

15. Parallel Boiler Royal Scot Class 4-6-0 (ex-Mainline model)

D34	6127 'Old Contemptibles'	crimson	LMS, ex-Mainline stock	85-94	30	37
D35	46137 'Prince of Wales Volunteers, South Lancashire'	green	BRb, ex-Mainline stock	85-94	32	40

16. Rebuilt Royal Scot Class 4-6-0 (ex-Mainline model)

D36	6115 'Scots Guardsman'	black	LMS, ex-Mainline stock	85-88	30	38
D41	46115 'Scots Guardsman'	green	BRc, ex-Mainline stock	85-93	35	42
D58	6100 'Royal Scot'	crimson	LMS as preserved, bell on front, name on smokebox door, ex-Mainline stock	85-96	30	38

17. Jubilee Class 5XP 4-6-0 (ex-Mainline model)

D37	5687 'Neptune'	black	LMS lined, Stanier tender, ex-Mainline stock	85-88	30	35
D38	45691 'Orion'	green	BRc lined, Stanier tender, ex-Mainline stock	85-88, 98	37	42
D42	45700 'Amethyst'	black	BRb lined, Fowler tender, ex-Mainline stock	85-95	30	37
D43	45698 'Mars'	green	BRb lined, Fowler tender, ex-Mainline stock	85-88	35	40

18. Rebuilt Patriot Class 4-6-0 (ex-Mainline model)

D39	45536 'Private W.Wood V.C.'	black	BRa, ex-Mainline stock	85-88	34	40
D40	45532 'Illustrious'	green	BRc, ex-Mainline stock	85-93	35	40

19. Manor Class 4-6-0 (ex-Mainline model)

D44	7808 'Cookham Manor'	green	GWR (button), ex-Mainline stock	85-86	35	38
D45	7819 'Hinton Manor'	green	GWR, ex-Mainline stock	85-86	28	33
D46	7827 'Lydham Manor'	green	BRc, ex-Mainline stock	85-86	33	40

20. Class 43XX Mogul 2-6-0 (ex-Mainline model)

D47	5328	black	BRb (large), ex-Mainline stock	85-00	37	43
D48	5322	green	Great Western, ex-Mainline stock	85-90	28	34
D49	4358	green	BRb (small) lined, ex-Mainline stock	85-90	30	35

21. Class N2 Tank 0-6-2T (ex-Airfix model)

Cat.No.	Name / Number	Colour	Details	Years	£	£
D51	4744	black	*LNER*, red lining, ex-Mainline stock	85-00	28	34
D52	69531	black	BRb (small) lined, ex-Mainline stock	85-00	22	26
D53	9522	green	*LNER* lined, ex-Mainline stock	85-96	20	25

22. Class J72 0-6-0T (ex-Mainline model)

Cat.No.	Name / Number	Colour	Details	Years	£	£
D54	581	green	*LNER*, ex-Mainline stock	85-88	18	25
D55	68745	black	BRa, Ross pop safety valves, ex-Mainline stock	85-86	20	25
D56	'Joem'	green	*North Eastern*, ex-Mainline stock	85-86	18	25
D57	69001	black	BRb, enclosed safety valves, ex-Mainline stock	85-86	17	23

23. Class 66XX Tank 0-6-2T (ex-Mainline model)

Cat.No.	Name / Number	Colour	Details	Years	£	£
D59	6655	black	BRb (large), ex-Mainline stock	85-94, 98	30	35
D60	6697	green	*GWR*, ex-Mainline stock	85-89	30	35

24. Class 57XX Pannier Tank (ex-Mainline model)

Cat.No.	Name / Number	Colour	Details	Years	£	£
D61	5768	black	BRb (small), ex-Mainline stock	85	30	38

25. Class 42 'Warship' Diesel Hydraulic B-B (ex-Mainline model)

Cat.No.	Name / Number	Colour	Details	Years	£	£
D64	827 'Kelly'	blue	BRe, as D65 with diesel sound and klaxon, ex-Mainline stock	85-88	25	35
D65	827 'Kelly'	blue	BRe, ex-Mainline stock	85-89	18	25
D66	D824 'Highflyer'	green	BRc, ex-Mainline stock	85-87	22	30

26. Terrier 0-6-0 tank

Cat.No.	Name / Number	Colour	Details	Years	£	£
D69	662	brown	LBSC Marsh Umber	89-95	25	30
D70	2635	green	SR lined	89-90	25	35
D71	32640	black	BRb lined	89-91	22	30
D72	6	green	GWR	89-94	22	30
D100	82 'Boxhill'	yell-brn	LBSC Stroudley 'Green'	89-95	25	32
D101	82 'Boxhill'	yell-brn	LBSC, as D100 but Ltd Edn	90-99	35	45
D102	55 'Stepney'	yell-brn	LBSC Stroudley 'Green'	90-98	53	65
?	?	black	SR, wartime 'Sunshine' lettering Ltd Edn 100	97	150	180
?	?	black	SR, Ltd Edn 125	99	160	195
?	?	green	SR, Ltd Edn 125	99	160	195

27. Class 150/2 Sprinter

Cat.No.	Name / Number	Colour	Details	Years	£	£
D82+ D82A	150237(57237/52237)	grey+blue	BRe, Provincial, 2-car	92-99	50	70
D108	?		Centro, 2-car	not made	NPG	NPG

28. Class 155 Super Sprinter

Cat.No.	Name / Number	Colour	Details	Years	£	£
D83	155329(57329/52329)	grey+blue	BRe, Provincial, 2-car	92-98	50	70
D110	?	maroon	BRe, Metro PTE, 2-car	not made	NPG	NPG
D106	?	grey+blue	BRe, Regional Railways, 2-car	not made	NPG	NPG

29. Class 124 Trans-Pennine DMU (ex-Trix model)

These were assembled using mouldings made at Dapol's Winsford factory and fitted with their Sprinter motor bogie with new sideframes clipped on. The units were adapted to take Dapol coach weights to give them extra weight.

Cat.No.	Name / Number	Colour	Details	Years	£	£
D94	?	blue	BRe, 2-car, single motor	not made	-	-
D95	NE51953/NE51954	green	BRc, 2-car, single motor	94-95	75	85
D105	NE51953/NE51954	green	BRc, 2-car, 2 motors	94-95	85	100
?	NE51953/NE51954	green	BRc, 2-car, 2 motors, a batch of 200-300 is expected	00	NPG	100

30. Class A4 4-6-2 (ex-Trix model)

Cat.No.	Name / Number	Colour	Details	Years	£	£
D84	4468 'Mallard'	blue	LNER with valances	not made	-	-
D85	2512 'Silver Fox'	silver	LNER with valances	not made	-	-
D86	60027 'Merlin'	green	BRc	not made	-	-

31. Class A3 4-6-2 (ex-Trix model)

Cat.No.	Name / Number	Colour	Details	Years	£	£
D87	4472 'Flying Scotsman'	green	LNER	not made	-	-
D88	60103 'Flying Scotsman'	green	BRc	not made	-	-

32. Class A2 4-6-2 (ex-Trix model)

Cat.No.	Name / Number	Colour	Details	Years	£	£
D89	525 'A.H.Peppercorn'	green	LNER	not made	-	-
D90	60532 'Blue Peter'	green	BRc	not made	-	-

33. Class 81 (ex-Trix model)

D91	?	blue	BRd electric blue	not made	-	-
D92	?	blue	BRe rail blue	not made	-	-
D93	?	grey	BRe Executive	not made	-	-

Coaches

For its coaches, Dapol depended principally on old stock and Airfix tooling. Initially they sold the large surpluses of stock they acquired from Airfix and Palitoy but then produced variations of the former Airfix models. These included Mk2D coaches in Executive livery and the 12 wheel LMS diner which was planned by both Airfix and Palitoy but not actually released until Dapol took it over. The coaches were numbered with an 'E' prefix and E41 seems to have been the highest number reached. Dapol's own versions generally fetch higher prices than the old stock from Airfix and Palitoy with Executive Mk2s selling for around £15-£20 each and LMS diners for around £25. Other Dapol coaches are generally in the £10 range.

Wagons

Dapol had hoped to acquire the Airfix wagon tooling when Airfix collapsed but it went to Palitoy with much of it being put back into use to produce new Mainline wagons. Instead, Dapol had a series of wagons tooled up for them in Hong Kong. These were very much like the Airfix ones and it is often difficult to tell them apart without turning them over. The first Dapol wagons were released in 1983 and were numbered with a 'B' prefix. The wagon range was the most prolific of all the ranges produced by Dapol and by 1998 the wagon numbering had reached B268. There will be rarer ones amongst them but as yet collecting has not had sufficient impact to affect prices which seem to average around £5 per wagon.

Sets

Dapol sets go under the prefix 'F' in their catalogue numbering scheme and tended to be made up with surplus stock to help shift it. Like other companies, Dapol found it difficult to compete with Hornby whose name was familiar to first-time buyers. In 1983 there were just three sets but these rose to ten by 1987. While a few were added as more were dropped, the sets were not pushed very hard from this time on and were soon dropped from the advertising. If they did not sell well they are likely to become collectable in the future but their time has not yet arrived. At present they are valued on their contents rather than as a collector's item in their own right. The best advice is to hang on to them and hope that their value will rise.

Dapol Class 0F L&Y Pug LMS 11217 (D1)   [table 1]

Dapol Class 1000 1027 'County of Stafford' (D4)   [table 2]

Former Airfix Castle renamed 'Powderham Castle' by Dapol   [table 3]

Dapol Terrier tank LBSC 82 'Boxhill' (D100)   [table 26]

Dapol Class 56 diesel Railfreight 56064 (D14A)   [table 6]

Dapol Class 2361 Dean Goods GWR 2517 (D18A)   [table 8]

Dapol Class J94 68034 (D8B)   [table 5]

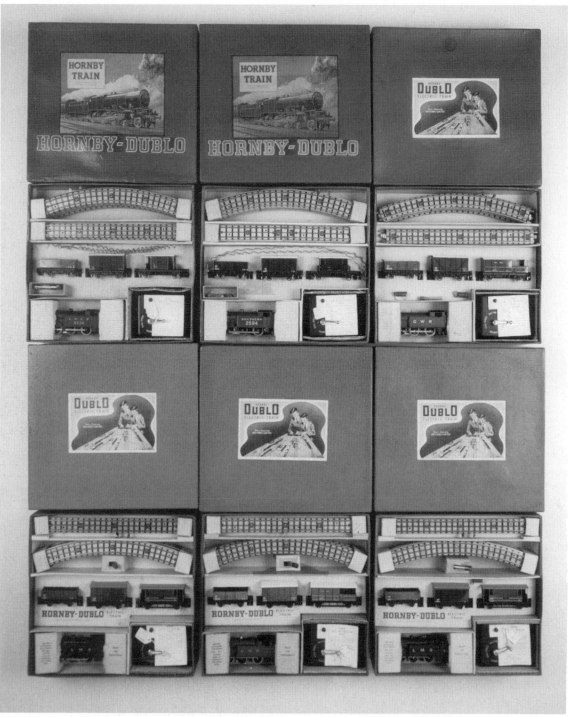

Top row, L-R: (1) First post-war issue LNER EDL7 Tank Goods Train Set with Royal Scot label 1947, locomotive with gold label.
(2) First post-war issue SR EDL7 Tank Goods Train Set with Royal Scot label 1947, locomotive with gold label.
(3) EDG7 GWR Tank Goods Train Set, guarantee stamp '11.48', first type mid-blue box without suppressor label, locomotive with gold label.
Bottom row, L-R: (1) EDG7 LMS Tank Goods Set, guarantee stamp '5.52', mid-blue box, locomotive with silver label.
(2) EDG7 GWR Tank Goods Set, guarantee stamp '11.50', mid-blue box, locomotive with silver label.
(3) EDG7 LMS Tank Goods Set, guarantee stamp '5.52', mid-blue box, locomotive with silver label.
(Christie's South Kensington)

Hornby-Dublo

These models were made by Meccano at Binns Road, Liverpool between 1938 and 1964

History

In pre-Second World War Britain, 0 gauge ruled supreme but as early as the 1920s a bid had been made to have a smaller gauge accepted. That was the Bing Table Top Railway which was a victim of the growth of Nazi influence in Germany. The German Trix system sprang from the Bing version and when the inventors fled to Britain to avoid Nazi persecution a British version of the system was developed at Northampton in association with Bassett-Lowke.

Seeing the possible risk this created for Hornby's market, Meccano Ltd decided to launch their own 00 scale system. Thus, in 1938, Hornby Dublo was born.

Initially it was a small version of the 0 gauge system except that the locomotives had cast metal bodies, the track looked like that sold by Märklin and the buildings were made of wood. Both clockwork and electric sets were available before the war and the couplings could not be uncoupled automatically. Pre-war locomotives were limited to an LNER valanced A4 Pacific named 'Sir Nigel Gresley' and an 0-6-2 tank engine that looked like an LNER Class N2 but which, in true Hornby tradition, was available in the liveries of the big four companies (with detail concessions to the GWR).

After the war, the Peco automatic coupling was adopted as standard and the buildings, when they reappeared, were diecast in aluminium. Clockwork did not reappear but the long awaited LMS 'Duchess of Atholl' did.

In 1953 the system was 'Nationalised' and the old liveries were dropped almost overnight. One of Hornby Dublo's finest locomotives was soon to appear – the 2-6-4 Standard tank. The Castle, 8F and Bo-Bo diesel quickly followed. By 1957 it was clear that Hornby Dublo was losing ground to the Tri-ang Railways system and something drastic had to be done. The first change was the adoption of plastic for wagon bodies, the first, the grain wagon, appearing the following year.

The possibility of a 2-rail electric system had been discussed as long ago as 1938 but was not adopted until 1959. Plastic buildings arrived the same year and the Super Detail coaches followed the year after. Too late it was realised that the system was not gaining the loyalty of beginners whose parents were being wooed by the low prices of Tri-ang and Playcraft sets. In a last ditch attempt to save the system, in 1963 two beginners sets were launched but, with unsold stock piling up in the factory, production of the Hornby Dublo system was halted.

With Meccano Ltd facing strong competition in the areas of railways (Tri-ang), diecast cars (Corgi) and construction systems (Lego) it had nowhere to go and consequently invited Lines Bros. (the makers of Tri-ang) to take them over - which they did. The name Hornby was transferred to the Tri-ang Railways system. This was done in the guise of an amalgamation but the only Hornby-Dublo models to be adopted into the newly named Tri-ang Hornby range (and then only for a few years) were the terminus station and the E3000. Thus Tri-ang Railways carried on, renamed Tri-ang Hornby (later renamed Hornby Railways), and the Hornby products in the shops today are therefore direct descendants of Tri-ang Railways and not Hornby Dublo. The name 'Hornby Dublo', was retained by Tri-ang although not used again and it is still owned by Hornby Hobbies who are still based in the Tri-ang factory in Margate.

Milestones

1901	Frank Hornby invents Meccano.
1914	Meccano Ltd moves to Binns Rd, Liverpool.
1915	Frank Hornby announces he is to make `toy trains.
1920	Toy train production starts at Binns Road.
1938	Launch of electric and clockwork Hornby Dublo through Meccano Magazine.
1941	Toy production closes and this sees the end of the clockwork system.
1947	Post-war Hornby-Dublo reach the shops and with it a new automatic coupling.
1948	Duchess of Atholl released.
1950	New motors introduced.
1953	Change to British Railways liveries.
1957	'Bristol Castle' released.
1957	Dublo Dinkies arrive.
1958	The first plastic wagons appear.
1958	Head and coachboards introduced.
1958	First diesel added to the range (Class 20).
1959	First plastic building appears.
1959	2-rail electric system introduced.
1960	Decals on loco models now show only left facing lion.
1960	Ringfield motor announced.
1961	Plastic couplings first appear.
1963	First beginners sets released
1964	Last model, the AL1 electic, released after other Hornby Dublo production of had stopped.
1964	Lines Bros. Ltd. invited to take over Mecanno Ltd.
1966	Hornby Dublo tools sold to G& R Wrenn.

The Hornby Dublo tools were sold to Tri-ang subsidiary, G&R Wrenn, and formed the basis of the Wrenn Railways model range which started to appear in the late 1960s and is described elsewhere in this book.

At the time Meccano Ltd were taken over by Tri-ang they had various models planned. With the approval of Hornby Hobbies, two of the proposed locomotives have now been produced by Michael Foster, in association with the Hornby Railway Collectors Association (HRCA), using former Hornby-Dublo chassis. These are the V2 and the 56XX 0-6-2 tank.

Further Reading

Anyone interested in further study of this important and popular model railway system is recommended to read 'Hornby Dublo Trains' by Michael Foster and published by New Cavendish Books (ISBN 0 904568 18 0). There is also a compendium to this work by Alan F Ellis, called 'Hornby Dublo Compendium', which is also published by New Cavendish Books (ISBN 0 904568 80 6).

Collectors Club

You may also wish to join the Hornby Railway Collectors Association (HRCA) who publish, for their members, an excellent monthly magazine, called The Hornby Railway Collector, devoted to the toy train and model railway products of Meccano Ltd. Details of this organisation may be obtained from the membership secretary, Bob Field, on Tel: 0115 962 5693.

Locomotives

Prices – The chance of finding mint boxed Hornby Dublo is relatively small and so the use of the 'mint/boxed' column (right hand one) for this purpose would have little meaning. We have therefore used both price columns to indicate the price range one may expect for examples in very good condition.

2-rail/3-rail – Unless otherwise stated, all of the locomotives in this section have three rail power contact (i.e. means to collect power from a centre rail) . Clockwork models (c/w) are suitable for use on both systems but not on 2-rail track at the same time as it is being used for electric locomotives.

After-Sale Factory Variations – Hornby Dublo variations marked 1 resulted from the model being returned to the factory for a repair and a revised part being used, thus altering the model.

Identification Aids – pre-war models had flat sprung metal couplings while post-war they were fitted with Peco style couplings. Pre-war and early post-war models did not have the model number (e.g. EDL7) under the running board while later ones did. On early post-war locomotives the maker's decal, on the back of the tender or bunker, was a gold block with a red border and inscribed 'Hornby Meccano Ltd, Made in England'. Later models had a silver coloured decal with a red border.

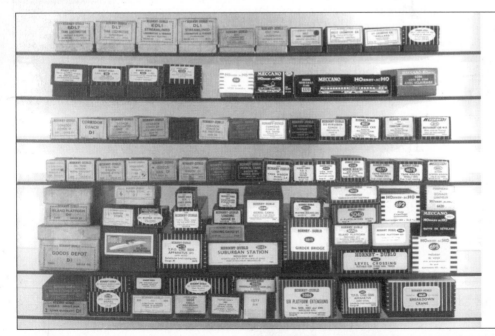

Hornby Dublo

25 years of box design

(Christie's)

1. 0-6-2T Class N2 (and similar)

p-wb = pre-war body (one without notch in buffer beam for postwar coupling)   p-wc = pre-war couplings

DL7	2594	green	*Southern*, olive, p-wc, c/w	38-40	700	800
DL7	6917	black	*LMS*, p-wc, c/w	38-40	400	450
DL7	2690	black	*LNER*, p-wc, c/w	38-40	450	550
DL7	6699	green	*GWR*, p-wc, c/w	38-40	700	800
EDL7	2594	green	*Southern*, olive, p-wc	38-41	600	700
EDL7	6917	black	*LMS*, p-wc	38-41	300	400
EDL7	2690	black	*LNER*, p-wc	38-41	300	400
EDL7	6699	green	*GWR*, p-wc	38-41	500	600
EDL7	2594	green	*Southern*, olive, p-wb	47	550	700
EDL7	2690	black	*LNER*, p-wb	47	NPG	NPG
EDL7	9596	black	*LNER*	47	NPG	NPG
EDL7	6917	black	*LMS*, lettering with serifs	47-48	175	250
EDL7	6699	green	*GWR*	47-53	200	250
EDL7	6231	green	*GWR*	?	NPG	NPG
EDL7	2594	green	*Southern*, malachite green	48-53	250	350
EDL7	9596	green	*LNER*	48-53	110	175
EDL7	6917	black	*LMS*, sans serif lettering	49-53	50	100
EDL7	69567	black	BRb, gloss finish, no coal	53-54	100	150
EDL17	69567	black	BRb, matt finish, no coal	54-58	40	70
3217	69567	black	BRc, matt finish, coal in bunker	61-63	150	300
2217	69550	black	BRc, 2-rail, small safety valve, coal in bunker	60-63	80	125
2217	69550	black	BRc, 2-rail, large safety valve dome, coal in bunker	63-64	100	150

2. 4-6-2 Class A4

DL1	4498 'Sir Nigel Gresley'	blue	*LNER*, c/w	38-41	600	800
EDL1	4498 'Sir Nigel Gresley'	blue	*LNER*	38-41	300	480
EDL1	7 'Sir Nigel Gresley'	blue	*LNER*,	47-53?	80	120
EDL1	7 'Sir Nigel Gresley'	blue	*LNER*,'EDL11' inside cab roof 1	47-53?	150	250
EDL1	7 'Sir Nigel Gresley'	blue	*LNER*, prewar loco with postwar tender 1	?	150	200
EDL11	60016 'Silver King'	green	BRb, gloss finish	53-54	100	150
EDL11	60016 'Silver King'	green	BRb, matt finish	54-58	75	100
L11/3211	60022 'Mallard'	green	BRc	58-63	75	100
2211	60030 'Golden Fleece'	green	BRc, 2-rail	59-64	90	120
3211	60022 'Mallard'	green	BRc, nickel plated driving wheels	62-63	250	320

3. 4-6-2 Duchess

EDL2	6231 'Duchess of Atholl'	maroon	*LMS*	47-53	75	100
EDL2	6231 'Duchess of Atholl'	maroon	*LMS*, lump beneath one nameplate where depression should be	?	180	250
EDL2	6231 'Duchess of Atholl'	maroon	*LMS*, cream nameplate	?	180	250
EDL2	6231 'Duchess of Atholl'	maroon	*LMS*, smoke defectors, 'EDL12' inside cab roof 1	?	350	500
EDL2	1215	black	*Canadian Pacific*, revised smokebox	52	400	600
EDL12	46232 'Duchess of Montrose'	green	BRb, gloss finish	53-54	100	140
EDL12/ 3212	46232 'Duchess of Montrose'	green	BRb, matt finish	54-58	60	90
2226	46245 'City of London'	maroon	BRc, 2-rail	59-64	100	130
3226	46274 'City of Liverpool'	maroon	BRc	61-63	250	320

4. 2-6-4T 4MT Standard Tank

EDL18	80054	black	BRb	54-58	60	80
2218	80033	black	BRc, 2-rail	59-64	90	120
3218	80059	black	BRc	61-63	300	400

5. 4-6-0 Castle Class

EDL20	7013 'Bristol Castle'	green	BRc	57-61	75	100
2220	7032 'Denbigh Castle'	green	BRc, 2-rail	59	100	150
2221	4075 'Cardiff Castle'	green	BRc, 2-rail	60-64	75	100
3221	5002 'Ludlow Castle'	green	BRc	61-63	300	400

6. 2-8-0 Class 8F

LT25/ 3225	48158	black	BRc	58-61	90	120
2225	48109	black	BRc, 2-rail	59	75	100
2224	48073	black	BRc, 2-rail	60-64	75	100
3224	48094	black	BRc	61-63	200	280

Cat.No.	Name / Number	Colour	Details	Years	£	£
7. Bo-Bo (Class 20) Diesel						
L30/3230	D8000	green	BRc	58-62	50	80
2230	D8017	green	BRc, 2-rail	59-62	45	70
8. 0-6-0T Class R1						
2206	31337	black	BRc, 2-rail	59-64	50	70
2206	31337	black	BRc, 2-rail, red buffers	59-64	75	100
2207	31340	green	BRc, 2-rail	59-64	40	60
9. 0-6-0DS (Class 08) Diesel Shunter						
2231	D3303	green	BRc, 2-rail	60-64	60	80
3231	D3763	green	BRc	61-63	100	150
10. 4-6-2 Rebuilt West Country Class						
2235	34005 'Barnstaple'	green	BRc, 2-rail	61-64	100	150
3235	34042 'Dorchester'	green	BRc	61-63	175	260
11. Co-Co Deltic Type Diesel						
2232	-	green	BRc, 2-rail	61-64	75	100
3232	-	green	BRc	61-63	120	150
2234	D9012 'Crepello'	green	BRc, 2-rail	62-64	90	130
3234	D9001 'St Paddy'	green	BRc	62-63	200	300
12. Co-Bo Met-Vic Diesel						
2233	D5702	green	BRc, 2-rail	61-64	100	140
3233	D5713	green	BRc	61-64	120	160
13. Suburban EMU						
2250	S65326	green	BR, 2-car unit , 2-rail	62-64	120	160
3250	S65326	green	BR, 2-car unit	62-63	300	400
14. 0-4-0T Tank						
2001	-	black	BRd, from 'Ready to Run' set, c/w	63-64	25	30*
2001	-	blue	map of Australia, from 'Ready to Run' set for Australia, c/w	?	90	150*
15. 0-4-0DS Diesel Shunter						
from 2004	-	yellow	from 'Ready to Run' set, c/w	64	35	50*
16. Class AL1 Electric						
2245	E3002	blue	BRd, 2-rail	64	250	320

4075 'Cardiff Castle' W.R.   (Barry Potter Auctions)

Coaches

Early coaches were tinplate but from 1960 they were a combination of tinplate and plastic. The only pre-war coaches were LNER Gresley teaks and consisted of an articulated pair (all 3rd and a brake/3rd) (£650-£850) and a single (composite) (£100-£150). All other coaches were fitted with Peco type automatic couplings. The articulated coaches were made after the war but were produced in a very small quantity and for export only (£750-£1000).

Of the post-war non-super detailed coaches the LNER teaks (£30-£60) and LMS coaches (£40-£60) are the most sought after and, where coaches in the mid '50s were produced with plastic wheels, they are usually slightly higher priced than those with metal wheels (£15-£25).

Super Detail coaches are generally priced between £15 and £30 but some are particularly in demand. These include suburbans (£50-£70), the 6-wheeld Stove (£100-£150) and the restaurant cars. There are two versions of these: WR chocolate and cream (£90-£120) and ER maroon (£120-£180). Sleeping cars were available from Hattons of Liverpool long after production ceased (£15-£35) and Pullman cars (£30-£50) were the only former Hornby Dublo coaches to be made later by Wrenn.

Wagons

Initially wagons were all tinplate with the flat spring pre-war couplings. These mostly sell for between £25 and £35 but there are exceptions : GWR van (£55-£75), GWR brake van or LMS cattle truck (£45-65), high capacity wagon (£60-£75), NE high-sided wagon (with or without coal), SR open wagon and SR coal wagon (£40-£50), SR van (£75-£85), any tank wagon (£80-£100) and SR brake van (£125-£150). Pre-war wagons frequently suffer from metal fatigue which has caused the diecast chassis to crumble and so care must be taken when buying these.

The tinplate wagons reappeared after the war but with Peco couplings and, in some cases, such as the tank wagons, with minor differences. These mostly sell for £15-£20 but exceptions include: GWR and LMS open wagons (£30-£40), GWR van (£75-£100), GWR brake van (£70-£90), NE high-sided wagon and GWR cattle wagon with long window cut-outs (£40-£60), NE high-sided wagon with greeny-grey body (£80-£120), Royal Daylight tank wagon, SR open wagon, brake van and coal wagon (£80-£100), Power Ethyl tank wagon, SR meat van with silvery grey roof ,SR brake van with one window on end and SR goods van (£100-£150), SR meat van (£60-£80) and Esso buff tank wagon (£140-£180).

Prior to 1953 customers had a wide choice of wagons as they were produced in the liveries of the big four companies but, that year, the whole system changed to BR liveries and where there had previously been four open wagons or vans there was now only one. This was partly compensated for with the release of the first of a series of wagons with diecast bodies, starting that year with the mineral wagon and bogie bolster. Post-nationalisation wagons with metal wheels (3-rail) sell for £10-£15 each. Exceptions include: all tank wagons but the Esso silver one (£20-£35) and the Canadian Pacific caboose (£90-£140).

The first plastic bodied wagon (the bulk grain wagon) arrived in 1958 and was the start of a trend which eventually saw the disappearance of all of the tinplate stock. with the exception of the tank wagons which, along with the diecast wagons, received plastic wheels. The range expanded fast and, today, some of the models that arrived late in the day are commanding high prices. Common wagons sell for £10-£15: others are a little more and there are quite a few minor variations that can increase the price. Models to particularly look for include: the brown plastic mineral wagon (£30-£45), SR Utility van, passenger fruit van and 'Aluminium Wire and Cable Co' cable drum wagon (£35-£45), low-sided wagon with Dublo-Dinky tractor (£40-£55), ICI bogie tank wagon (£65-£85), the same model with diamond bogies (£200-£300), the hopper wagon and maroon horse box with horse (£75-£100), green horse box with horse (£100-£125), the gloss red breakdown crane (£200-£300) and the rail cleaning wagon (£300-£500).

Accessories

Pre-war wooden station buildings, which were made with either a red or green roof, are the most sought-after lineside accessories. They include: the main station building, the arched roof, island platform (green roof), engine shed and goods depot (£200-£250), red roof island platform and the through station (£150-£175), platforms from the central station (£20-£40), sets of boxed staff or passengers figures (£75-£100), wooden signal cabin (£50-£75), tunnels (340-£50), buffer-stops (£15-£20), footbridge (£30-£40 and signal £7-£12).

The most expensive item of track is the clockwork track point at £30-£40 each. Pre-war electric points, in contrast, are £6-£12 and other pieces of track usually sell at between £1 and £2 each. Of post-war track, the most demanded are 3-rail straights (£1-£2), hand points (£5-£10) and electric points (£10-£15). There is little demand for 2-rail plastic sleeper track.

After the war the buildings were made of cast aluminium. These included the through station (£50-£70), island platform (£30-£40), straight platform extensions for either (£35-£45), footbridge or red roof signal cabin (£20-£30), green roof signal cabin (£150 - £200), girder bridge (£40-£50), 6 station staff or 6 passengers (£40-£50) and level crossing (£10-£15). Also from this period is the turntable (£40-£60).

Signals sell for between £7 and £18 while lever switches are £7-£10 or, in the case of green coloured ones, £20-£30.

Plastic kits for stations and lineside buildings came in 1959 replacing the aluminium ones. Most expensive are the large terminus station (£200-£300), station extension canopy in red and yellow box (£400-£500), the same in a white box (£200-£300), plastic girder bridge (£300-£400) and set of 12 railway staff (£100-£125). Other items from this period to look for include: 2-road engine shed (£60-£70), engine shed extension kit (£20-£30), suburban station kit (£30-£40), plastic tunnel (£50-£100), island platform kit (£30-£40), goods depot kit (£30-£50), buff coloured water crane (£35-£45), buffers with electric lights on them (£15-£20), 12 plastic passengers and goods (£30-£40), lighting kit (£10-£15), set of 12 gradient and mile posts (£40-£50), set of 6 lineside notices (£25-£35) and box of 12 telegraph poles (£50-£75).

Sets

As one might expect, pre-war train sets fetch the highest prices. Clockwork passenger DP1 sets are priced £1,000-£1,250 and DG1 clockwork goods sets sell for £300-£900; with the level of price depending on which livery is carried. Pre-war electric passenger EDP1 sets are £900-£1,250 but, again the goods sets vary: EDG7 GWR and LMS (£300-£900), EDG7 LNER and SR (£700-£900) while EDGA7 GWR sets are in the £500-£750 price range.

Amongst post-war sets, ones to look out for are the very first ones released in 1947 and 1948. They differ slightly, in various ways, from those produced after 1948 and the date on instruction leaflets will help to identify them. Or these the prices are as follows: LNER passenger EDP1 (£600-£800), LMS passenger EDL7 (£300-£400), LNER goods EDL7 (£500-£900) and SR goods (£1,000-£1,500).

Other post-war pre-Nationalisation sets are priced: LNER passenger EDP1 (£150-£200), LMS passenger EDL2 (£120-£160), LMS, LNER and SR goods EDL7 sets (£300-£900), GWR goods EDL7 (£300-£500). Either of the Canadian Pacific sets sells for £650-£850.

As with the solo models, the BR liveried sets replaced the pre-Nationalisation ones in 1953 following which the range of sets grew quite fast. The following are some of the sets worth looking for: EDP15 with matt locomotive finish (£200-£250), G19 (£350-£450), P15 or P20 (£350-£450), P22 (£250-£350), 2015, 2020, 2021, 2022, 2025, 2033, 2034, 2035, 2049 or 2050 (£200-£300) and 2035 (£1,000-£1,250). Other sets are mostly priced £100-£125 for good boxed examples.

Previously published information

As stated in the introduction, the main objective of this catalogue is to provide comprehensive lists of the locomotives with detailed listings of rolling stock destined to appear in the next edition. As a consequence, the listings of rolling stock, accessories, sets and catalogues which appeared in the first edition have not been included here. However, if this information is required please send £2 in postage stamps and we will be pleased to send you a copy.

60030 'Golden Fleece' E.R.

(Barry Potter Auctions)

Top down: (1) EDP15 BR (East) 'Silver King' Passenger Train Set. (2) Rare G25 LMS 2-8-0 8F Freight Train Set
(3) EDP20 'Bristolian' Passenger Train Set. (4) Rare G19 2-6-4 Tank Goods Train Set.
(5) P22 'The Royal Scot' Passenger Train Set (locomotive with nickel-silver unbushed wheels, plastic bogie and pony wheels)
(Christie's South Kensington)

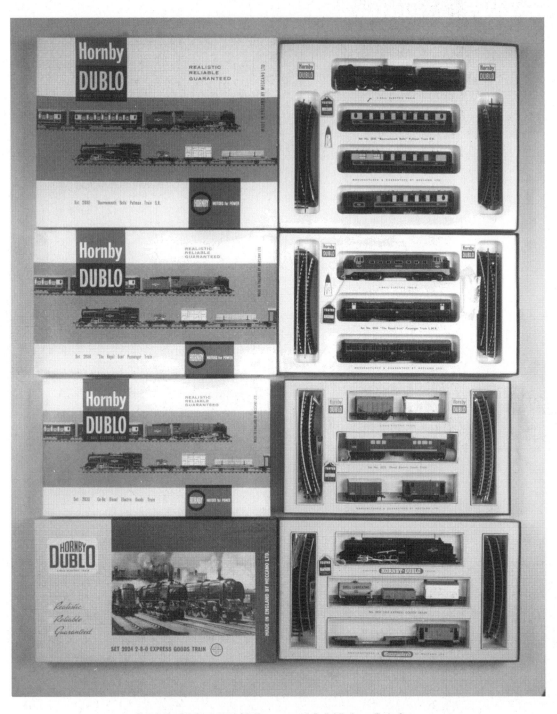

Top down: (1) Rare 2035 SR 'Bournemouth Belle' Pullman Train Set.
(2) 2034 'The Royal Scot' Passenger Train Set (rare final issue blue and white picture box).
(3) 2033 Co-Bo Diesel Electric Goods Train Set (rare final issue blue and white picture box).
(4) 2024 2-8-0 Express Goods Train Set (early Ring-field motor).
(Christie's South Kensington)

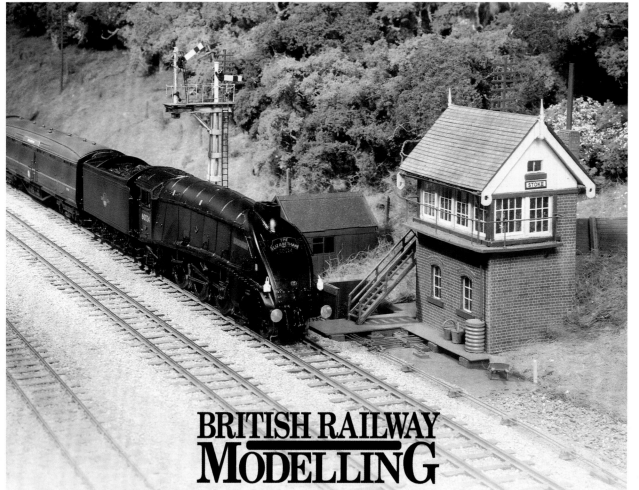

Hornby Dublo Class 8F 48073 [table 6]

Hornby Dublo Class N2 69550 [table 1]

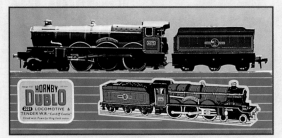

Hornby Dublo Castle Class 4075 'Cardiff Castle' [table 5]

Hornby Dublo Class 08 D3302 [table 9]

Hornby Dublo Princess Coronation 46245 'City of London' [table 3]

Hornby Dublo Deltic diesel D9012 'Crepello' [table 11]

Hornby Dublo West Country 34005 'Barnstaple' [table 10]

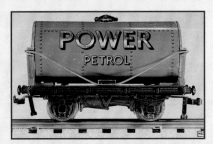

1. Hornby Dublo 3-rail 'Power' tank

2. Hornby Dublo 2-rail 'Esso' fuel oil tank

3. Hornby Dublo 3-rail 'Esso' buff tank

4. Hornby Dublo 2-rail 'Mobil' tank

5. Hornby Dublo 3-rail 'Mobil' tank

6. Hornby Dublo 2-rail 'Vacuum' tank

7. Hornby Dublo 2-rail 'Shell lubricating Oil' tank

8. Hornby Dublo 3-rail 'Esso Royal Daylight' tank

9. Hornby Dublo 3-rail 'Pool' tank. One of four finished privately as a spoof

1. Hornby Dublo EDG7 Southern Tank Goods Set
(Barry Potter Auctions)

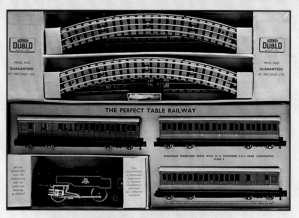

2. Hornby Dublo EDP14 Passenger Train Set
(Barry Potter Auctions)

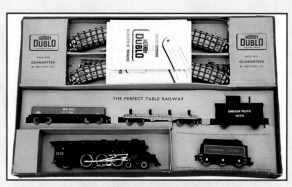

3. Hornby Dublo EDG3 Freight Train Set for Canada
(Barry Potter Auctions)

4. Hornby Dublo 2050 Suburban Electric Train
(Barry Potter Auctions)

5. Hornby Dublo 2021 'The Red Dragon' Passenger Train
(Barry Potter Auctions)

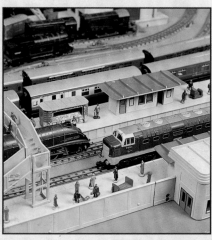

6. Hornby Dublo layout

Kitmaster

History

Nene Plastics Ltd was founded in Raunds by T. Eric Smith in 1940, immediately prior to his call-up for war service. On his return he set about developing and launching his Rosebud Dolls range. In 1954 a new injection moulding plant was brought into operation. The following year the name of the company was changed to Rosebud Dolls Ltd. with a target of 5 million dolls per year.

In 1958, Rosebud Kitmaster was formed to make kits using spare capacity in the injection moulding room. The subject was chosen because kits were a growing market and at that time locomotive kits in plastic were not being done by anyone else. In the UK, the kits were available between 1959 and 1962 and were moulded in polystyrene. They were complementary to a range of railway kits made by Airfix but were much more expensive. The subjects were chosen by Dennis Franklin who was Rosebud's Assistant Technical Manager and who took charge of the Kitmaster project. He travelled far and wide choosing and studying the models to be made and obtaining official drawings for them.

A crucial error was an early decision to model only in a 'constant' 00 scale which meant that models of foreign locomotives would not sell abroad where H0 scale was the norm. The foreign outline models were generally of little interest to the British public and, with tools costing between £6,000 and £10,000 per model, income from sale of these kits fell a long way short of repaying the development costs.

Trix had made a similar mistake in modelling in H0 for the British market and an interesting connection with Trix Products Ltd was through the latter's chief designer, Michael Catalani. He had designed the new range of Trix plastic coaches but was not prepared to move to Birmingham when that company was moved there. Instead, he went to work for Rosebud Kitmaster for three weeks before being lured back by his previous employer. While at Rosebud he was involved with the design of the Pullman cars.

Initially, the Kitmaster kits were released at a rate of one a month but after the first year the strain of this was beginning to show. As a result of pressure put on them a number of skilled staff left. Up until the release of the Beyer-Garratt model in 1960, the pattern making was done in-house but, after that, it was subcontracted to freelance model makers. Most of these patterns were made in brass by model-maker Jack Gain.

The Kitmaster project was clearly over ambitious and badly planned as described above. Within a short time this was creating financial strains on the Company. The policy of a new model every month required large amounts of capital for new tools and Rosebud Kitmaster had been slow in getting their distribution and marketing sorted out. As a result, money was not coming in to the Company as fast as it was going out with the result that a crisis was looming.

The solution was to sell the Kitmaster business and the obvious buyer was Airfix Ltd. Late in 1962 the Kitmaster tools and stock were sold to that company. Some of the surplus kits were released to the public through a Shredded Wheat promotion conducted by the Hermes Supply Company; a subsidiary of Airfix Ltd.

A number of the British subjects were absorbed into the Airfix kit range and were later acquired by Palitoy and then by Dapol, who are still making them!

By 1964 things were looking desperate for Rosebud Dolls Ltd and in June that year the Receiver was called in. The Company remained in administrative receivership, with the doll business recovering, until July 1967 when it merged with Mattel Inc. (famed for Barbie doll) to form Rosebud Mattel Ltd. (renamed Mattel (UK) Ltd in 1971).

Further Reading

The book 'Let's Stick Together' by Stephen Knight contains everything you are ever likely to want to know about the Kitmaster range and what happened to the kits in later years. This very thorough work was published in 1999 by Irwell Press (ISBN 1-871608-90-2) and is strongly recommended to anyone interested in further study.

Collectors Clubs

Enthusiasts of the Kitmaster kit range are well catered for by the Kitmaster Collectors Club which was founded in 1980. The Club publishes a magazine called 'Signal' twice a year and includes in the subjects covered the railway kits by Airfix and Dapol. The Club has a web site at www.kitmaster-club.org.uk and for enquiries regarding membership fax: 01787 478226.

Kits

Dates – The dates given below are those when the kit is believed to have first been available in the shops. Remaindered stock was available in shops, often for considerable periods, after the demise of Kitmaster.

Prices – The two prices given show the range of prices one can find on unmade kits; the second column being for mint examples in their original cellophane wrapping.

Cat.No.	Subject	Colour	Details	Years	£	£
1.	**00 Kits** Note that Continental outline models are to 4mm/1ft in this table.					
1	'Rocket'	yellow	L&M 0-2-2	59	15	25
2	D3421	black	Class 08 0-6-0DS	59	15	25
4	46225 'Duchess of Gloucester'	black	Princess Coronation Class (Duchess) 4-6-2	59	35	50
5	30919 'Harrow'	black	Schools V Class 4-4-0	59	5	15
6	51212	black	ex-L&Y Saddle Tank 0-4-0ST	59	4	8
7	6167	black	Class 6100 Prairie Tank 2-6-2T	59	4	8
8	162	black	Italian Class 835 Tank 0-6-0T	59	35	50
9	1	green	Stirling Single 4-2-2	59	35	50
10	'Deltic'	blue	Deltic Prototype Diesel Co-Co	60	35	50
11	34057 'Biggin Hill"	black	Battle of Britain Class 4-6-2	60	15	25
12	13305	black	Swiss Crocodile Series Be6/8	60	25	35
13	M16001, M15627, M15019, M15243, W15111, W15598, W15430, E15307, E15144, E16017	maroon	Mk1 Corridor Composite Coach	60	10	20
13	S15042, S15573, S15888, S15903, S15580, S15873	green	Mk1 Corridor Composite Coach	60	15	25
14	M25589, M24133, M24405, M24861, W24165, W24341, W24719, E24222, E24531, E25027	maroon	Mk1 Corridor 2nd Coach	60	10	20
14	S24320, S24305, S24169, S24326, S24318, S24311	green	Mk1 Corridor 2nd Coach	60	15	25
15	M35114, M34090, M34105, M34671, W34152, W34297, W34763, E34422, E34590, E35157	maroon	Mk1 Corridor Brake 2nd Coach	60	10	20
15	S34256, S34621, S34158, S34945, S34279, S35020	green	Mk1 Corridor Brake 2nd Coach	60	15	25
19	23001, 23008, 23014	black	German Baureihe Class 23	60	35	50
22	92220 'Evening Star', 92203, 92134	black	Class 9F 2-10-0	60	15	25
23	241P.026, 241P.027, 241P.029	black	French 241P Mountain	60	35	50
24	3440 'City of Truro'	black	GWR City Class	60	15	25
25	7971, 7987, 47994	black	LMS Beyer-Garratt 2-6-6-2	61	70	100
26	68022, 68028, 68051, 68076	black	J94 Tank 0-6-0ST	61	15	25
28	M4, M5, M6, S9, W7, W8, E1, E2, E3, E10, E11	maroon	Mk1 Restaurant Car	61	15	25
28	M4, M5, M6, S9, W7, W8, E1, E2, E3, E10, E11	green	Mk1 Restaurant Car	61	25	35
30	76000, 76093, 76114	black	Class 4MT BR Mogul	61	25	35
31	A F	blue	Midland Pullman Power Car	61	35	60
32	B E	blue	Midland Pullman Kitchen Car	61	50	70
33	C D	blue	Midland Pullman Parlour Car	61	25	35
35	-	-	USA Tank 0-6-0T	not made	NA	NA
36	'Flying Scotsman'	-	Class A3	not made	NA	NA
2.	**H0 Kits** Note that these are genuine 3.5mm/1ft models.					
3	'General'	black	Early American General 4-4-0	59	35	50
27	-	-	DB B4yge Coach	61	5	10
29	-	silver	SNCF A9 myfi/1958 Coach	61	5	10
34	5405	black	New York Central Hudson J3a 4-6-4	61	70	100
37	-	-	Canadian National U-4-A	not made	NA	NA
3.	**TT Kits**					
16	46100 'Royal Scot', 46110 'Grenadier Guardsman', 46169 'The Boy Scout'	black	Rebuilt Royal Scot	60	35	50
17	M35114, M34090, M34105, M34671, W34152, W34297, W34763, E34422, E34590, E35157	maroon	Mk1 Corridor Brake 2nd	60	5	10
17	S34256, S34621, S34158, S34945, S34279, S35020	green	Mk1 Corridor Brake 2nd	60	5	10
18	M16001, M15627, M15019, M15243, W15111, W15598, W15430, E15307, E15144, E16017	maroon	Mk1 Corridor Composite	60	5	10
18	S15042, S15573, S15888, S15903, S15580, S15873	green	Mk1 Corridor Composite	60	5	10
20	M25589, M24133, M24405, M24861, W24165, W24341, W24719, E24222, E24531, E25027	maroon	Mk1 Corridor 2nd	60	5	10
20	S24320, S24305, S24169, S24326, S24318, S24311	green	Mk1 Corridor 2nd	60	5	10
21	M4, M5, M6, S9, W7, W8, E1, E2, E3, E10, E11	maroon	Mk1 Restaurant Car	60	5	10
21	M4, M5, M6, S9, W7, W8, E1, E2, E3, E10, E11	green	Mk1 Restaurant Car	60	5	10

4.   Presentation Sets

P1	100 Years of British Steam	-	'Rocket', 'Duchess of Gloucester' and Stirling Single	59	100	150
P2	Battle of Britain Set	-	34057 'Biggin Hill" and 3 Mk1 coaches	60	NPG	200
P3	Royal Scot Set (TT)	-	Rebuilt Royal Scott and 4 Mk1 coaches	61	NPG	300

5.   Motor Kits

KM1	Motor Bogie	-	00	60	10	15
KM2	Motor Box Van	-	00	60	10	15
KM3	Motor Bogie	-	TT	not made	NA	NA

Footnote: Airfix produced two locomotive kits of their own, not using Kitmaster tools. These were the Park Royal Railbus (R201) in green (1960) which sells for £15 in good condition and £25 when mint and the 204HP Drewry shunter (R7) in black (1961) for which you might expect to pay £7 for a good example or £10 for a mint one.

The TT scale Rebuilt Royal Scot Class model (16) and coaches
[table 3]   (Tony Wright)

Some of the early OO scale kits
(Tony Wright)

133

Lima Class 08 in Virgin 'Pit Stop' livery as 08887 (L204658)   [table 1]

Lima Class 20 in BR rail or corporate blue as 20222 (L204634)   [table 2]

Lima

History

Lima is one of a handful of model railway manufacturers that are truly international; producing models for many different overseas markets. They date from 1946 but did not entered the British market until 1973, first with an unsuccessful range of British HO models before recognising that, if they were to sell to British modellers, they would need to make their products in the uniquely British 00 scale. This they did in 1976.

In the 1980s Lima made a serious bid for the modern image market and greatly improved the quality of their models. They recognised that modern image modellers were interested in the minor variations between different members of a class of locomotives. They employ batch production which means that a limited number of each model is made before it is replaced by another version of it. As a result, the range in shops is constantly changing with new releases each month.

Today, Lima's production for the British market is almost exclusively diesel and electric locomotives and Mk3 coaching stock, with collectors forming a major part of their market. Lima, more than any other manufacturer supplying the British market, have been prepared to accept commissions, from retailers, to produce exclusive short runs of special editions. This has resulted in a vast range of model variations over the last twenty years.

The models are made at Vicenza in Italy and, since 1983, have been imported by Riko International Ltd who are based in Hemel Hempstead and recommend what should be made. In 2000, the dealership changed to The Hobby Company Ltd.

Collectors Club

You may also wish to join the Lima Collectors Society who publish a bimonthly newsletter, called Modelimage, which keeps members informed of news of new products and reviews aspects of the Lima range. The Society also publishes an extensive list of Lima models which is available to members. Details of this organisation may be obtained from the chairman, Peter Baker, who may be contacted on Tel: 01782 519267.

Dates

Only single years are shown in the tables below. This is because most Lima models are produced in single batches and therefore production is not spread over several years.

Listing

As Lima models are almost exclusively of modern image locomotives, they are of prototypes which today are referred to by their British Railways TOPS codes - Class 08, Class 20, Class 37 etc.. This provides easy numerical listing and so we have used it to provide the order in which models are described here.

Milestones

1946	Lima formed.
1973	Lima enter the UK market.
1976	Lima change production for the British market to 00 scale.
1977	Deltic model appears.
1979	Last steam outline models launched.
1985	The Class 73 is released.
1987	The most prolific UK model, Lima's Class 47, is launched.
1994	The highly detailed Class 59 is released.
1999	Lima become the first manufacturer to market a model of the new Class 66.

Range Development

Lima modern image locomotives were introduced in the following years:

1977	Classes 33 and 55
1978	Class 09
1979	Classes 52 and 87
1980	Classes 42, 117 and GWR autocoach
1982	Class 43
1984	Class 50
1985	Class 20
1986	Class 37 and 73
1987	Class 47
1988	Class 40
1989	Classes 26, 27 and 31
1990	Class 60
1992	Class 156
1994	Classes 59 and 92
1996	Class 373 (ex- Jouef)
1997	Class 101
1998	Class 121
1999	Classes 57 and 66

Cat.No.	Name / Number	Colour	Details	Years	£	£
1. Class 08/09/10/11						
L205108	3004	green	BRc, Class 08	78	25	30
L205109	7120	black	LMS, Class 11	78	25	30
L205151	D3489 'Colonel Tomline'	lt. green	Townsend Thoresen, chevron ends, Class 10	83	28	35
L205297	08331	navy	GNER Redstripe	00	25	30
L204638	08611	red	Virgin	99	25	30
L205259	08720	maroon	*EWS*	00	NPG	30
L205200	08874	blu+grn	*Silverlink*	99	25	30
L204658	08887	black	Virgin Pit Stop	99	25	30
L204677	08899	green	*Midland Mainline*, teal green	99	25	30
L149972	08899	green	*Midland Mainline*, teal green, train pack	99	NA	40
L204701	09007	blue	Mainline	96	30	40
L204758	09009 'Three Bridges'	maroon	EW&S	97	32	45
L205090	09012 'Dick Hardy'	grey	BRe InterCity Executive	89	28	40
L205201	09023	maroon	*EWS*	99	30	40
L205107	09026	blue	BRe, chevron ends	79	25	30
L101806TW	09026	bt. blue	NSE, no con rods	88	15	20
L205225	09026	bt. blue	NSE	88	28	35
L205112	09027	grey	Railfreight, Scottie motif	86	25	35
L103409	09027	blue	BRe, Scottie motif, no con rods, no yellow ends	86	35	60*
L205058	09101	grey	BRe, Departmental grey	94	30	40
2. Class 20						
L204827	D8040	green	BRc, grey roof, Sp Edn (MR&ME) 475 paired with D8041, 5 pole motor	93	35	50
L204828	D8041	green	BRc, grey roof, Sp Edn (MR&ME) 475 paired with D8040, 5 pole motor	93	35	50
L205156	D8138	green	BRc	85	30	45
L205066	2014	grey	*RFS*	93	30	40
L204707	20042	black	Waterman Railways	95	30	45
L205220	20048	blue	BRe, scottie motif, Sp Edn 300 (Harburn Hobbies) (further 250 used in West Highland train pack L149779	99	30	50
L205220	20048	blue	BRe, scottie motif, from above train pack	99	30	40*
L204865	20059	grey	*Railfreight* red stripe	95	30	40
L205240	20064 'River Sheaf'	green	BRe, grey roof, red solebar	88	30	45
L205067	20066	blue	BRe	94	30	40
L205241	20088	grey	Railfreight unspecified triple grey	89	30	45
L204821	20092	red+gry	BRe RTC, paired with 20169, Sp Edn 500 (Greenyard/Hattons)	93	35	50
L205203	20112	blue	BRe, Ltd Edn 850	92	75	90
L204836	20131 'Almon B Strowger'	grey	*BRT*	94	30	40
L204822	20169	red +gry	BRe RTC, dummy, paired with 20092, Sp Edn 500 (Greenyard/Hattons)	93	35	50
L205158	20171	blue	BRe LL, grey roof	85	30	40
L149974	20172 'Redmire' + 20173 'Wensleydale'	grey	Railfreight Redstripe Sp Edn 300 (Beatties) sold as pair	00	NPG	125
L149974	20172 'Redmire'	grey	Railfreight Redstripe from above pack	00	50	NA
L149974	20173 'Wensleydale'	grey	Railfreight Redstripe from above pack	00	50	NA
L205157	20183	blue	BRe	85	30	40
L103807 TW	20183	blue	BRe, no detail	85	NPG	80
L205068	20187	grey	BRT (incorrect livery)	93	30	40
L204881	20188	black	Waterman Railways, code boxes 3D94	94	25	35
L205159	20215	grey	BReLL Railfreight red stripe	85	30	40
L204634	20222	blue	BRe	98	25	35
L204662	20227 'Traction'	grey	*Railfreight* red stripe, Sp.Edn. 550 (Traction)	98	35	50
L205263	20901	blue	DRS, Sp.Edn. 750 (Rail Express)	00	NPG	NPG
L204813	20906 'Kilmarmock 400'	grey	Hunslet Barclay, Ltd Edn 850	93	50	65
3. Class 26						
L204699	D5300	green	BRc, Sp Edn 550 (Harburn Hobbies), yellow half panels, etched plaques and shedplates, moulded plastic headlights	99	30	40
L205075	D5301 'Eastfield'	green	BRc, Ltd Edn 550	93	65	80
L204878	D5310	green	BRc	94	25	30
L205242	26001	grey	Railfreight Coal	90	25	30
L205246	26003	blue	BRe, discs	89	25	30

L205008	26004	gry+yel	BRe Dutch livery	91	25	33
L205245	26004	grey	*Railfreight* red stripe	90	25	29
L204677	26006	grey	BReLL *Railfreight* red stripe	99	25	30
L106306	26010	grey	Railfreight	90	35	70*
L205244	26027	blue	BRe, discs	90	20	30
L205243	26038	grey	*Railfreight* red stripe, scottie motif	90	30	40
L205173	26040	gry+yell	BRe Dutch, scottie motif	00	NPG	40

4. Class 27

L205248	D5394	green	BRc	90	25	30
L204671	27001	blue	BRe, Scottie motif	99	25	30
L205252	27037	blue	BRe, Scottie motif	89	30	40
L205247	27102	blue	BRe	89	30	40

5. Class 31

L205239	D5500	green	BRc, discs, no yellow panel	90	30	40
L205093	5518	green	BRe Royal Train, white roof	00	NPG	45
L204640	D5551	green	BRc, Sp Edn 550 (MR&ME)	98	30	60
L204614	D5578	blue	BRc, experimental livery code box 7M68	98	25	36
L204624	D5579	brown	BRc, 'golden ochre' experimental livery	98	25	34
L204859	D5583 'Stratford Major Depot'	green	BRc, BR No.31165, yellow panel and white wrap windows	94	30	40
L205092	D5679	green	BRc	89	30	40
L205093	D5830	green	BRc, half yellow panel	89	30	40
L205238	31004	blue	BRe, discs	90	30	40
L204868	31105 'Bescot TMD'	grey	*Transrail* triple grey	96	30	40
L204637	31106 'The Black Countryman'	gry+yel	BRe Dutch, Sp Edn 300 (Langdale) paired with 31107	98	35	50
L204637	31107 'John H. Carless VC'	gry+yel	BRe Dutch, Sp Edn 300 (Langdale) paired with 31106	98	35	50
L205282	31110	green	Ltd.Edn (Traction)	?	NPG	NPG
L204704	31112	gry+yel	*Transrail* Dutch	96	30	40
L205072	31116 'Rail 1981-1991'	gry+yel	BRe Dutch (sold in Scotland)	91	40	65
no code	31116 'Rail 1981-1991'	gry+yel	BRe Dutch, Sp Edn 500 (Rail) with headcodes	91	30	55
L205172	31019	blue	BRe, grey roof	99	30	40
L205232	31160 'Phoenix'	grey	Railfreight Distribution	90	30	40
-	31199	grey	BReLL, Railfreight Distribution	?	320	400
L205095	31201 'Fina Energy'	grey	Railfreight Petroleum	91	30	40
L205031	31206	grey	*Railfreight* red stripe	91	30	40
L205237	31275	grey	Railfreight Coal	89	30	40
L205236	31283	blue	BRe, large numbers, Kingfisher motif	90	30	40
L205213	31296 'Amlwch Freighter/ Tren Nwyddau Amlwch'	grey	BReLL *Railfreight* grey, yellow cab	90	30	40
L205190	31309 'Cricklewood'	blue	BRe, white stripe Sp Edn 500 (Beatties)	99	30	45
L205091	31325	blue	BRe	89	30	40
L205234	31327 'Phillips Imperial'	grey	*Railfreight* red stripe, large numbers	89	30	40
L205235	31402	blue	BRe	89	30	40
L204730	31407	blue	*Mainline*	96	30	40
L205255	31410 'Granada Telethon'	gry+blu	BRe *Regional Railways*	00	30	40
L205032	31413 'Severn Valley Railway'	blue	Severn Valley Blue	91	30	50
L204845	31421 'Wigan Pier'	gry+blu	BRe *Regional Railways*	96	30	40
L205233	31423	grey	Mainline InterCity	90	30	40
L205069	31439	gry+blu	BRe *Regional Railways*, Ltd Edn 850	93	45	60
L204673	31452	black	*Fragonset Railways*	99	30	40
L205196	31455 'Our Eli'	gry+blu	BRe *Regional Railways*	99	30	40
L204661	31466	maroon	*EWS*	98	25	37
L204687	31468	black	*Fragonset Railways*	99	30	40
L205096	31541	gry+yel	BRe Dutch	91	30	40
L205094	31568 'The Enginemans Fund'	grey	BRe Departmental grey	90	30	40
L205094	31601 'Bletchley Park Station X'	black	*Fragonset Railways*	00	30	40
L205229	31970	red+gry	BRe, Research Division - RTC Derby	90	30	40

6. Class 33   Body improved in 1986

L205115	D6506	green	BRc, big numbers, half yell front ends	81	25	35
L205129	D6506	green	BRc, big numbers, no yellow panel	81	25	35
L205114	D6524	blue	BRe	77	25	35

Lima

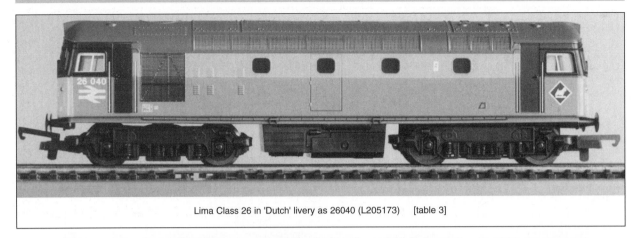

Lima Class 26 in 'Dutch' livery as 26040 (L205173)   [table 3]

Lima Class 33 in 'Dutch' livery as 33046 (L204610)   [table 6]

Lima Class 27 in BR blue as 27001 (L204671)   [table 4]

Lima Class 37 in DRS blue as 37607 (L204684)   [table 7]

Lima Class 40 in BR green as 337 (L204642)   [table 8]

Cat.No.	Name / Number	Colour	Details	Years	£	£
L205114	D6524	blue	BRe, chromatic blue	77	25	35
	D6535 'Herefordshire Rail Tours' (see 33116)					
L205221	33008 'Eastleigh'	green	BRc, snowploughs, half yellow ends	87	25	40
L205126	33008 'Eastleigh'	green	BRe, full yellow ends	86	25	35
L205114	33024	blue	BRe, yellow front ends	81	25	35
L205115	33025	blue	BReLL (but logo too small)	82	30	40
L104407V	33025	blue	BRe, small numbers, from set	82	28	35*
L204660	33025	maroon	EWS	98	25	50
L205114	33027 'Earl Mountbatten of Burma'	blue	BRe, white roof, red buffer beams	83	30	40
L103706V	33027 'Earl Mountbatten of Burma'	blue	BRe, white roof, black buffer beam, from set	83	28	35*
L204660	33030	maroon	EWS	98	25	45
L101008	33033	grey	Railfreight Construction, from set	89	28	35*
L104313	33033	grey	Railfreight Construction, from set	92	28	35*
L205070SI	33033	grey	triple grey for Railwayana, no body markings	89	25	35
L205074	33035	bt. blue	revised NSE, snowploughs	93	25	35
L204610	33046 'Merlin'	gry+yel	BRe Dutch	98	25	35
L205228	33050 'Isle of Grain'	grey	BRe Railfreight Construction	89	25	40
L105111	33051 'Shakespeare Cliff'	grey	Railfreight Construction, from set	89	28	35*
L204756	33051 'Shakespeare Cliff'	gry+yel	BRe Dutch, Sp Edn 500 (Rail Express)	97	40	55
L205174	33056 'The Burma Star'	blue	BRe, white roof, red beam large buffers	87	30	40
L103407V	33056 'The Burma Star'	blue	BRe, white roof, red beam small buffers, from set	87	28	35*
L103807V	33056 'The Burma Star'	blue	BRe, white roof, black beam large buffers, from set	87	28	35*
	33056 'The Burma Star'	blue	BRe, white roof, black beam small buffers, from set	87	28	35*
L204705	33063	grey	BRe triple grey Mainline	95	25	35
L205030	33065	gry+yel	BRe Dutch, side body numbers small	91	25	35
L205116	33105	blue	BRe, push-pull	87	30	40
L205073	33109 'Captain Bill Smith RNR'	grey	BRe Departmental grey	94	30	45
L205185	33114 'Ashford 150'	bt. blue	Revised NSE, headboard, Ltd Edn 850	92	80	120
L204841	33116/D6535 'Hertfordshire Rail Tours'	blue	BRe, Sp Edn 500 (Hertfordshire Rail Tours Sales Ltd.)	94	40	55
L205070	33205	grey	Railfreight Distribution, side body numbers small	89	30	45

7. Class 37   sno = snowploughs fitted   syep = small yellow end panels   scb = split code box

Cat.No.	Name / Number	Colour	Details	Years	£	£
L204858	D6607 'Ben Cruachan'	green	BRc, Sp Edn 500 (Harburn Hobbies), numbered 403 on ends, etched Eastfield Depot motifs and nameplates, syep, sno	94	90	150
L204644	D6700	green	BRc, Sp Edn 500 (ModelRail),	98	35	50
L205222	D6722	green	BRc, no yellow ends	87	30	45
L205173	D6755	green	BRc, half yellow panel, oversize nos.	86	30	45
L204834	D6916 'Great Eastern'	green	BRc, Ltd Edn1000, numbered 216 on ends, syep	94	50	65
L204772	D6999	green	BRc, Sp Edn 550 (MR&ME), 300th diesel electric, 5T17 code in boxes	97	50	65
L205172	37012 'Loch Rannoch'	blue	BRe, white stripe, red buffer beams, silver handrails, sno, Scottie motif, scb	86	45	50
L106206	37012 'Loch Rannoch'	blue	BRe, white stripe, black buffer beams, sno, Scottie motif, scb, no end detail	86	35	65*
L204717	37013	grey	Railfreight triple grey unspecified, Sp Edn 500 (Geoffrey Allison)	96	40	55
L205198	37013	blue	Mainline blue, scb	99	30	45
L204866	37023 'Stratford TMD Quality Assurance'	blue	Mainline blue, Stratford Depot motif, split headcodes	94	35	50
L204879	37025 'Inverness TMD'	blue	BReLL (extended), Sp Edn 500 (Harburn Hobbies), etched nameplates, yellow cab, stag motif, sno, scb	95	90	125
L204693	37027 'Loch Eil'	blue	BReLL, Sp Edn 550 (Geoffrey Allison), Scottie motif, yellow cab, sno, scb	99	30	45
L204786	37032 'Mirage'	grey	Railfreight red stripe, Sp Edn 550 (Macclesfield Model Centre), unofficial name	98	35	47
L205189	37043 'Loch Lomond'	blue	BRe, Sp Edn 550 (Harburn Hobbies) small scottie motif, etched metal nameplates	99	35	49
L205294	37049	blue	BRe, scb	89	30	45
L106307	37051	grey	Railfreight Metals, from set	92	50	70*
L204613	37057 'Viking'	maroon	EW&S	98	28	37
L106307	37063	grey	Railfreight Distribution, from sets	89	50	70*

140

L205076	37069	gry+yel	BRe, Dutch, scb	91	30	45
L205190	37081 'Loch Long'	blue	BReLL, 'computer' style numbers, small Scottie motif, sno, scb, yellow cabs	87	50	65
L205171	37082	grey	BReLL, *Railfreight* (unauthentic)	87	30	45
L205177	(37093)	white	BR painted in Police car livery for a TV advert, no number carried	87	45	85
L204760	37095 'British Steel Teeside'	blue	BRe, white cantrail stripe, kingfisher motif, scb	97	30	45
L205077	37099 'Clydesbridge'	grey	Railfreight Metals	93	30	45
L204680	37111 'Loch Eil Outward Bound'	blue	BReLL, Sp Edn 500 (Moray's), Scottie motif	98	30	45
L205091	37112	blue	BRe, scb, wrap round yellow ends, 1981 hybrid livery	00	NPG	45
L205286	37113	blue	BRe, scb, large Scottie motif	89	30	45
L205288	37114 'Dunrobin Castle'	blue	BReLL, numbers and logo too small, Highland Stag motif, sno	89	45	80
L204714	37116 'Sister Dora'	blue	*Transrail* on Rail blue, Sp Edn 500 (Rail Express) etched plates enclosed	96	50	100
L205299	37133	grey	BRe Departmental grey	91	30	45
L205218	37137 'Clyde Iron'	grey	Railfreight Metals, sno	99	30	40
L205289	37140	blue	BRe, Stratford Cockney Sparrow motif	89	30	45
L205124	37180 'Sir Dyfed/ County of Dyfed'	grey	Railfreight all-over grey, sno	87	35	50
L205018	37184	grey	Railfreight Petroleum, Immingham Depot motif	91	30	45
L205019	37185	grey	Railfreight Distribution	91	30	45
L204700	37201 'Saint Margarets'	gry+yel	BRe *Transrail* on Dutch	96	30	45
L204788	37209 'Phantom'	blue	BReLL, Sp Edn 550 (Geoffrey Allison) unofficial name, sno	98	30	45
L208434	37216 'Great Eastern'	green	Ltd Edn 1000, D6916	94	NPG	60
L204711	37219	blue	*Mainline* blue, number at wrong end one side	96	30	45
L205297	37223	grey	BRe Railfreight Coal	90	40	55
L205017	37232 'The Institution of Railway Signal Engineers'	gry+yel	Dutch	91	35	50
L205079	37251 'The Northern Lights'	grey	*InterCity* Swallow	93	30	45
L205262	37261 'Caithness' + 37262 'Doonray'	blue	BReLL, Ltd Edn 300 (Geoffrey Allison)	00	NA	100
-	37261 'Caithness'	blue	BReLL, from above set	00	40	NA
-	37262 'Doonray'	blue	BReLL, from above set	00	40	NA
L204663	37275 'Oor Wullie'	blue	BRe, Sp Edn 550 (Rails)	98	30	44
L205123	37310 'British Steel Ravenscraig'	blue	BReLL, dark roof small logo, leaping salmon motif	87	50	80
L205287	37350/D6700	green	BRc, small yellow panel	89	35	50
L205193	37351	gry+yel	*Transrail* on Dutch, scb	99	30	45
L205215	37370	grey	BReLL Railfreight red stripe, leaping salmon motif, sno	99	30	45
L205290	37401 'Mary Queen of Scots'	grey	*InterCity* Mainline, sno	89	35	50
L204711	37401 'Mary Queen of Scots'	grey	BRe Railfreight Dist. triple grey, Sp Edn 500 (Harburn Hobbies), sno, etched nameplates and arrows, info sheet	97	75	90
L205178	37402 'Oor Wullie'	blue	BReLL, incorrect mould, no sealed beam headlight	87	35	50
L204773	37402 'Bont-y-Bermo'	grey	Railfreight unspecified triple grey, Sp Edn 550 (Geoffrey Allison), sno	97	30	45
L205129	37404 'Ben Cruachan'	grey	*InterCity* Mainline, Sp Edn 550 (Harburn Hobbies) + metal etched nameplates	00	35	50
L204812	37405 'Strathclyde Region'	blue	BReLL, small nos., small logo, large Scottie motif, sno	94	35	50
L205241	37405 'Strathclyde Region'	grey	*InterCity* Mainline, Sp Edn 350 (Moray's), sold with 37417	00	35	50
L205219	37406 'The Saltire Society'	grey	*Transrail* on triple grey, Sp Edn 550 (Harburn Hobbies), sno, etched nameplates, info sheet	99	35	49
L204863	37407 'Blackpool Tower'	grey	*Transrail*, triple grey 407 on front end	95	30	45
L204863	37407 'Blackpool Tower'	grey	*Transrail*, triple grey	95	30	45
L204696	37407 'Loch Long'	grey	*InterCity* Mainline red stripe Sp Edn 500 (Morays), sno	99	35	50
L204882	37408 'Loch Rannoch'	blue	BReLL, large Scottie motif, sno	95	30	70
L204882	37408 'Loch Rannoch'	blue	BReLL, large Scottie motif, sno, no detail on front, from set	95	45	65*
L204675	37409 'Loch Awe'	blue	BReLL, Sp Edn 550 (Harburn Hobbies), sno, Scottie motif, etched nameplates, yellow cabs	98	35	47

Cat.No.	Name / Number	Colour	Details	Years	£	£
L204762	37411 'Ty Hafan'	maroon	*EWS*, sno	97	30	45
L204632	37413 'Scottish Railway Preservation Society'	maroon	*EWS*, Sp Edn 700 (Harburn Hobbies and SRPS), etched nameplates and SRPS Railtours headboard, ticket + info sheet	98	35	50
L204817	37414 'Cardiff Cathays C&W Works'	gry+blu	BRe *Regional Railways*, Ltd Edn 850	93	90	120
L205241	37417 'Highland Region'	grey	*InterCity* Mainline, Sp Edn 350 (Moray's), sold with 37405	00	35	50
L205266	37417 'Rail Magazine'	maroon	*EWS*, black and gold nameplates, sno	00	NPG	45
L204625	37418 'East Lancashire Railway'	gry+blu	BRe *Regional Railways*	98	30	45
L204820	37418 'Pectinidae'	grey	Railfreight Petroleum, Sp Edn 250 (Langdales) paired with 37421	99	35	50
L20****	37418 'An Comunn Gaidhealach'	blue	BReLL, stag motif + metal etched nameplates, Sp Edn 550 (Harburn Hobbies)	00	35	50
L104311	37419	grey	*InterCity* Mainline, from set	92	65	100*
L204641	37420 'The Scottish Hosteller'	blue	BReLL, Sp Edn 550 (MR&ME)	98	30	45
L204697	37420 'The Scottish Hosteller'	bt. blue	BRe *Regional Railways*, Sp Edn 1000 (Morays + Geoffrey Allison), sno, etched nameplates and logo	99	35	50
L204731	37421 'The Kingsman'	gry+blu	BRe *Regional Railways*, sno	96	30	45
L204819	37421 'Strombidae'	grey	Railfreight Petroleum, Sp Edn 250 (Langdales) paired with 37418	99	35	50
L204763	37422 'Robert F.Fairlie'	gry+blu	BRe *Regional Railways*, spelling mistake, sno	97	30	45
L149932	37423 'Sir Murray Morrison'	grey	Railfreight Distribution, Sp Edn 300 (Langdales) paired with 37428	98	30	45
L204784	37424 'Isle of Mull'	grey	*Mainline*, Sp Edn 550 (Harburn Hobbies), sno, etched nameplates + info sheet	98	35	50
L204782	37425 'Sir Robert McAlpine/ Concrete Bob'	gry+blu	BRe *Regional Railways*, Sp Edn 550 (Rails), sno	97	50	65
L204897	37425 'Sir Robert McAlpine/ Concrete Bob'	grey	Railfreight Construction, Sp Edn 500 (Rails), sno	96	75	100
L204655	37425 'Sir Robert McAlpine/ Concrete Bob'	blue	BReLL, Sp Edn 550 (Rails), sno, yellow cab, Scottie motif	98	30	45
L204612	37426	maroon	*EWS*	98	30	45
L204842	37427 'Highland Enterprise'	gry+blu	BRe *Regional Railways ScotRail*, Sp Edn 500 (D&F) uncertificated	94	90	150
L149932	37428 'David Lloyd George'	grey	Railfreight Petroleum, Sp Edn 300 (Langdales) paired with 37423	98	30	45
L204659	37428 'Loch Awe'	maroon	Royal Claret livery for the Royal Scotsman train, EWS motif, Sp Edn 550 (Harburn Hobbies), sno	98	50	70
L204887	37429 'Eisteddfod Genedlaethol'	gry+blu	BRe Regional Railways	94	30	60
L205298	37430 'Cwmbran'	grey	*InterCity* Mainline, number wrong end one side	92	50	80
L205176	37431 'County of Powys'/ 'Sir Powys'	blue	BReLL, red dragon motif, county coat of arms, yellow cabs	00	30	45
L204824	37431 'Bullidae'	blue	*Mainline*, Sp Edn 250 (Langdales)	99	55	70
L205230	37501 'Teeside Steelmaster'	lt.blue	BReLL British Steel blue, Kingfisher motif, BSC motif	90	50	65
L205231	37502 'British Steel Teeside'	grey	BReLL *Railfreight* red stripe, large numbers	90	45	60
L205078	37506 'British Steel Skinningrove'	grey	BReLL *Railfreight* red stripe, Kingfisher motif	94	30	45
L204843	37510	grey	*InterCity* Swallow	95	30	60
L205293	37511 'Stockton Haulage'	grey	BRe Railfreight Metals, large numbers, Thornaby Depot motif	89	50	65
L204709	37517 'St. Aidens'	blk+org	*Loadhaul*	96	30	45
L107157	37519	grey	*Railfreight* red stripe, large nos., from set, Kingfisher motif	89	55	65*
L204647	37605	grey	*EPS*, Channel Tunnel motifs, triple grey	98	55	70
L204684	37607	dk.blu	*DRS* blue, Ltd Edn 750	99	30	45
L204796	37609	dk.blu	*DRS* blue	98	50	65
L204605	37610	dk.blu	*DRS* blue, Sp Edn 550 (Rail Express)	98	35	100
L204683	37611	dk.blu	*DRS* blue	99	50	65
L204737	37671 'Tre Pol And Pen'	grey	Railfreight Distribution triple grey, St Blaxey Depot motif, sno	97	40	70
L205285	37673	grey	Railfreight Distribution, St Blazey Depot motif	87	45	60
L205208	37675 'William Cookworthy'	grey	*Railfreight* red stripe, Ltd Edn 850	92	50	65
L204754	37682 'Hartlepool Pipe Mill'	maroon	*EW&S*	97	30	45

L205296	37688 'Great Rocks'	grey	BRe Railfreight Construction, Buxton Depot motif	90	40	70
L204891	37692 'The Lass O Ballochmyle'	grey	BRe Railfreight Coal, Sp Edn 500 (D&F Models), Eastfield Depot motif	95	75	150
L20****	37693 'Sir William Arrol'	grey	Railfreight Coal, Sp Edn 550 (Harburn Hobbies), etched name and depot motif and arrows	00	35	50
L204765	37698 'Coedbach'	grey	Railfreight Coal	97	30	45
L204735	37702 'Taff Merthyr'	grey	Railfreight Coal triple grey, Canton Depot motif	96	30	45
L204856	37713	blk+org	*Loadhaul* sticker attached	94	30	45
L204793	37714	maroon	*EWS*	98	25	38
L204892	37715 'British Petroleum'	grey	BRe Mainline on Railfreight unspecified triple grey, Stewarts Lane Depot motif, BP motif	95	30	45
L204740	37717 'Maltby Lilly Hall'	maroon	*EW&S*	97	30	45
L204886	37798	blue	Mainline blue, revised moulding, Stewarts Lane Depot motif	94	30	45
L204622	37884 'Gartcosh'	blk+org	*Loadhaul*	98	22	34
L205284	37892 'Ripple Lane'	grey	Railfreight Petroleum triple grey, Ripple Lane Depot motif	87	50	65

8.   Class 40   scb = split code box

L205064	D205	green	BRc, early green, discs	89	30	45
L205233	D210 'Empress of Britain'	green	BRc, Sp Edn (Rails)	99	30	40
L204728	D233 'Empress of England'	green	BRc, discs, Sp Edn 550 (Rails), half yellow panel	97	40	55
L205060	D261	green	BRc, centre headcode	88	30	45
L205065	D334	green	BRc, scb	89	30	45
L205201	D335	green	BRc, scb	88	30	45
L205062	D354	green	BRc, centre headcode	89	30	45
L204642	337	green	BRc, scb	98	30	45
L205189	40001	blue	BRe, discs	88	30	45
L204698	40012 'Aureol'	blue	BRe, Sp Edn 500 (Moray's)	99	35	50
L205063	40052	blue	BRe, discs	90	30	45
L205217	40063	blue	BRe, centre headcode	89	30	45
L205187	40066	blue	BRe, black centre headcode	89	30	45
L205188	40106 'Altantic Conveyor'	green	BRc, discs, revised green, full yellow ends	88	35	50
L205200	40122/D200	green	BRc, discs	88	30	45
L205278	40126	blue	BRe, scb	89	30	45
L205202	40140	blue	BRe, scb	90	30	45
L205061	40145	blue	BRe, centre headcode	88	30	45

9.   Class 42 (Warships)

L204894	D807 'Caradoc'	blue	BRe	96	30	40
L204669	D809 'Champion'	maroon	BRc	99	30	40
L149966	D809 'Champion'	maroon	BRc, train pack with 3 coaches	99	NA	70
L107307	D814 'Dragon'	blue	BRe, from a set	80	35	45*
L204861	D815 'Druid'	maroon	BRc	95	30	40
L204837	D819 'Goliath'	green	BRc, Ltd Edn 1000, spelling mistake	94	35	50
L205128	D838 'Rapid'	maroon	BRc	80	30	45
L205135	D843 'Sharpshooter'	green	BRc	80	30	45
L205127	814 'Dragon'	blue	BRe	80	30	40
L205083	828 'Magnificent'	blue	BRe	93	30	40

10.   Class 43 HST Power & Dummy Cars

L205253	43024 + 43025	green	*First Great Western*	00	NPG	NPG
L149909	43043 'Leicestershire County Cricket Club'+ 43075	turqu	*Midland Mainline*, train pack	98	50	65
L205080	43051 'Duke and Duchess of York'	grey	*InterCity* Swallow	89	25	35
L106520 L205082	43051 + 43072	grey	*InterCity* Swallow, from set	89	50	60*
L205197 L205199	43053 'County of Humberside' + 43136	grey	BRe, *InterCity* grey and yellow, from L149811 set	87	50	60*
L149806	43058 'Midland Pride' + 43059	turqu	*Midland Mainline*, train pack	98	65	78
L205160 L205164	43113 'City of Newcastle Upon Tyne' + 43063	blue	BRe, L149751 train pack	84	45	60
L205160	43113 'City of Newcastle Upon Tyne'	blue	BRe	84	25	35
L205164	43063	blue	BRe	84	18	25
L205169	43085 'City of Bradford'	grey	BRe, *InterCity* Executive	87	25	35

Cat.No.	Name / Number	Colour	Details	Years	£	£
L205198	43091					
	'Edinburgh Military Tattoo'	grey	BRe, *InterCity* grey and yellow, dummy	87	18	25
L149849	43093 'Lady in Red' +					
	43155 'The Red Arrows'	red	*Virgin XC*, in train pack	98	65	80*
L149872	43096 'The Great Racer' +					
	43110	navy	*GNER* white lettering, train pack	97	60	75
L204681	43100 'Blackpool Rock' +					
	43101 'The Irish Mail'	red	*Virgin*, double pack	99	35	50
L149908	43109 + 43167	navy	*GNER* pearl lettering, train pack	98	45	60
L149918	43117 + 43118	navy	*GNER* gold lettering, train pack	98	50	65
L106506	43122 + 43178	red	*Virgin*	99	45	60
L205184						
L205180	43125 + 43126 (253028)	grey	*InterCity125* Executive, from L104416V set	85	50	60*
L204733	43129	grey	*InterCity* Swallow, dummy	96	15	20
L149849	43155 'The Red Arrows'	red	*Virgin XC*	98	NPG	NPG
L205254	43157 'HMS Penzance'	red	*Virgin XC*	99	25	35
L149916	43160 'Storm Force' + 43090	red	*Virgin*, train pack	98	50	65
L205160						
L205164	43167 + 43168	blue	BRe, from L103416V set	82	50	60*
L205160	43167	blue	BRe,	82	25	35
L205164	43168	blue	BRe, dummy,	82	18	25
L149975	43172 + 43009	green	*First Great Western* + 2 Mk3 coaches	00	80	95
L106522	43177 'University of					
	Exeter' + 43139	grey	*InterCity* Swallow, from set	97	65	75*
L106522	43177 + 43139	grey	*InterCity* Swallow, from set	98	65	75*
L205081						
L205082	43178 + 43072	grey	*InterCity* Swallow, from set	89	40	50*
L204732	43181					
	'Devonport Royal Dockyard'	grey	*InterCity* Swallow	96	35	40
L149871	43185 'Great Western' +					
	43168	green	*Great Western* Trains, from train pack	97	65	75*
L205165						
L205168	-	org+silv	from Australian XPT set, no numbers	84	35	45*

11. Class 47

Cat.No.	Name / Number	Colour	Details	Years	£	£
L205215	D1574	green	BRc 2 tone green, original as built livery	89	30	40
L204718	D1664 'George Jackson					
	Churchward'	green	BRc 2 tone green, Sp Edn 500 (MR&ME)	96	50	90
L204775	D1733	blue	Sp Edn 240 (Langdales) XP64, without red panels	97	70	85
L204775	D1733	blue	Sp Edn 280 (Langdales) XP64, with red panels			
			fitted after leaving the factory	97	60	80
L205049	D1761	green	BRc 2 tone green	89	30	50
L205219	D1842	green	BRc 2 tone green	89	30	50
L205192	D1957	blue	BRe	99	30	40
	D1962 (see 47833)					
L204835	47004/D1524					
	'Old Oak Common T&RSMD'	green	BRc 2 tone green	95	40	60
L205255	47006	grey	Railfreight Construction, snowploughs	90	30	50
L149930	47010 'Xancidae'	grey	Railfreight Petroleum, Sp Edn 200			
			(Macclesfield Mod. Cntr) part of 4 pack	98	50	65
L205210	47016 'Atlas'	grey	BReLL Railfreight grey '1546', yellow cabsides	99	30	45
L204710	47033					
	'The Royal Logistics Corps'	grey	*Railfreight Distribution* European, Channel Tunnel	96	30	50
L205266	47079	grey	Railfreight Metals	88	30	40
L204600	47114 'Freightliner Bulk'	grey	2 tone green, *Freightliner*,			
			Sp Edn 550 (Rail Express)	97	50	75
L149930	47125 'Tonnidae'	grey	Railfreight Petroleum, Sp Edn 200			
			(Macclesfield Mod. Cntr) part of 4 pack	98	60	65
L204789	47142 'Traction'	grey	*Railfreight* red stripe, Sp Edn 550			
			(Macclesfield Mod. Cntr), unofficial name	98	35	50
L204860	47145 'Merddin Emrys'	blue	Tinsley blue, Speedlink symbols, Ltd Edn 850	94	50	75
L204885	47157	grey	Railfreight unspecified triple grey,			
			Sp Edn 500 (Goeffrey Allison)	95	50	65
L205210	47164	blue	BRe, with Union Jack (Silver Jubilee)	87	30	60
L205043	47190 'Pectinidae'	grey	Railfreight Petroleum, flush both ends	89	30	40
L205298	47193	green	*Freightliner*	00	30	46
L205092	47210 'Blue Circle'	grey	Railfreight Construction	00	30	46

144

Lima Class 31
in BR green for royal
duties as 5518
(L205093)
[table 5]

Lima Class 50
in BR blue large logo
livery as 50046
'Ajax'
(L206920)
[table 12]

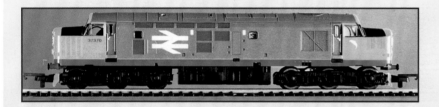

Lima Class 37
in Railfreight red
stripe livery as 37370
(L205215)
[table 7]

Lima Class 37
in Railfreight Metals
livery as 37137
'Clyde Iron'
(L205218)
[table 7]

Lima Class 50
in Network South
East livery as 50033
'Glorious'
(L205179)
[table 12]

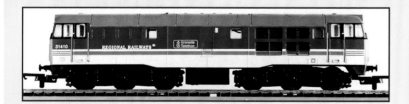

Lima Class 31
in Regional Railways
livery as 31410
'Granada Telethon'
(L205255)
[table 5]

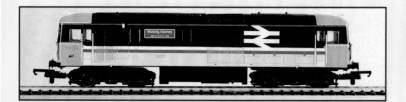

Lima Class 73
in Intercity livery as
73134
'Woking Homes 1885-1985'
(L205194)
[table 19]

Lima

Lima Class 60
in Mainline livery as
60044
'Ailsa Craig'
(L205169)
[table 17]

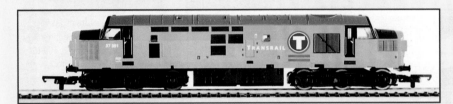

Lima Class 37
in 'Dutch' livery as
37351
(L205193)
[table 7]

Lima Class 60
in Steel livery as 60006
'Scunthorpe Ironmaster'
(L204783)
[table 17]

Lima Class 37
in European
Passenger Services
(EPS) livery as 37605
(L204647)
[table 7]

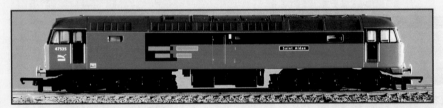

Lima Class 47
in RES livery as
47535
'Saint Aidan'
(L205184)
[table 11]

Lima Class 08
in Midland Mainline
livery as 08899
(L204677)
[table 1]

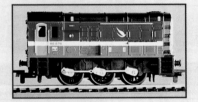

Lima Class 08
in Silverlink livery as
08874
(L205200)
[table 1]

Lima Class 47
in Virgin livery as
47702
'County of Suffolk'
(L204636)
[table 11]

Where do you think your fellow collectors get their models?

Code	Number / Name	Colour	Description			
L149930	47233 'Strombidae'	grey	Railfreight Petroleum, Sp Edn 200 (Macclesfield Mod. Cntr) part of 4 pack	98	50	65
L204844	47241	grey	Railfreight Distribution European, Channel Tunnel	95	30	40
L149930	47278 'Vasidae'	grey	Railfreight Petroleum, Sp Edn 200 (Macclesfield Mod. Cntr) part of 4 pack	98	50	65
L205045	47283 'Johnnie Walker'	grey	Railfreight Distribution	89	30	45
L205048	47298	blue	BRe	89	30	40
L205039	47301	grey	*Railfreight* LL modified red stripe, large numbers, Kingfisher motif	89	30	50
L205260	47305	blue	Chemical blue with yellow stripe	88	30	40
L205257	47315	grey	Departmental grey	90	30	40
L205044	47317 'Willesden Yard'	grey	Railfreight Distribution	89	30	45
L204759	47348 'St Christophers Railway Home'	grey	*Railfreight Distribution* European Channel Tunnel	97	30	40
L205212	47363 'Billingham Enterprise'	grey	Railfreight grey LL, Kingfisher motif	87	30	40
L204832	47365 'Diamond Jubilee'	grey	*Railfreight Distribution* European, Channel Tunnel	95	30	40
L204633	47369	green	BRc, 2 tone green with yellow cab	98	25	35
L204889	47375 'Tinsley Traction Depot'	grey	*Railfreight Distribution*	95	30	40
L204874	47376 'Freightliner 1995'	grey	triple grey *Freightliner*, panther motif	95	30	40
L205033	47380 'Immingham'	grey	Railfreight Petroleum	91	30	40
L205269	47401 'North Eastern'	blue	BRe	89	30	40
L204666	47402 'Gateshead'	blue	BRe, yellow cab windows	99	30	40
L205216	47455	blue	BReLL extended	88	40	60
L107210	47461 'Charles Rennie Mackintosh'	blu+gry	*ScotRail*, from set, highland motif, front end not detailed	88	50	100*
L205264	47461 'Charles Rennie Mackintosh'	blu+gry	*ScotRail*, highland motif	88	30	130*
L205209	47471 'Norman Tunna G.C.'	grey	*InterCity*, yellow cabs + cab roofs, No.1 end flush	99	30	40
L205036	47474 'Sir Rowland Hill'	red	Parcels	90	30	50
L205254	47475	gry+blu	Provincial blue	90	30	40
L104318	47475 'Restive'	red	RES, from set	93	50	60*
L105114	47476 'Night Mail'	red	Parcels, from set	91	50	60*
L205040	47484 'Isambard Kingdom Brunel'	green	BRe, Brunswick green, GWR 150, No.1 end flush	89	40	60
L205218	47487	blue	BRe	87	30	40
L205214	47487	grey	BRe, Original *InterCity* Executive, yellow doors, Cockney Sparrow motif	88	40	60
L204682	47488	green	*Fragonset Railways*, 2 tone green	99	30	40
L205071	47489 'Crewe Diesel Depot'	red	Parcels	91	30	50
L104318	47490 'Restive'	red	RES, as 47475 but numbered incorrectly, should have been 'Resonant'	93	40	60*
L20 5046	47508 'SS Great Britain'	grey	*InterCity* Mainline	89	30	60
L204619	47513 'Severn'	blue	BReLL, grey roof, yellow cabs	98	30	40
L205042	47522 'Doncaster Enterprise'	green	BRe, *Parcels*, LNER green, flush both ends	89	30	70
L105112	47530	bt.blue	Revised NSE, from set	90	50	60*
L205184	47535 'Saint Aidan'	red	RES, panther motif	99	30	40
L205211	47541 'The Queen Mother'	grey	InterCity *ScotRail* red stripe + stag motif, wood plinth, coat of arms, Sp Edn 550 (Harburn) etched nameplates, individually numbered models matching certificate	00	60	77
L107206	47549 'Royal Mail'	grey	*InterCity* Executive, from set	91	50	60*
L204734	47555 'The Commonwealth Spirit'	blue	BRe, small logo, yellow cab windows	96	30	40
L204774	47564 'Colossus'	blue	BReLL, Sp Edn 550 (MR&ME)	97	30	45
L204729	47565 'Responsive'	red	RES, including headboard, panther motif	96	30	40
L205259	47567 'Red Star'	blue	BRe	88	30	50
L105110	47569 'The Gloucestershire Regiment'	red	Parcels, from set	90	50	60*
L107108	47576 'Kings Lynn'	bt.blue	NSE, from set	88	70	100*
L205038 50	47579 'James Nightall VC'	bt.blue	BRe, revised NSE (original blue), nameplates both at one end	89	30	
L205220	47581 'Great Eastern'	bt.blue	BRe NSE, Cockney Sparrow motif	87	30	60
L205209	47582 'County of Norfolk'	bt.blue	NSE, Cockney Sparrow motif	87	30	50
L205261	47583 'County of Herefordshire'	bt.blue	NSE	88	30	50
L205127	47583 'County of Herefordshire'	bt.blue	BReLL with extended stripes, Sp Edn 500 (Langdale)	00	NPG	45
L205084	47588 'Resurgent'	red	BRe, RES	93	30	50
L104314	47594 'Resourceful'	red	BRe, RES, from set	92	50	60*

Cat.No.	Name / Number	Colour	Details	Years	£	£
L205047	47596 'Aldeburgh Festival'	blue	BRe, grey roof	89	30	50
L205034	47599	grey	Railfreight Metals, wrong size symbols	91	30	50
L205268	47609 'Fire Fly'	grey	*InterCity* Executive	89	30	50
L107106	47613 'North Star'	grey	*InterCity* Executive, no details to front end, from set	88	55	65*
L205262	47613 'North Star'	grey	*InterCity* Executive	88	50	130*
L205041	47620 'Windsor Castle'	grey	*InterCity* Executive, flush No.2 end	89	30	60
L205205	47625 'Resplendant'	red	RES	92	30	50
L205213	47628 'Sir Daniel Gooch'	green	Brunswick green, GWR 150	87	30	60
L205206	47635 'Jimmy Milne'	blue	BReLL extended, Ltd Edn 850	92	50	65
L205258	47637	grey	*InterCity* ScotRail red stripe, Highland Stag motif	88	30	50
L204818	47701 'Old Oak Common T&RSMD'	bt.blue	Revised NSE (later blue), flush No.2 end	94	30	50
L204636	47702 'County of Suffolk'	red	*Virgin*, Sp.Edn.	99	35	50
L204898	47703	black	Fragonset	98	30	40
L205211	47705 'Lothian'	gry+blu	*ScotRail*, one side incorrect	87	30	60
L204703	47705 'Guy Fawkes'	black	*Waterman Railways*	96	30	40
L205267	47709 'The Lord Provost'	gry+blu	*ScotRail*	88	30	60
L204880	47710 'Lady Godiva'	black	*Waterman Railways*	95	30	40
L204688	47710	black	*Fragonset Railways* with logos (also in pack 149971)	99	30	40
L149779	47711 'Greyfriars Bobby'	gry+blu	BRe *ScotRail*, Sp Edn 300 (Harburn Hobbies), from train pack, yellow cab roof	95	70	80*
L205037	47711 'Greyfriars Bobby'	gry+blu	BRe *ScotRail*, Sp Edn 200 (Harburn Hobbies), etched name and workplates, Scottie figurine + info sheet	95	70	85
L20****	47713 'Tayside Region'	grey	*InterCity* ScotRail, Sp Edn 350 (Moray's), sold with 47714	00	35	50
L20****	47714 'Grampian Region'	grey	*InterCity* ScotRail, Sp Edn 350 (Moray's), sold with 47713	00	35	50
L205037	47716 'The Duke of Edinburgh's Award'	gry+blu	*ScotRail*	88	30	40
L204739	47726 'Manchester Airport - Progress'	red	RES, Sp Edn 500 (Langdale)	96	30	45
L149784	47747 'Res Publica'	red	BRe RES, from train pack	95	50	60*
L149808	47749 'Atlantic College'	red	RES, from train pack with NFX 92714, NOX 95133 + NJX 95138	97	50	60*
L204690	47758 'Regency Rail Cruises'	maroon	*EWS*	99	30	40
L205258	47760 'Ribblehead Viaduct'	maroon	EWS	00	30	46
L204767	47785 'Fiona Castle'	maroon	EWS	97	30	45
L204792	47786 'Roy Castle OBE'	maroon	EWS	98	30	40
L204864	47798 'Prince William'	dk purple	RES Royal EIIR, panther motif	95	30	40
L204794	47798 'Prince William'	dk purple	EWS Royal, new logos	98	30	40
L204888	47799 'Prince Henry'	dk purple	RES Royal EIIR, panther motif	95	30	40
L204795	47799 'Prince Henry'	dk purple	EWS Royal, new logos	98	30	40
L204853	47803	yellow	BRe Infrastructure (transfers optional), Sp Edn 500 (Greenyards/Hattons)	93	50	65
L204753	47807	pur+wht	*Porterbrook* Leasing Co	97	45	60
L205085	47809 'Finsbury Park'	grey	*InterCity* Swallow	94	30	60
L149949	47810	grey?	*InterCity* Swallow Porterbrook, Ltd Edn 200 (Macclesfield M C), part of pack of 4	99	35	50
L149949	47811	grey	*InterCity* Swallow, Ltd Edn, part of pack of 4	99	35	50
L204825	47811	green	*First* Great Western	00	30	43
L204645	47813 'SS Great Britain'	green	*Great Western* Trains	98	25	35
L204761	47814 'Totnes Castle'	red	*Virgin*	98	30	40
L204727	47817	pur+wht	*Porterbrook* Leasing Co	96	30	40
L204635	47827	red	*Virgin*	99	30	40
L204685	47830	green	*Great Western* Trains (also in 149970 sleeper pack)	99	30	40
L204685	47830	red	*Virgin* issued in error and the bulk were recalled and reissued as 47827	99	60	100
L105108	47833	grey	*InterCity* Swallow, from set	93	65	75*
L205089	47833/D1962 'Captain Peter Manisty RN'	green	BRc 2 tone green, Ltd Edn 850	93	90	110
L205013	47835 'Windsor Castle'	grey	*InterCity* Swallow, flush No.2 end, Sp Edn 650 (Cheltenham Model Centre)	93	50	65
L205256	47838	grey	*InterCity* Mainline/Swallow, incorrect white skirting to body sides	90	30	50
L205256	47838	grey	*InterCity* Swallow, correct white skirting to body sides	90	30	50
L149960	47840 'North Star'	grey	*InterCity* Swallow, Ltd Edn, part of pack of 4	99	35	50
L205202	47841 'Institute of Mechanical Engineers'	grey	*InterCity* Swallow	99	30	45
L204621	47844	red	*Virgin*	98	30	40
L205171	47846 'Thor'	green	*Great Western* Trains	99	30	40

L205268	47849 'Cadeirlan Bangor Cathedral'	red	*Virgin* Ltd Edn 550, coat of arms above nameplate	00	NPG	45
L149960	47853	grey	*InterCity* Swallow, Ltd Edn, part of pack of 4	99	35	50
L204823	47972 'Royal Army Ordnance Corps'	red+gry	BRe RTC(Technical Services), Sp Edn 850 (Beatties)	93	50	65
L205035	47976 'Aviemore Centre'	gry+yel	Dutch	91	30	40
L205253	97561 'Midland Counties Railway 150'	maroon	yellow cabs and lined border	90	40	50

12. Class 50

L205009	D400	blue	BRe, Sp Edn 400 (Rail Magazine) including headboard	91	110	140
L205009	D400	blue	BRe	92	30	45
L205170	50001 'Dreadnought'	blue	BRe	99	30	45
L205265	50003 'Tremeraire'	bt. blue	Revised NSE	92	35	50
L205140	50007 'Sir Edward Elgar'	green	BRe Brunswick green, original mould	85	30	45
L205140	50007 'Sir Edward Elgar'	green	BRe Brunswick green, modified mould	91	30	45
L205121	50008 'Thunderer'	blue	BRe, Ltd Edn 550	92	110	130
L204811	50009 'Conqueror'	blue	BReLL	94	30	45
L205232	50010 'Monarch'	blue	BReLL, blue roof Sp Edn (Traction)	99	35	47
L205226	50015 'Valiant'	blue	BReLL	87	30	45
L205007	50015 'Valiant'	gry+yel	BRe Dutch	91	30	45
L205135	50017 'Royal Oak'	bt. blue	NSE	86	30	45
L205175	50017	maroon	VSOE Northern Pullman (LMS Royal Scot type livery)	00	NPG	45
L204896	50019 'Ramillies'	blue	BRe, grey roof, Sp Edn 600 (Model Railway Enthusiast)	94	45	60
L205141	50020 'Revenge'	blue	BRe, original mould	84	30	45
L205279	50021 'Rodney'	blue	BReLL	89	30	45
L205131	50023 'Howe'	bt. blue	NSE	86	30	45
L103408	50023 'Howe'	bt, blue	NSE, from set, no cab detail	86	35	45*
L205177	50025 'Invincible'	bt. blue	BRe, NSE	93	30	45
L205280	50028 'Tiger'	bt. blue	Revised NSE	89	30	45
L107208	50030 'Repulse'	bt. blue	BRe, revised NSE, from set	89	40	55
L205011	50031 'Hood'	blue	BReLL, Sp Edn 650 (Cheltenham Model Centre)	93	60	75
L104317	50033 'Glorious'	bt. blue	Revised NSE, from set	93	45	55*
L105179	50033 'Glorious'	bt. blue	Revised NSE	00	NPG	45
L205027	50034 'Furious'	bt. blue	Revised NSE	91	30	45
L205207	50035 'Ark Royal'	bt. blue	Revised NSE, Ltd Edn 850	92	50	65
L204787	50036 'Victorious'	blue	BReLL, yellow cab, grey roof	98	30	40
L205227	50038 'Formidable'	blue	BReLL	87	30	45
L104312	50041 'Bulwark'	bt.blue	Revised NSE, from set	92	45	55*
L106207	50042 'Triumph'	blue	BReLL, black cab surrounds, from set	89	100	120
L205142	50043 'Eagle'	blue	BReLL, original mould	84	30	40
L205142	50043 'Eagle'	blue	BReLL, revised mould	84	40	55
L205224	50044 'Exeter'	bt. blue	NSE	87	30	45
L246920	50046 'Ajax'	blue	BReLL, with black roof and yellow cab, Ltd Edn 550 (MR&ME)	99	30	45
L204716	50050 'Peco Golden Jubilee 1946-1996'	blue	BReLL, Sp Edn 500 (Peco)	96	30	45
L205281	50149 'Defiance'	grey	BRe, Railfreight General (experimental motif)	87	30	45

13. Class 52

L205134	D1003 'Western Pioneer'	green	BRc	80	30	40
L204800	D1004 'Western Crusader'	green	BRc, red numberplate	94	30	45
L204846	D1013 'Western Ranger'	blue	BRe	95	30	40
L205010	D1015 'Western Champion'	golden ochre	BRc, Sp Edn 500 (Cheltenham Model Centre)	92	70	100
L205121	D1016 'Western Gladiator'	maroon	BRc	79	30	40
L205126	D1023 'Western Enterprise'	sand	BRd, incorrect name	79	30	40
L204776	D1023 'Western Fusilier'	blue	BRe, Ltd Edn 550 (Langdale)	98	30	45
L204668	D1043 'Western Duke'	blue	BRe	99	30	40
L205122	D1071 'Western Renown'	blue	BRe	79	30	40

14. Class 55

L204651	D9000 'Royal Scots Greys'	green	BRc 2 tone green, Sp Edn 550 (Geoffrey Allison)	98	35	50
L204781	D9001 'St Paddy'	green	BRc 2 tone green, Sp Edn 550 (Rails)	97	50	80
L205222	D9002 'Kings Own Yorkshire Light Infantry'	green	BRc 2 tone green, Sp Edn 500 (Moray's), no name on side - etched plates supplied	00	35	50

Lima Class 31 in experimental light blue livery as D5578 (L204614)
[table 5]

Lima Class 52 (Western Class) in BR blue as
D1043 'Western Duke' (L204668)   [table 13]

Lima Class 59 in EWS red and gold livery as 59203 'Vale of Pickering' (L204674)   [table 16]

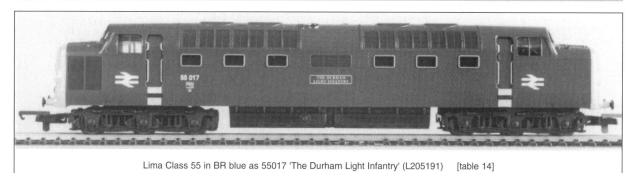

Lima Class 55 in BR blue as 55017 'The Durham Light Infantry' (L205191)   [table 14]

Lima Class 60 in Steel livery as 60033 'Tees Steel Express' (L204799)   [table 17]

Lima Class 66 in EWS red and gold livery as 66001 (L204679)   [table 18]

Cat.No.	Name / Number	Colour	Details	Years	£	£
L205105	D9003 'Meld'	green	BRc 2 tone green, white cab surround	77	30	40
L205105	D9008 'The Green Howards'	green	BRc 2 tone green, handrails not picked out	82	30	40
L204657	D9009 'Alycidon'	green	BRc 2 tone green, Sp Edn 550 (Rails/DPS)	98	30	45
L204816	D9013 'The Black Watch'	green	BRc 2 tone green, Sp Edn 650 (MR&ME), half yellow panel, windows not picked out	93	60	75
L204656	D9015 'Tulyar'	green	BRc 2 tone green, Sp Edn 550 (DPS/Rails)	98	30	45
L204607	D9016 'Gordon Highlander'	green	BRc 2 tone green, Ltd Edn 850	98	30	60
L205269	D9018 'Ballymoss'	green	BRc 2 tone green, half yellow panel	00	NPG	45
L204743	D9019 'Royal Highland Fusilier'	green	BRc 2 tone green, Sp Edn 550 (MR&ME), half yellow panel, steps not picked out	97	40	55
L205106	9006 'Fife and Forfar Yeomanry'	blue	BRe also chromatic blue	77	30	40
L205260	9016 'The Gordon Highlander'	purple	*Porterbrook*, Ltd Edn 1200	00	35	50
L204802	55002 'Kings Own Yorkshire Light Infantry'	green	BRc 2 tone green, white cab surround, full yellow end	94	40	60
L204801	55007 'Pinza'	blue	BRe, white cab surround	93	30	60
L204869	55009 'Alycidon'	blue	BRe, silver grills and batteries	94	30	60
L204738	55015 'Tulyar'	blue	BRe, Sp Edn 550 (DPS + Rails)	96	45	60
L205191	55017 'The Durham Light Infantry'	blue	BRe, Ltd Edn 1000	99	30	45
L205230	55019 'Royal Highland Fusilier'	blue	BRe, Sp Edn (Deltic Preservation Soc)	00	35	47
L204702	55021 'Argyll and Sutherland Highlander'	blue	BRe, Sp Edn 500 (Harburn Hobbies), etched nameplates and crests plus replica Argyll's badge, info sheet	96	35	60
L205106	55022 'Royal Scots Grey'	blue	BRe, handrails not picked out	82	30	40

15. Class 57

Cat.No.	Name / Number	Colour	Details	Years	£	£
L204649	57001 'Freightliner Pioneer'	green	*Freightliner*, Ltd Edn 750 (Rail Express)	99	60	75
L204686	57002 'Freightliner Phoenix'	green	*Freightliner*	99	30	40
L204686	57003 'Freightliner Evolution'	green	*Freightliner*	99	30	40

16. Class 59

Cat.No.	Name / Number	Colour	Details	Years	£	£
L204838	59001 'Yeoman Endeavour'	silv+blue	Foster *Yeoman*	94	40	50
L204804	59002 'Yeoman Enterprise'	silv+blue	Foster *Yeoman*	94	40	55
L204849	59003 'Yeoman Highlander'	silv+blue	Foster *Yeoman*	96	40	60
L204643	59003 'Yeoman Highlander'	silv+red+blue	*DB* Yeoman, Ltd Edn 500 (Beatties)	98	45	70
L204850	59005 'Kenneth J Painter'	silv+blue	Foster *Yeoman*	95	40	55
L204646	59005 'Kenneth J Painter'	silv+blue	Foster *Yeoman*, revised livery	99	30	45
L204851	59101 'Village of Whatley'	yellow	*ARC*	96	40	55
L204667	59101 'Village of Whatlet'	silv+yell	*ARC*, revised livery	99	30	45
L204839	59102 'Village of Chantry'	yellow	*ARC*	94	40	55
L204803	59103 'Village of Mells'	yellow	*ARC*	94	40	55
L204665	59103 'Village of Mells'	org+blue	*Hanson*	99	40	55
L204852	59104 'Village of Great Elm'	yellow	*ARC*	95	35	50
L205257	59104 'Village of Great Elm'	org+blue	*Hanson*	00	40	52
L204805	59201 'Vale of York'	blue	*National Power*	94	45	60
L204664	59201 'Vale of York'	maroon	*EWS*	99	35	50
L204674	59203 'Vale of Pickering'	maroon	*EWS*	99	30	45

17. Class 60

Cat.No.	Name / Number	Colour	Details	Years	£	£
L204867	60000	blk+org	*Loadhaul*, Sp Edn 100 (for Loadhaul personnel)	95	250	450
L205020	60001 'Steadfast'	grey	Railfreight Construction	90	30	45
L205021	60002 'Capability Brown'	grey	Railfreight Petroleum, incorrect side grill	90	30	45
L204764	60003 'Freight Transport Association'	maroon	*EWS*, spelling mistake	97	30	45
L205024	60003 'Christopher Wren'	grey	Railfreight Petroleum	91	35	50
L205022	60004 'Lochnager'	grey	Railfreight Coal	90	35	50
L204783	60006 'Scunthorpe Ironmaster'	bt. blue	*British Steel* blue	98	30	45
L205023	60008 'Moel Fammau'	grey	Railfreight Metals	90	35	50
L204736	60008 'Gypsum Queen II'	blk+org	*Loadhaul*	97	30	45
L204715	60011	vio/blue	*Mainline*	96	30	45
L204755	60012	maroon	*EW&S*	97	30	45
L204875	60015 'Bow Fell'	grey?	*Transrail* on triple grey	95	30	45
L204741	60019	maroon	*EW&S*	96	30	45
L204806	60032 'William Booth'	grey	Railfreight Coal	93	35	60
L204799	60033 'Tees Steel Express'	bt. blue	*British Steel* blue	98	35	50

L204807	60039 'Glastonbury Tor'	grey	Railfreight Construction	93	35	50
L204876	60040 'Brecon Beacons'	grey	BRe *Mainline* on triple grey Railfreight	95	30	45
L205169	60044 'Ailsa Craig'	blue	*Mainline*	99	30	45
L204808	60050 'Roseberry Topping'	grey	BRe Railfreight Metals	94	30	45
L204857	60050 'Roseberry Topping'	grey	BRe *Loadhaul* on Railfreight	95	30	45
L204854	60051 'Mary Somerville'	grey	Railfreight Petroleum	94	30	45
L205025	60055 'Thomas Barnardo'	grey	Railfreight Coal	91	35	50
L204867	60059 'Swinden Dalesman'	blk+org	*Loadhaul*	95	30	45
L204768	60063 'James Murray'	grey	*Transrail* on triple grey	97	30	45
L204620	60083 'Mountsorrel'	maroon	*EWS*	99	30	40
L205025A	60098 'Charles Francis		BRe Railfreight Construction			
	Brush'	grey	Sp Edn 250 (for Brush personnel)	93	230	320
L205026	60100 'Boar of Badenoch'	grey	BRe, Railfreight Construction, Ltd Edn 850	92	45	60

18. Class 66

L204679	66001	maroon	*EWS*	99	35	50
L204691	66016	maroon	*EWS*	99	35	50
L205197	66100	maroon	*EWS*, Ltd Edn	99	35	50
L205229	66501	green	*Freightliner*, Sp Edn 750 (Rail Express)	99	45	75
L205227	66502	green	*Freightliner*	99	35	50

19. Class 73

L205276	E6001	green	BRc 2 tone green			
			(SR EMU green and lime waistband)	87	40	60
L205192	E6003	green	BRc Brunswick green	87	30	60
L149929	E6003 'Sir Herbert Walker'	green	BRc, Sp Edn 500 (Rails) paired with 73128	98	30	45
L205223	E6012	blue	BRe in original blue with grey band along			
			bottom of sides	87	30	50
L205275	73001	blue	BRe	87	30	50
L205275	73001	blue	BRe, grey roof	87	30	50
L205274	73002	blue	BReLL	89	30	50
L205273	73004 'The Bluebell Railway'	bt.blue+ yellow	NSE	89	30	50
L204618	73101					
	'Brighton Evening Argus'	brown + cream	*Pullman* livery	98	30	75
L205186	73101 'The Royal Alex'	brn+crm	*Pullman* livery, commemorative edition			
			first 3000 certificated	92	35	75
L205270	73105	blue	BReLL	90	25	40
L205170	73108	blue	BRe, early blue, roof dark grey	87	30	50
L205001	73109 'Battle of Britain					
	50th Anniversary'	bt. blue	Revised NSE, Ltd Edn 550	92	100	130
L204862	73114 'Stewarts Lane					
	Traction Maintenance Depot'	vio. blue	*Mainline*, Stewarts Lane motif	94	25	40
L204877	73118	grey	triple grey EPS, code 73	94	25	40
L205193	73123 ' Gatwick Express'	grey	BReLL, *InterCity* Executive,			
			large numbers, full yellow ends	87	30	40
L205191	73125 'Stewarts Lane		BReLL *InterCity* Executive,			
	1860-1985'	grey	half yellow and half black cab ends	86	30	40
L103406	73125 'Stewarts Lane		*InterCity* Executive, without running numbers,			
	1860-1985'	grey	enlarged shedplate on cabside	86	90	110*
L205012	73126 'Kent & East					
	Sussex Railway'	bt. blue	Revised NSE, Sp Edn 650 (Signal Box)	93	75	80
L204742	73128	maroon	*EW&S*	96	30	40
L149929	73128 'OVS Bullied'	gry+yel	BRe Dutch, Sp Edn 500 (Rails) paired with E6003	98	30	45
L205178	73129 'City of Winchester'	bt. blue	NSE (without branding), city coat of arms	00	NPG	45
L205277	73130 'City of Portsmouth'	grey	BRe, *Intercity* Mainline	89	30	40
L204757	73131	maroon	*EW&S*	97	30	45
L204648	73133 'Bluebell Railway'	gry+yel	BRe Dutch	98	25	35
L205194	73134					
	'Woking Homes 1885-1985'	blk+gry	BReLL InterCity, yellow cab roof	99	30	45
L205169	73136	grey	BRe Departmental grey, code 20	91	25	35
L205271	73138 'Poste Haste'	grey	BRe, *InterCity* Mainline, full yellow to front end only	89	30	40
L205169	73142 'Broadlands'	blue	BReLL	86	30	40
L205194	73142 'Broadlands'	grey	BReLL, *InterCity* Executive	87	30	40
L204847	73212 'Airtour Suisse'	grey	*Gatwick Express*	94	25	35
L204770	73901	yellow	Merseyrail, Sp Edn 500 (Langdale)	97	40	55

Cat.No.	Name / Number	Colour	Details	Years	£	£
20. Class 87						
L204810	87002 'Royal Sovereign'	grey	*InterCity* Swallow	94	30	45
L205195	87003 'Patriot'	red	*Virgin*	99	30	45
L205125	87005 'City of London'	blue	BRe	79	30	40
L205125	87005 'City of London'	grey	BRe, InterCity Executive	87	30	40
L204631	87006 'George Reynolds'	red	*Virgin*	98	30	35
L204798	87009	red	*Virgin*	98	30	40
L205195	87009 'City of Birmingham'	grey	BRe, InterCity Executive	86	30	40
L205130	87012 'Couer de Lion'	grey	BRe, InterCity Executive	85	30	40
L205185	87018 'Lord Nelson'	grey	BRe, InterCity Executive	85	30	40
L205175	87019 'Sir Winston Churchill'	blue	BRe	84	30	40
L205155	87022 'Cock O' The North'	blue	BReLL, unauthentic LL livery	82	30	40
L205179	87031 'Hal O' The Wind'	grey	InterCity Mainline	90	30	35
L204809	87101 'Stephenson'	grey	BRe Railfreight Distribution	93	30	35
21. Class 92						
L204855	92001 'Victor Hugo'	grey	BRe Railfreight Distribution, Channel Tunnel, Commemorative Edn. 3000 certificated	94	30	35
L204672	92001 'Victor Hugo'	maroon	*EWS*, Channel Tunnel	99	30	45
L204893	92003 'Beethoven'	grey	BRe Railfreight EPS, Channel Tunnel	95	35	50
L204672	92015 'DH Lawrence'	grey	Railfreight Unspecified	95	30	40
L204871	92017 'Shakespeare'	grey	BRe Railfreight Unspecified, Channel Tunnel	95	35	40
L204870	92022 'Charles Dickens'	grey	BRe *Railfreight Distribution*, Channel Tunnel	94	35	40
L204873	92023 'Ravel'	grey	Railfreight *SNCF*, Channel Tunnel	94	35	50
L204708	92030 'Ashford'	grey	BRe Railfreight Distribution, Ltd Edn 850**	98	30	40
L204884	92034 'Kipling'	grey	Railfreight Unspecified	96	30	45
L204777	92041 'Vaughan Williams'	grey	Railfreight Unspecified, Sp Edn 300 (Beatties)	97	75	90

** Both 300 and 850 appear on certificates.

Cat.No.	Name / Number	Colour	Details	Years	£	£
22. Class 101						
L149894	51228/51506	gry+blu	BRe *Regional Railways*	97	40	55
L149895	M50321/M50303	green	BRc, white stripe and whiskers	97	45	60
L149896	53311/53322	bt. blue	NSE	97	40	55
L149897	50304/50338	blue	BRe	97	40	55
L149898	51188/53268	gry+blu	BRe *Regional Railways* ScotRail	97	40	55
L149899	E51433/E51503	green	BRc	97	45	60
L149814	SC51800/SC51808	green	BRc, destination *Dundee*	98	45	60
L149915	E51425/59108/E51503	blu+gry	BRe	99	35	50
L149927	51177/59303/53269	gry+blu	BRe *Regional Railways*	99	35	50
L149959	51253/53171	maroon	Strathclyde PTE, 2 car set, Sp Edn 300 (D&F)	99	50	85
L149973	M53331/M59125/M53308	blu+gry	BRe, blue/grey rework, destination Crewe	00	60	75
23. Class 117						
L 117305	51410/59520/51368	brn+crm	BRc GWR colours, Sp Edn 300 (Model Railway Enthusiast)	94	NA	140
L204829	51410	brn+crm	BRc power car, GWR colours, from above set	94	55	NA
L204830	59520	brn+crm	BRc centre car, GWR colours, from above set	94	20	NA
L204831	51368	brn+crm	BRc dummy power car, GWR colours, from above set	94	20	NA
L205137/ 46/39	W51342/W59518/W51340	green	BRc, 3-car set	80	40	55
L205136/ 45/38	W51334/W59493/W51332	blue	BRe, 3-car set	80	40	50
L205147/ 48/49	W51350/W59508/W51332	blu+gry	BRe, 3-car set	81	40	50
L205152/ 53/54	W51350/W59484/W51346	wht+blu	BRe, 3-car set	82	40	50
L205086/ 87/88	51369/59521/51411	gry+blu	BRe *Regional Railways*, 3-car set	92	40	50
L205097/ 98/99	51362/59514/51404	bt.blue	BRe NSE, 3-car set	94?	45	50
24. Class 121/2 (Bubble Car)						
L204608	W55035 (B135)	blue	BRe, destination *Bath*	98	30	40
L204611	55027	bt. blue	NSE	98	30	40
L204617	W55026	green	BRc, small yell. warning panel, code 2T55	98	30	45
L204623	W55028	blu+gry	BRe	98	30	40
L204630	W55025	green	BRc, whiskers	98	30	45

25. Class 156

L205053	156470 (52470)	blue	BRe Provincial Blue, single car only	92	15	20
L204706	156402 (52402/57402)	grey	BRe *Regional Railways* Express, Class 158 style livery	96	40	55
L204895	156420 (52420/57420)	gry+blu	BRe *Regional Railways*, green stripe	96	40	55
L204791	156433 'The Kilmarnock Edition' (52433/57433)	crim+ cream	Strathclyde PTE, Sp Edn 300 (Harburn Hobbies), etched nameplates, info sheet	98	75	125
L205050	156443 (52443/57443)	blue	BRe Provincial Blue	92	35	50
L204676	156454 'Whitby Endeavour' (52454/57454)	blu+gry	BRe Provincial Blue		30	50
L204712	156465 'Bonnie Prince Charlie' (52465/57465)	blue	Provincial *ScotRail*, Sp Edn 500 (Harburn Hobbies), etched nameplates, info sheet	96	40	65
L205051	156480 (52480/57480)	blue	BRe Provincial Blue	92	35	50
L205052	156481 (52481/57481)	blue	BRe Provincial Blue	92	35	50
L205054	156501 (52501/57501)	org+blk	BRe Strathclyde PTE	93	40	55
L205054D	156501 (57501)	org+blk	BRe Strathclyde PTE, dummy car only	93	25	30
L204840	156502 (52502/57502)	org+blk	BRe Strathclyde PTE, Sp Edn 500 (D&F) uncertificated	94	60	75
L205055	156512 (52512/57512)	org+blk	BRe Strathclyde PTE, Sp Edn 500 (Harburn Hobbies) uncertificated	92	65	90
L204713	156513 (52513/57513)	org+blk	BRe Strathclyde PTE, Sp Edn 400 (D&F Models) uncertificated	96	40	65

26. Class 373 (Eurostar)

L106530	F5 (3211 + 3212)	grey	*Eurostar*, from set, HO Ex-Jouef	96	40	50*

27. GWR Railcars

L205132	22	brn+crm	*GWR* (button)	80	30	45
L205133	W22	mrn+crm	1948 numbering	80	30	45
L204639	29	brn+crm	*Great* (crest) *Western*	98	25	35
L205150	W30W	green	BRc	83	30	40
L205267	W32W	green	BRc, white roof domes	00	NPG	40
L205143	34	brn+crm	*GWR* (button), *Express Parcels*	82	30	40
L205144	W34W	maroon	*Express Parcels*	82	30	40

28. Class J50 0-6-0

L205101	8920	green	*LNER*, dark shade of green, no steps to smokebox and works plate, plastic whistle	76	25	30
L205101	8920	green	*LNER*, lighter shade of green	77	25	30
L205102	68920	black	BRb	77	25	35

29. King Class

L205103	6000 'King George V'	green	*Great* (crest) *Western,* moulded handrails, single boiler bands, crests separate	77	30	40
L205103	6000 'King George V'	green	*Great* (crest) *Western,* separate handrails, double boiler bands, crests joined	77	30	40
L205104	6009 'King Charles II'	blue	BRb, moulded handrails, thin lining	77	30	45
L205104	6009 'King Charles II'	blue	BRb, moulded handrails, thick lining	77	30	45
L205176	6026 'King John'	green	BRb	90	40	55
L205056	6012 'King Edward VI'	green	*Great* (crest) *Western,* Ltd Edn 500	93	55	70

30. Prairie 2-6-2T

L205111	4589	green	*GWR*	79	25	35
L205110	5574	black	BRb, lined	79	30	40
L205015	4581	green	*GWR*	93	25	35
L205014	5557	black	BR, lined	93	30	40
L100000	5549	black	BR	?	45	60

31. Pannier 0-6-0PT

L205117	9400	green	*GWR*	79	25	35
L205118	9420	black	BRb	79	30	40
L204815	9401	black	BRb	94	30	40

32. Mogul (Crab) 2-6-0

L205119	13000	maroon	LMS, number on tender	79	30	45
L205120	42700	black	BRb, lined	79	35	50
L204814	42760	black	BRc, Ltd Edn 850	94	40	65

Coaches

Lima coaches have been limited to only a few prototypes. These fall into two categories - BR standard coaching stock and non-passenger stock. The latter includes Syphons, CCTs and GUVs while the former are made up of Mk1s, Mk2s and Mk3s. As with Lima locomotives, the emphasis has been on extending the range of liveries that can be carried by each basic model. The coaches sell quite cheaply on the second-hand market and good examples may be bought for between £8 and £12. Some rarer examples including GUVs loose from train packs (which have exclusive numbers) and limited editions commissioned by shops can sell for up to £20.

Wagons

The range of Lima wagons is limited to a few types and models vary considerably according to the age of the model design. Early models such as the 7-plank wagon, small tanker and closed van lacked detail while more recent ones are far better. Understandably, the emphasis in recent years has been on modern wagons such as a PCA depressed centre tank, JCA tanker, grain hopper, bogie pallet van, Seacow, bogie ballast hopper, six wheel tank wagon, bogie covered wagon and ore tippler. The early wagons sell for around £4-£5 in mint boxed condition while the later bogie wagons, in similar condition could cost £10-£15 each. Modellers often want them in quantity to make-up realistic trains.

Sets

There have been many train sets over the years as well as some train packs. Special value is applied to these only where they contain models unique to them. To establish which these are, the locomotive list is worth studying. Other sets sell for between £25 and £50.

Lima Class 101 in BR green as
SC51800 and SC51808 (L149814)   [table 22]

Lima Class 121 (Bubble Car) in BR blue as
W55035 (L204608)   [table 24]

Lima Class 73 in 'Dutch' livery as 73133 'The Bluebell Railway' (L204648)   [table 19]

Lima Class 92 in EWS tunnel livery as 92001 'Victor Hugo' (L204672)   [table 21]

Lima Class 87 in Virgin livery as 87003 'Patriot' (L205159)   [table 20]

Lima Class156
in
Strathclyde PTE
maroon and cream as
156433
'The Kilmarnock Edition'
(L204721)

[table 25]

Lima Class GWR Railcar in chocolate and cream as No.29 (L204639)   [table 27]

Mainline

History

Palitoy was a division of the General Mills Corporation of America and had previously been in the model railway market when, in the early 1950s, they had made and marketed an S gauge train set. They already used the Kader Industrial Company in Hong Kong to manufacture toys for them and so it was natural for them to go to Kader when, in the mid 1970s, they decided to produce an 00 scale model railway system for the British market.

The new system was launched at the 1976 Harrogate Toy Fair followed by the Brighton Toy Fair. For their stand at Harrogate, Kader supplied the pre-production working chassis of the J72 and Palitoy provided cast resin shells for the bodies - they looked excellent. For the Brighton Fair a number of J72 pre-production models were running and attracted much attention. There were also pre-production wagons and coaches to be seen plus a pair of static 4MTs and a running Peak, all with cast resin shells.

The new system was called Mainline Railways and the excellent BR Standard 4MT 4-6-0, a Class 45 diesel and some Mk1 coaches quickly followed. Development and expansion carried on apace and 1981 saw the release of the model of a Manor Class locomotive which set the highest standards so far.

In 1981 Palitoy took over the rival Airfix GMR system and the Airfix models were gradually absorbed into the Mainline range.

Unlike Airfix, Palitoy did not own the tools with which its models were made. When Mainline models were ordered from Kader it was on the understanding that Kader retained ownership of the tools. When Palitoy acquired Airfix, it became owners of the Airfix tools and, at the advice of Palitoy (Far East) office, placed the ex-Airfix wagon tooling with Todco who were third manufacturing company involved with Airfix tools after Sandakan and Cheong Tak. This was to lead to complications and misunderstandings later when the Mainline Railways assets were sold.

In 1983, General Mills decided to withdraw from toy development in Europe. This was not a sign of failure on the part of the Mainline range but rather a sweeping decision made many miles away on the other side of the Atlantic which affected various European toy ranges. The design department at Coalville was officially closed on August 31st 1983 and the research and development facility within the Company, for most product ranges, came to an end. The Company was acquired by Kenner Parker (later Kenner Parker Tonka) and subsequently the Palitoy name disappeared.

On the 17th of May 1985 the Mainline stock and intellectual assets were sold to Dapol.

Further Reading

A detailed listing of the Airfix and Mainline model railway systems was produced by the late Charles Manship in the 1980s but this is no longer available. However, there has been a series of articles by Graham Smith-Thompson, in Model Railway Enthusiast magazine, profiling the Airfix and Mainline ranges together with other systems that later used the tools. There were six parts devoted specifically to Mainline Railways published in the January-May and July 1999 issues of the magazine.

Dates – Those shown in the following lists are based on catalogue and price list appearances and are provided for guidance only.

Listing – The models are arranged in the order we believe they became available.

Samples on the Market – Far East manufacturers sent samples to their customers for approval before proceeding with full production. These samples often ended up in collections and today they command a good price. In some cases samples exist of Mainline models that did not reach the production stage and these are of even greater interest to collectors.

Catalogue Numbers – In some cases these were used for more than one item, as in the case of trade packs - e.g. 37067. Later numbers were often prefixed by a '9' when a new computer was installed at Palitoy. From that time, all products carried a six figure code and it is probable that the '9' prefix indicated that the item was from the Hobbies Division. Brackets applied

---

Milestones

1976	Mainline Railways is launched by Palitoy.
1981	Release of the Manor Class model.
1981	Palitoy acquire Airfix assets.
1983	General Mills decide to pull out of toy production in Europe.
1983	Design Department closes in August
1985	Dapol acquire the intellectual assets of the Mainline range.

to catalogue numbers indicate that the number applied to more than a solo model, i.e. a train set or trade pack.

Smoke – Some models were advertised 'with smoke' in 1982 but mention of it was immediately dropped after this. It seems that the locomotives described were produced but without smoke generators fitted.

Locomotives

1. Class J72 0-6-0T

Cat.No.	Name / Number	Colour	Details	Years	£	£
37054	581	green	*LNER* lined, Ross pop safety valves	76-79	18	25
37055	68745	black	BRa, Ross pop safety valves	76-79	20	25
37070	69001	black	BRb, enclosed safety valves	80-81	17	23
37067**	69023 'Joem'	green	*North Eastern*, enclosed safety valves, as preserved	80	18	25
937506	?	black	*LNER* modified model	not made	-	-
937507	?	green	BR/NER, York Station Pilot	not made	-	-

** This catalogue number was also used for a trade pack of 6 mixed J72s.

2. Class 45 Diesel 1Co-Co1

Cat.No.	Name / Number	Colour	Details	Years	£	£
-	-		Unpainted grey plastic. Only 12 made and distributed to the trade for comments. Not all were returned	76?	100	120*
37050	D49 'The Manchester Regiment'	green	BRc, early matt, later semi-gloss	77-79	25	35
37051	45039 'The Manchester Regiment'	blue	BRe, early matt, later semi-gloss	76-79	22	32
(37068)[1]	45046 'Royal Inniskilling Fusilier'	blue	BRe	80	22	30*
(37068)[1]	D52 'The Lancashire Fusilier'	green	BRc	80	22	32*
9/37040	45048 'Royal Marines'	blue	BRe, split headcode boxes	82-84	34	45
9/37041	D100 'Sherwood Forester'	green	BRc, split headcode boxes	82-84	45	65
(37048)[2]	45048 'Royal Marines'	blue	BRe, split headcode boxes, as 37040 but with diesel sound and klaxon	82-83		
(37048)[2]	D100 'Sherwood Forester'	green	BRc, split headcode boxes, as 37041 but with diesel sound and klaxon	82-83		

[1] In 1980, retailers were offered packs of six Class 45s consisting of two each of these two plus two of Cat. No. 37051 (above).
[2] Also sold together in a trade pack.

3. Standard Class 4 4-6-0

Cat.No.	Name / Number	Colour	Details	Years	£	£
37052	75006	black	BRb (small) lined	76-80	38	45
37053	75001	green	BRc lined, matt finish	76-80	38	45
937052	75033	black	BRc lined, traction tyres fitted, sold in tray only	83-84	NPG	260*
937053	75027**	green	BRc lined, traction tyres fitted	not made	-	-

** Three samples were made and one of these was sold by auction in 1997 for £500.

4. Class 6P/7P 'Rebuilt Royal Scot' 4-6-0   All were fitted with the Stanier 4000 gallon tender.

Cat.No.	Name / Number	Colour	Details	Years	£	£
37056	6115 'Scots Guardsman'	black	*LMS* lined straw	77-79	30	38
37057	46100 'Royal Scot'	green	BRb (large)	77-79	33	40
37060	6100 'Royal Scot'	crimson	*LMS* as preserved, bell on front, name on smokebox door	79	32	38
37060	6100 'Royal Scot'	crimson	As above but all black cab fronts **	79	38	45
37080	6100 'Royal Scot'	crimson	*LMS* as 37060 but with Mk1 steam sound	80	45	60
937088	46115 'Scots Guardsman'	green	BRc, new pattern matt silver cadmium plated driving wheels	83-84	35	42

** Due to a production fault, a batch was made with all black cab fronts instead of LMS crimson.

5. Class 2251 'Collett Goods' 0-6-0

Cat.No.	Name / Number	Colour	Details	Years	£	£
37058	3205	green	*GWR* semi-gloss	78-80		
37059	2213	black	BRb (small) lined	78-80	30	35
37077	3210	green	BRc lined	80	32	40

37059 was demonstrated at the 1981 Harrogate Toy Fair with steam and whistle sound. This was to also be fitted to 37058.

6. Class 5XP 'Jubilee' 4-6-0

Finer quality wheels were proposed for the Jubilee but due to technical difficulties all models were released with Scot type wheels. In 1981, the Jubilee received a re-profiled chimney with skirt mounting studs. Some had turned brass safety valves fitted.

Cat.No.	Name / Number	Colour	Details	Years	£	£
9/37046	5719 'Glorious'	crimson	*LMS*, advertised with smoke, Fowler 3500 gallon flush-sided tender	82-84	40	48
37034	5719 'Glorious'	crimson	*LMS*, advertised with steam sound, Fowler 3500 gallon flush-sided tender	82	NPG	NPG

37034	45698 'Mars'	green	BRb (small), advertised with smoke, Fowler 3500 gallon riveted tender	82	35	40
9/37047	45698 'Mars'	green	BRb (small), advertised, Fowler 3500 gallon riveted tender, with smoke and steam sound	82-84	45	50
37061	5690 'Leander'	crimson	*LMS*, Stanier 4000 gallon tender, small nameplate	79-80	28	34
9/37061	5690 'Leander'	crimson	*LMS*, Stanier 4000 gallon tender, correct size nameplate	80-83	30	36
37095	5690 'Leander'	crimson	*LMS*, as 37061 but with Mk2 steam + whistle sound	81	58	70
37089	45690 'Leander'	green	BRc, Stanier 4000 gallon tender	81-82	32	38
37062	45691 'Orion'	green	BRc, Stanier 4000 gallon tender, small nameplate	79-80	30	36
9/37062	45691 'Orion'	green	BRc, Stanier 4000 gallon tender, correct size nameplate	80-83	32	38
37081	45691 'Orion'	green	BRc, as 37062 but with Mk1 steam sound	80-81	37	42
37095	45691 'Orion'	green	BRc, as 37062 but with Mk2 steam + whistle sound	81		
37074	5687 'Neptune'	black	*LMS* straw lining, Stanier 4000 gallon tender, small nameplate (samples only produced)	80	NPG	NPG
37074	5687 'Neptune'	black	*LMS* straw lining, Stanier 4000 gallon tender, correct nameplate	80-81	30	35
37095	5687 'Neptune'	black	*LMS* as 37074 but with Mk2 steam + whistle sound	81	75	100
936153	45700 'Amethyst'	black	BRb (small) lined, Fowler 3500 flush-sided tender, new cab glazing, turned brass safety valves	83-84	30	37

7. Class 42 'Warship' Diesel Hydraulic B-B

9/37063	827 'Kelly'	blue	BRe	79-84	18	25
9/37064	D824 'Highflyer'	green	BRc	79-84	22	30
9/37073	D823 'Hermes'	maroon	BRc	80-84	25	32
37087	D825 'Intrepid'	green	BRc	81-82	25	32
37094	827 'Kelly'	blue	BRe, As 37063 but with diesel sound and klaxon	81	25	35
37094	D824 'Highflyer'	green	BRc, As 37064 but with diesel sound and klaxon	81		

8. Class 6P/7P 'Rebuilt Patriot' 4-6-0

37065	5530 'Sir Frank Ree'	black	*LMS*, not in catalogue	80	35	42
37066	45532 'Illustrious'	green	BRc	80-81	35	40
37075	45540 'Sir Robert Turnbull'	exp. green	BRa	80-81	38	50
37076	45536 'Private W. Wood V.C.'	black	BRa	80-81	34	40
37082	5530 'Sir Frank Ree'	black	BR, not in catalogue, with steam sound	80	70	100
37082	45536 'Private W. Wood V.C.'	black	BRa, not in catalogue, with steam sound	80	70	100

9. Class 78XX 'Manor' 4-6-0

9/37043	7827 'Lydham Manor'	green	BRc, advertised with smoke	82-84	33	40
9/37078	7819 'Hinton Manor'	green	*GWR*	80-84	28	33
37079	7812 'Erlestoke Manor'	black	BRb (small) lined	80-81	42	50
937100	7808 'Cookham Manor'	green	*GWR* (button)	83-84	35	38
-	7822 'Foxcote Manor' **	green	BR with Cambrian Coast headboard, 2 white lamps and whitened buffers	not made	-	-

** This was to be the power unit for the Cambrian Coast Express passenger set but production was cancelled. The pre-production sample was sold at auction in 1997 for £340.

10. Class 57XX Pannier Tank 0-6-0PT

9/37084	5764**	green	*GWR* (button)	not made	-	-
9/37084	5764	green	*Great Western*	82-84	22	30
9/37085	5768	black	BRb (small)	82-84	30	38

** advance samples exist and one sold at auction in 1997 for £300.

11. Royal Scot Class 'Parallel Boiler Scot' 4-6-0

9/37092	6127 'Old Contemptibles'	crimson	*LMS*, finish improved '83	82-84	30	37
9/37093	46137 'Prince of Wales 's Volunteers, South Lancashire'	green	BRb (large), finish improved '83	82-84	32	40
937509	?	crimson	*LMS*, Fowler 3500 flush-sided tender without coal rails or smoke deflectors	not made	-	-

12. Class 43XX Mogul 2-6-0

9/37045	4358	green	BRb (small) lined, advertised with smoke	82-84	30	35
37090	5322	green	*Great Western*	82	35	40
9/37091	5328	black	BRb (large)	81-84	37	43
937090	4375	green	*Great Western*	83-84	28	34

13. Class 03 Diesel Shunter 0-6-0DS

9/37036	03382	blue	BRe, yellow coupling rods and buffer stocks	82-84	18	24
9/37037	D2179	green	BRc	82-84	20	25

14. Class N2 Tank 0-6-2T (ex-Airfix model)
The completed models arrived too late to be sold by Airfix and instead were marketed by Palitoy. They carried the Airfix logo beneath the keeper plate.

Cat.No.	Name / Number	Colour	Details	Years	£	£
9/54154	9522	green	*LNER* lined	82-84	20	25
9/54155	69531	black	BRb (small) lined	82-84	22	26
954158	4744	black	*LNER* lined	83-84	28	34

15. Class 2361 'Dean Goods' 0-6-0 (ex-Airfix model)
The moulds for the plastic parts of this model were made for Airfix by Heller in France and taken over by Palitoy who shipped them out to Sandakan in Hong Kong to make.

Cat.No.	Name / Number	Colour	Details	Years	£	£
9/54156	2516	green	*GWR*	82-84	28	36
9/54157	2538	black	BRb (large)	82-84	28	35

16. Class 66XX 0-6-2T

Cat.No.	Name / Number	Colour	Details	Years	£	£
937038	6697	green	*GWR*	83-84	30	35
937039	6655	black	BRb (large)	83-84	30	35
937508	?	green	BRc, lined	not made	-	-

17. Class 61XX Prairie 2-6-2T (ex-Airfix model)
Unlike the Airfix versions of this model, those made by Palitoy had flanged centre drivers.

Cat.No.	Name / Number	Colour	Details	Years	£	£
937083	6169	green	*GWR*	83-84	25	30
937086	6167	green	BRc lined	83-84	27	33

18. Class 14XX 0-4-2 Tank (ex-Airfix model)

Cat.No.	Name / Number	Colour	Details	Years	£	£
937096	1403	green	*GWR*	not made	-	-
937097	1442	black	BRb (small)	not made	-	-

See Dapol D19.

19. Class 56 Diesel Co-Co

Cat.No.	Name / Number	Colour	Details	Years	£	£
937035	56079	blue	BRe	83-84	25	30
937044	56084	blue	BReLL	83-84	22	28

20. Class B1 4-6-0
Pre-production models were made and finished as listed here ready for the 1984 catalogue which did not materialise.

Cat.No.	Name / Number	Colour	Details	Years	£	£
937510	1000 'Springbok'	green	*LNER*, apple green	not made	-	-
937511	61007 'Klipspringer'	black	BR lined	not made	-	-

21. Class 4F 0-6-0 (ex-Airfix model)
This was to have been a revised version from the Airfix tooling.

Cat.No.	Name / Number	Colour	Details	Years	£	£
937512	?	black	*LMS* as preserved at Butterley	not made	-	-
937513	?	black	BR	not made	-	-

22. Class 2P 4-4-0

Cat.No.	Name / Number	Colour	Details	Years	£	£
937514	635	black	*LMS* lined, former 4F tender	84	30	40
937515	40568	black	BR lined, former 4F tender	84	30	38

Mainline Class 57XX Pannier Tank (9/37085)   [table 10]

Coaches

The first coaches Palitoy produced were BR Mk1s and these were followed by some early LMS panelled stock. With the exception of livery changes, expansion of this range was slow until 1981 when a full brake and some Collett type coaches were announced. After that the coach range was greatly enlarged by the addition of the former Airfix models. Mint boxed examples of Mainline coaches may be bought for between £10 and £15 with the ex-Airfix models fetching the higher prices along with the Colletts.

The maroon Mk1s (37107 and 37108) were reissued in 1983 fitted with Commonwealth bogies and a semi-gloss finish (937107 and 937108) but with the descriptions in the catalogue and on the boxes transposed.

A pair of LNER Gresley coaches was developed but never got to the mould-making stage in the Far East.

Wagons

A large range of Mainline wagons was made the later ones coming from Airfix tooling. Typically Mainline were the small hopper, small tank wagon, cattle truck and the coke wagon. Other models included a 5 and 7-plank, mineral, sliding door van, vent van, Mogo van, 1-plank, fruit van, toad, short NE brake van, well wagon and a long bogie bolster.

Many of the open wagons had private owner liveries and some later ones had loads. The latter are scarcer and sell for up to £10 mint boxed while most of the small wagons are usually priced £5 and upwards.

Some Mainline wagons were reissued with Airfix style chassis. A new 10' chassis was tooled up from the acquired Airfix drawings and improved by the incorporation of such features as the small integral 'dummy' hooks on the buffer headstocks and seperately attached vacuum-cylinder to the underside for 'fitted' wagons, with 3-hole disc wheels on shouldered steel axles.

In 1984, a completely new, modern style hopper wagon, type HEA, was tooled up, but it did not attain production due to the termination of the range.

Accessories

Palitoy accepted Peco's offer of their Setrack which was made by Garnet in Austria. Airfix, who used the same source, had chosen black sleeper bases and so, for Mainline, a brown moulded sleeper base were ordered. Both had steel rails. Due to continual production difficulties in Austria, none of the correct specification isolating points was ever delivered to Palitoy. Instead, Peco were compelled to supply their own UK-made ones from the Steamline range, with their nickel silver rails, for the assembly of Mainline train sets at the Coalville factory.

The only other accessories produced were power and circuit controllers, electronic steam sound with whistle and diesel sound with klaxon modules. There was also a series of card building kits, by Gilmour. Palitoy had planned to reintroduce some of the former Airfix plastic lineside kits in 1984 but this was abandoned.

Sets

Sets do not seem to have been too prominent and the Company were not encouraged along this line as they did not sell well. Over the years a total of 20 were made. At present these are not attracting enough attention from collectors to push the prices up and are best valued according to their contents.

Mainline Standard Class 4 (37052)   [table 3]

Mainline Class 43XX Mogul (9/37091)   [table 12]

Mainline Class 2361 Dean Goods (9/54157)   [table 15]

1981 Mainline catalogue cover
depicting the Class 45   [2]
and Jubilee

[table 6]

Boxed Mainline wagon

Mainline Class 56 in 'large logo' blue livery (937044)   [table 19]

Mainline Class 2251 Collett Goods (37058)   [table 5]

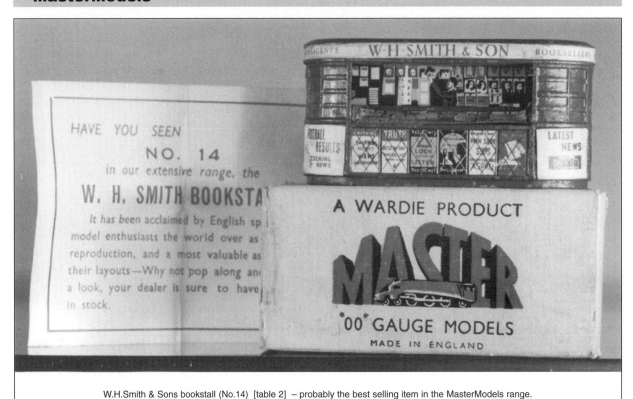

W.H.Smith & Sons bookstall (No.14) [table 2] – probably the best selling item in the MasterModels range.

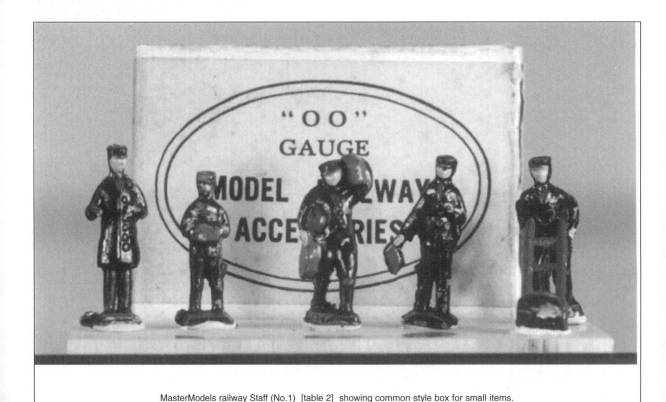

MasterModels railway Staff (No.1) [table 2] showing common style box for small items.

MasterModels

History

The 00 scale lineside accessories, which were to become MasterModels, were started by Don Bowles of Croydon. His first advertisement appeared in July 1950 and referred to 'realistic' models which were 'hand-built to scale and not diecast'. The illustration accompanying the advert showed six lineside accessories ranging from a telegraph pole to a water tower. Bowles advertised on a regular basis until February 1951 when B.J.Ward of Grand Buildings, Trafalgar Square, London, advertised that they were now the sole distributors of MasterModels. Don Bowles moved to Angel Hill, Tiverton in July 1951 and reverted to being a model railway retailer.

B.J.Ward was founded by Bertram (Bertie) John Ward and the Company's address was soon being given as 130 Westminster Bridge Road. From the time Ward became involved, a cottage industry gave way to mass production by die casting which was carried out by a company called Kenlow.

The MasterModels series was manufactured until 1962 and during that time more than 100 lineside accessories were introduced including, towards the end, some rather poor looking plastic figures.

Several items were dropped from the B J Ward catalogue by 1954 but a number of new models were introduced into the range as well. The range appeared to have reached its peak by 1956 and it seems likely that 1958 was the last year any new models were introduced; with the final release being in October of that year.

The models were initially sold in grey boxes and these were later replaced by the more familiar cream coloured ones. A few, especially when a special size of box was needed, came in plain brown cardboard boxes with a MasterModel label attached. Small translucent paper envelopes were sometimes used, each with a stapled MasterModel card. Box labels were usually off-white or cream but strange colours, such as bright blue do sometimes turn up.

MasterModels were advertised in the model railway press and in both the Gamages and Bradshaw's catalogues. The Company also produced their own sales leaflet and in 1956, 1957 and 1958 published their 'Catalogue and Handbook' which provided good detail of the range and their associated series.

Like all good model ranges, MasterModels had its imitators. A Japanese company called AHI Brand Toys produced 'Tru-Size Metal Miniature Figures and Animals in HO gauge' a series which definitely contained copies of the British range. They had a larger and thicker base than their MasterModels originals but were otherwise identical. As far as we know, two sets were made. One contained the No. 23 track repair party but with the flag waving figure replaced by a cable drum. The other set was a mixture of figures from sets 2, 3, 23 and 67.

Apart from MasterModels, B.J.Ward also marketed platform and building series that including Woodside, Rickwood, Clarewood (kits), Hailey and Dudley. Rickwood and Clare-wood were named after his children but who were Hailey and Dudley? They also sold the 'Wardie' tunnels and road bridge and the 'K' Series garage accessories which were larger than 00 scale. The 'Gilco' sets, which B.J.Ward distributed, contained some of the 'Wardie' garage accessories, such as petrol pumps. Puck sponge rubber scenery (made by Grovewell Ltd), Kentoys (presumably made by Kenlow), the Wee World Series and the Anorma range of building kits were all advertised in the MasterModels catalogue and handbook.

Further Reading

Listing of MasterModels has been done by various people in the past including Bob Smith and Paul & Jennifer Brookes but the only published work we know to be available at present is 'MasterModels - Listing of Models for Collectors' by the latter. Model Railway Enthusiast magazine had a long running series called 'The MasterModels Gallery' which included coloured

---

Milestones

1950	First MasterModels made by Don Bowles.
1951	Don Bowles hands over to B.J.Ward and a new numbering system introduced.
1952	Special value sets released.
1952	Bestseller Smith's bookstall released.
1954	Apparent end of Don Bowles influence .
1954	Tudor building series launched.
1954	Girder bridge released.
1956	Earliest known catalogue.
1957	Major changes to the range.
1958	Building papers.
1958	Last known catalogue and last diecast model introduced.
1962	The year the set of plastic figures is thought to have been released.
1962	MasterModels range peters out.

photographs of most of the range. This may be found in every issue of the magazine from June 1998 to March 2000.

Identifying MasterModels

There have been a number of makes of 00 scale figures available in Britain and it is not easy to identify them as they rarely carry a maker's mark. The most common are MasterModels and Britains Lilliput. While Britains figures are quite smooth and nicely proportioned, those of MasterModels are a little more rugged. The MasterModels range included many lineside and platform accessories and some of the larger ones carry the tooled-in inscription "British Made".

Some figures, such as the wheelbarrow and track repair workmen with tools, turn up in several sets while some castings, such as the telephone kiosk, turn up in a variety of disguises. Very early models were made in brass sheet by modeller Don Bowles and these are quite different from the later cast models and have a 'tinplate' feel about them. At the very end, B.J.Ward started using plastic mouldings instead of metal castings for some of its figures but these were quite crude and generally unattractive.

Colours – Colours of many of the items in the sets vary. The colour of the clothes worn by figures were changed from time to time. Seats, lamps, hoardings, signs etc. changed between light green, dark green, red brown, chocolate, grey and cream. We have not recorded these colours here as there is little evidence of when changes occurred and which colour combinations were brought together in sets. No doubt some colours are rarer than others but we have little information on this to offer you.

Packaging – Most items/sets sold in a cream coloured box. Early boxes were printed in black in an oval on a cream, yellow or blue (very rare) label. Later ones were printed in three colours with a 'Master 00 Gauge Models' logo. Some early models were sold in translucent paper envelopes.

Dates – The dates given in the following table are taken from when advertisements for the models appeared in the model railway press or in retailer's catalogues.

Qty. Column – An additional column has been provided to record the number of items in the box.

Cat.No.	Item / Set	Qty.	Description	Years	£	£

1. Early Lettered Items and Sets This untidy pattern of codes was used on early models some of which were later added to the numbered series above. **DB = thought to be a Don Bowles design**

Cat.No.	Item / Set	Qty.	Description	Years	£	£
A	Set of Track Signs	3	bar type signs on two posts and base: 'Catch Points', 'Danger', 'Weigh Bridge'	51-59	10	15
B	Set of Track Signs	2	squarish signs on single posts: 'Passengers Must Not Cross the Line', 'Beware of the Trains'	51-61	6	10
BBS/1	Bridge End Supports	2	embankment ends for No.68 in numbered table below, made from wood and cardboard	56	NPG	15
BBS/2	Bridge End Supports	2	as above but for No.77 double girder bridge	56	NPG	15
BC4	Track Signs	4	B (above) and C (below) sets of signs combined	55-60	10	15
BR/1	Dog & Partridge Inn	1	wood block building decorated with printed paper, sign Dog and Partridge Inn	54	20	35
BR/2	Black Horse Inn	1	wood block building decorated with printed paper, sign Black Horse Inn	54	20	35
BR/3	Tudor House	1	wood block building decorated with printed paper	54	20	35
BR/4	Blue Anchor Inn	1	wood block building decorated with printed paper, sign Blue Anchor Inn	54	20	35
BR/7	Transformer Station	1	these can vary considerably in appearance usually including a brick building, transformer, fence and notices	53-57	20	30
BR/8	House	1	wood block building decorated with printed paper, also referred to as TS/5	54-57	20	35
BR/9	Barber Shop	1	wood block building decorated with printed paper, sign S.Todd, Barber., possibly the same as TS/4	54-55	20	35
BR/10	The Rising Sun	1	wood block building decorated with printed paper, sign Rising Sun, also referred to as TS/2	54-57	20	35
BR/11	The Bell Inn	1	wood block building decorated with printed paper, sign The Bell	54-55	20	35
BR/12	The Coach Inn	1	wood block building decorated with printed paper, sign The Coach Inn, also referred to as TS/1	54-57	20	35
BR/13	The Smugglers Inn	1	wood block building decorated with printed paper, sign Ye Old Smugglers Inn, access to coaching yard beneath building	54-56	20	35
BR/14	Hotel Royal	1	wood block building decorated with printed paper	54-56	20	35

Code	Name	Qty	Description	Years		
BR/15	Antique Shoppe	1	wood block building decorated with printed paper, also referred to as TS/3	54-57	20	35
BR/16	Corner Shop	1	wood block building decorated with printed paper	54-56	20	35
BR/17	Manor House	1	wood block building decorated with printed paper	54-55	20	35
BS	Buffer Stop with Buffers	1	earlier code for BS1	50	4	8
BS1	Buffer Stop with Buffers	1	DB, single casting, grey with red buffer beam	51-57	4	8
BS2	Buffer Stop with Lamp	1	single casting with lamp but no buffers, grey with red buffer beam and lamp	51-60	4	8
BS3	Buffer Stop with Lamp and Buffers	1	single casting with lamp and buffers, grey with red buffer beam	52-57	4	8
C	Set of Track Signs	2	squarish signs on single posts: 'British Railways - Do not Touch Conductor Rails', 'British Railways - Take Care When Crossing'	51-57	6	10
C1	Imitation Coal	1	small bag of imitation coal	52?	NPG	8
C2	Imitation Coal (double size)	1	large bag of imitation coal	52-60	NPG	10
D1	Miniature Posters (00)	50	in packet, including coloured posters and monochrome railway signs	55-59	NPG	5
D2	Miniature Posters (00)	25	in packet	55-60	NPG	5
D3	Sheet of Miniature Posters (00)	12	on a sheet by 'Posterstamps'	55-58	NPG	5
	Miniature Posters (00)	80	sheet of 60 coloured posters and sheet of 20 monochrome railway signs	?	NPG	5
	Sheet of Miniature Posters (TT)	100	two thirds size posters in 2 packet of 50	55	NPG	8
DH/1	Building Paper	1	Red Brick, 30"x22"	58	NPG	4
DH/2	Building Paper	1	Stone, 30"x22"	58	NPG	4
DH/3	Building Paper	1	Parquet, 30"x22"	58	NPG	4
DH/4	Building Paper	1	Green Roman Tile, 30"x22"	58	NPG	4
DH/5	Building Paper	1	Red Roman Tile, 30"x22"	58	NPG	4
DS	Double Signal	1	earlier code for DS3 below	50	5	10
DS3	Double Signal (Home and Distant)	1	DB, no further information	52-53	5	10
ES	Electric Signal	1	no further information	52	8	15
F6	6" Fencing with Base	6	(see FB6 below)	51	12	15
F12	12" Fencing	6	9 post 3 rail flexible fencing made from wire with 5 lengthened posts for fixing into the baseboard	51-57	15	20
FB6	6" Fencing with bases	6	6" lengths of 3 rail flexible fencing made from wire with bases on 3 of the 5 posts	52	12	15
H1	Hoarding (Small)	1	small hoarding between 2 posts on a base with 1 coloured advert	51-54	3	5
H1/T3	Small Hoarding/ Large Timetable	2	set combining H1 (above) and T3 (below)	55-59	8	12
H2	Hoarding	1	large hoarding between 2 posts on a base with 2 coloured adverts	51-61	5	8
H2/T1	Large Hoarding/ Small Timetable	2	set combining H2 (above) and T1 (below)	55-61	8	12
H3	Hoarding (Warning Notice)	1	small hoarding between 2 posts on a base with notice: 'British Railways - Warning - Trespassers Will Be Persecuted - By Order'	51-53	3	5
H3/T4	Warning Notice and Departures Board	2	set combining H3 (above) and T4 (below)	55-59	8	12
LA2	Lamps with Advertisement Board	2	modern street lamps with curved tops and an advert board on the standard, square bases, 'Keep Death off the Roads', 'Buy British, Buy Master Models'	55-61	8	12
LCG	Level Crossing Gates	2	(see 9 in numbered list below)	51-52	8	12
LDB	Double Lamp	1	no further information	51	5	10
LG	Loading Gauge	1	DB, (see 80 in numbered list below)	50-51	5	10
LSA	Lamp with Advertisement Board	2	(see LA2 above)	51-55	4	10
LSB	Single Lamp	1	no further information	50-51	5	10
MP	Miniature Posters		(see D1, D2, D3 above)	55-60	NPG	NPG
MS/1	Office Building	1	5 storey modern building with clock	57	20	35
MS/2	Hospital Building	1	2 storey modern building	57	20	35
MS/3	Flats Building	1	4 storey modern building	?	20	35
00	Scale Scenic Background	4	(see 98 in numbered series)	52-61	10	15
00	Bus and Coach Stops	4	(see 94 in numbered series)	53-61	4	10
00	Posters		(see D1, D2, D3 etc.)	?	NPG	NPG
00	Telegraph Pole	1	made from steel wire with 2 or 3 arms	54	4	6
PL1	New Universal Plus Point Lever		no further information	?	NPG	NPG
Q1	Imitation Quarry Granite	1	no further information	56-61	NPG	10
RC1	Rail Cleaner	1	no further information	60-61	NPG	NPG

Cat.No.	Item / Set	Qty.	Description	Years	£	£
SA	Advertisement	1	small black brass hoarding with coloured advert: *'Chivers Jellies'*	51	8	12
SG	Grey Seat	1	small grey wrought-iron and plank seat	51-53	2	4
SG4	4 Grey Seats	4	4 of SG (above)	55-59	8	10
SM	Green Seat	1	small green wrought-iron and plank seat	51-53	2	4
SM4	4 Green Seats	4	4 of SM (above)	55-59	8	10
SS	Single Semaphore Signal	1	home or distant	52	4	6
SS1	Single Semaphore Signal (Home)	1	DB, home	50-53	4	6
SS2	Single Semaphore Signal (Distant)	1	DB, distant	50-53	4	6
	Signal Arms		upper and lower quadrant	53	5	8
ST	Timetable & Seat	1	DB, brass sheet and bar seat, GWR timetable on back of seat, later replaced by No.39	51	5	8
T	Water Tower	1	DB, a water column of early design	50	20	30
T1	Timetable (Small)	1	small hoarding between 2 posts on a base with a small timetable, sometimes with *'Arrivals'* on label on reverse	51-55	3	5
T2	Timetable	1	no further information	51	8	10
T3	Timetable (Large)	1	large hoarding between 2 posts on a base with large timetable	51-55	4	8
T4	Train Departure Board	1	large hoarding between 2 posts on a base with 2 small timetables, sometimes with *'Train Departures'* on label on reverse	51-55	4	8
TD6	Telegraph Pole	1	DB, double pole structure (joined by cross pieces) with 6 arms, no base, later coded TPD6, listed also as TPD	50-52	2	3
TH	Water Tower	1	water column	51	12	18
TNL	Water Tower	1	large water column with 2 moveable hoses and chains and a ladder	51-52	18	25
TNS	Water Tower	1	small water column with 2 hoses and chains but no ladder	51-52	18	25
TP	Telegraph Pole	1	DB, pole with 4 arms and no base, later coded TP4	50-52	4	6
	Telegraph Pole	1	pole with 2 arms, pole 3 ¾ " long	58-61	4	6
TP4	Telegraph Pole	1	(see TP above)	52-57	4	6
TPB	Telegraph Pole	1	DB, pole with 4 arms and a base, later called TPB4	50-52	4	6
TPB4	Telegraph Pole	1	(see TPB above)	52-57	4	6
TPD	Telegraph Pole	1	(see TD6 above)	50-52	4	6
TPD6	Telegraph Pole	1	(see TD6 above)	52-57	4	6
TS/1	The Coach Inn	1	(see BR/12 above)	55	20	35
TS/2	The Rising Sun	1	(see BR/10 above)	55	20	35
TS/3	Antique Shoppe	1	(see BR/15 above)	55	20	35
TS/4	Tea Shoppe	1	(possibly same as BR/9)	55	20	35
TS/5	House	1	(see BR/8 above)	55	20	35
TT	Posters		(see D1, D2, D3 etc.)	?	20	35
W	Track Signs	3	bar type signs on two posts and base: *'Whistle', 'Reduce Speed', 20 mph on Curve'*	51-57	10	15
WB4	Wagon Buffers (Round)	4	brass wagon buffers	50-53	NPG	8
WC	Water Crane	1	DB, water crane made from wire with hose and chain and a winding handle rising from the base, replaced by No.48	50-53	10	15
WT	Water Tower	1	(see WT1 below)	52-53	18	25
WT1	Water Tower	1	water tank on girder frame, also listed as WT	51-57	18	25
WT2	Water Tower	1	water tower on wooden block disguised as a building with brick paper, same casting as WT1	53-55	25	30
WT2	Water Tower	1	as above but with a lean-to attached to the building	?	25	30
	Imitation Grass Mat	1	sheet 12"x22", suede finish	58-60	NPG	8

2. Numbered Items and Sets

After a period of haphazard letter codes a straightforward numbering system was introduced for models in the MasterModels range and these are listed below.

1	Track Accessories	4	station nameboard (*Waterloo, Crewe, Cardiff or Glasgow*), telegraph pole, single lamp standard, level post (brown + white)	51-54	12	15
1	Railway Staff	5	porter with sack barrow, station master, porter with 3 cases, guard with flag, short porter with silver box,	51-57?	10	15
1	Railway Staff	5	porter with sack barrow, porter with 2 cases, porter with 3 cases, guard with flag, guard holding a lamp up high	57?-60	10	15
2	Railway Passengers	5	lady with coat over her arm, small boy, golfer with clubs, man with rolled brolly, postman	51-60	10	15
3	Assorted Figures	5	man in top hat and tails, woman in evening dress and cape, boy or girl, woman with handbag, man (green) with brolly and rolled newspaper	51-60	10	15
4	Seated Figures	5	two soldiers, a Wren, man in suit, woman in coat	51-60	10	15
5	Seated Figures	4	nun, woman in coat, man in overcoat, lovers	51-62	10	15
6	Double Seats	2	single casting double sided seats	51-60	5	10
7	Platform Accessories	7	weighing machine, chocolate machine, hand trolley, 3 churns, cycle	51-60	12	15
7	Platform Accessories	8	as above but with 4 churns	55-59	12	15
8	Milk Churns	12	12 cone shaped with flared top	51-57	12	15

No.	Name	Qty	Description	Years		
8	Milk Churns	12	6 bottle shaped and 6 cone shaped without flare	58-61	12	15
9	Level Crossing Gates	2	a pair, each mounted on a post with a green base, each with half red disc, originally coded LCG, (see also 76 below)	52-61	6	10
10	Station Equipment	4	round or oval pillar box, bus or coach stop, telephone kiosk, single or double street lamp	52-60	12	15
10	Station Equipment	4	round or oval pillar box, bus or coach stop, telephone kiosk, *Castrol* hoarding	58-60	12	15
11	Gradient Posts	6	brown posts and bases with white arms	51-55	18	20
11	4 Sheep in Pen	5	grey wooden base, green and cream metal fence	56-60	20	25
12	Electric Trolley + Trailer	7	trolley, trailer, driver (plugs into trolley), 2 barrels, 2 crates, trolley + trailer usually blue	52-59	12	15
14	W.H.Smith's Bookstall	1	green (shades), single casting with printed card for back of stall, other detail on printed labels	52-62	15	20
15	Telephone Kiosks	2	single casting, detail in wrap-round printed label	52-55	8	12
16	Single Station Lamp Standards	3	round base, cast-iron type standards, curved-over top with modern lamps	52-57	9	12
16	Single Station Lamp Standards	3	tall, small round base, concrete type standards, curved-over top with tiny modern lamps	58-61	9	12
17	Steel Girders	6	unpainted girder shaped metal, also coded 'FI'	52	15	20
18	Cable Drums	2	single casting, unlagged type, *Henley*	52-58	6	10
18	Cable Drums	2	one lagged + one unlagged type, *Henley*	58-60	6	10
19	Tar Barrels	6	crude castings, black with yellow ends	52-57	9	12
19	Tar + Oil Barrels	12	crude castings, 6 black + 6 grey	58-61	12	15
20	Oil Barrels	6	crude castings, grey with white ends	52-57	9	12
21	Platform Gardens	2	island beds, 1 rectangular + 1 diamond, single castings with 1 bush each	52-57	6	10
21/22	Platform Gardens	4	1 rectangular + 1 diamond + 2 semicircle	58-59	12	15
22	Platform Gardens	2	border beds, 2 semicircle, single castings with 2 bushes each	52-57	6	10
23	Track Repair Party	6	lookout with flags, man with shovel, man with sledge hammer, man with pickaxe, man and a wheelbarrow	52-60	12	15
24	Police Boxes	2	same casting as telephone kiosk but different wrap-round printed label, dark blue	52-58	10	15
25	Placards	3	each a casting with a printed label showing posters behind wire	52-57	12	15
26	Sleeper Buffer	1	buffer stops built from old railway sleepers filled with sand or ballast, single casting	52-60	4	6
27	Scales with Light Luggage	5	green, black and silver scales that turn up in other sets, 2 suitcases, golf bag, basket of fruit	52-57	15	20
28	Signal Ladders	6	stamped metal ladders mounted on a card. Probably sold separately	53-59	12	18
29	Glass Crates	3	single castings, painted cream and wrapped round with printed wood effect label	52-57	12	15
30	Corrugated Iron Sheets	3	grey castings	55-58	9	12
31	Enquiry Kiosks	2	same casting as telephone kiosk but with different printed wrap-round label, green	52-58	10	15
32	Lagged Cable Drums	2	as in 18 above but both lagged, *Henley*	53-57	6	10
33	Esso Oil Drums	3	red with white *Esso* labels, early box has been found with deep blue label	52-54	6	10
33	Esso Oil Drums	6	3 green and 3 red with white *Esso* labels	55-61	12	15
34	Watchman's Hut	2	open front covered seat and brazier with red foil fire, man with sledge hammer	52-60	6	10
35	Cable Laying Party	5	man with sledge hammer, man with pickaxe, man with wheelbarrow, *Henley* cable drum (either)	52-62	10	15
36	Finley's Tobacco Kiosk	1	same as 14 above but brown and with different printed card and stuck-on labels (these vary)	52-62	15	20
37	Walton's Fruit Kiosk	1	same as 14 above but black and with different printed card and stuck-on labels	52-62	15	20
38	Sand Bin & Fire Buckets	3	sand bin with red label, red rack and 4 fire buckets, man with shovel	52-61	8	12
39	Seat with Station Name	1	seat attached to a station nameboard (*Westbay, Glasgow, Crewe, Masterhalt, Waterloo, Swansea, Edinburgh*)	52-57	4	6
40	Permanent Way Cabin	2	'timber' hut on metal base with barrel and plastic pipe from gutter, man with pickaxe or shovel	53-60	8	12
41	Water Column	1	cylindrical tank on top of post with round base, ladder and plastic pipe	53-60	6	10
42	Railway Container	1	*Don't carry it...send it by Carter Paterson***	53-61?	6	10
42	Railway Container	1	*Smiths Bluecol the Safe Anti Freeze*	53-61?	6	10
42	Railway Container	1	yellow plank effect sometimes marked *British Railways Furniture*	53?-61	6	10
43	Cycle Rack & 4 Cycles	5	rack (grey cast slab with grooves), 4 cast cycles in different colours	52-60	10	15
44	Petrol Pumps	2	Esso pumps red or blue with plastic pipes, bit too large for 00	52-57	10	15
45	Coal Office	1	same as 40 above but sign on roof and no base, water butt or workman	53-60	10	15

Cat.No.	Item / Set	Qty.	Description	Years	£	£
48	Water Crane	1	very like Hornby Dublo water crane but marked *'MasterModels'* on the base	53-61	6	10
49	Level Crossing	1	two pairs of gates on a single cast metal roadway ramp base that goes under the track	53-57	18	25
49	Level Crossing	2	two pairs of gates on separate cast metal roadway ramps that abut the track	58-61	22	30
50	AA Box & Patrolman	3	traditional *AA* box (special casting), motorcycle and *AA* sidecar, AA patrolman to sit on bike	53-60	30	40
51	Semaphore Ground Signals	2	black ground signal with grey horizontal arm operated by sprung counter weight, dummy lights	53-57	10	15
51/2	Ground Signal and Disc Shunt Signal	2	one from set 51 above and one from set 52 below	58-59	10	15
52	Disc Shunt Signals	2	black shunting signal with grey disc with black bar operated by sprung counter weight, dummy lights	53-57	10	15
53	4 Aspect Searchlight Junction Signals	2	black searchlight signal with ladder and dummy lights, red light with grey surround	53-57	10	15
54	2 Arm Electric Banner Signals	2	black banner signal with ladder and 2 round discs (grey with red or green stripe) on horizontal arm	53-57	10	15
55	3 Aspect Colour Light Signals	2	black colour light signals with ladder and dummy lights in a grey surround	53-57	10	15
56	Aspect Searchlight Signals	2	black searchlight signal with ladder and dummy green light with grey surround	53-57	10	15
57	Crew Unloading Trucks	7	2 men carrying plank between them on their shoulders, man with box on head, man carrying box in front of him, man lifting something down, foreman in suit	53-60	12	15
58	Track Ballast	-	packet of track ballast	53-61	NPG	10
59	Tarpaulin Covers	2	black fabric (with strings) printed in white with cross and *BR317521*	53-61	8	12
60	Station Names	12	12 names on gummed paper	53-57	NPG	15
61	AA Boxes	2	2 of the traditional AA box No.54 from 50 above	53-61	12	20
62	Police Box with Patrolman	3	Police box from 24 above, motorbike without sidecar, police rider on bike (ex-AA man)	53-61	30	40
63	Pillar Boxes	2	2 oval pillar boxes	53-57	6	10
64	Wicket Gate	1	kissing type gate set in a short length of fence	53-60	6	10
65	Charrington's Coal Bunker	3	block of three coal bunkers with nameboard across the top, scales, man carrying sack on back	54-60	5	10
66	Station Clocks	2	2 double sided bracket clocks with crazed faces	54-61	6	10
67	Street Personnel	5	woman in coat, man having his shoes cleaned, policeman conducting traffic, news vendor	54-57	10	12
67/9	Street Personnel	8	sets 67 and 69 combined	58-62	16	18
68	Girder Bridge for Single Track	1	grey or brown hogs back bridge in cast metal pieces	54-62	25	35
69	Belisha Crossing Set	3	2 Belisha beacons and a crossing attendant with a stop board	54-57	6	10
70	Bus Shelter	1	single casting in shades of green with London Transport posters and map on printed paper	55-60	8	12
71	Loading Crane on Base	1	grey crane that swivels on a pyramidal stepped base, working jib and hook cable	55-62	15	20
72	Gent's Toilet	2	2 castings which together form an outdoors wrought-iron urinal block	54-61	10	15
73	Mine Workers	6	5 black workmen with silver kneepads, a wheelbarrow	55-57	18	20
74	6" Paling Fences	6	supplied 6 or 12 to a box they were sold singly, green single casting fence with top rail and base	55-60	12	15
75	Station Name and Seat with Figures	4	double seat with nameboard and three seated figures: nun, man in coat, woman in coat	55-59	10	15
76	Level Crossing Gates (Double Track)	2	pair of long reach gates on posts each with square base (2 sets needed)	55-61	8	12
77	Girder Bridge (Double Track)	1	same as 68 but extended in width with a second floor section and girder sections to join them	55-60	30	40
78	Sitting Army Figures	5	2 WRAC, 2 soldiers with hats, 1 soldier without	55-57	10	15
79	Sitting Naval Figures	5	2 WRN, 3 sailors	55-58	10	15
80	Loading Gauge	1	white with white pedestal fixed to a black base strip, white gauge suspended on short wires, originally coded 'LG'	52-61	6	10
81	Massey Harris Tractor & Roller	3	red tractor with black wheels, blue or green driver, blue roller with grey wheels, originally coded K49	55-61	35	50
82	Massey Harris Tractor & Rake	3	red tractor with black wheels, blue or green driver, blue rake with red wheels, originally coded K50	55-61	35	50
83	Massey Harris Tractor & Hay Trailer	3	red tractor with black wheels, blue or green driver, green trailer with black wheels, originally K47	55-60	35	50
84	Gantry Signal	1	dummy colour light signals on black gantry cast in two halves and riveted together ***	56-62	15	20

85	Service Personnel	5	Wren, seated sailor, army officer, soldier with kit bag, military policeman	57-62	10	15
86	BR Personnel	7	driver, fireman, porter and broom, coach window cleaner and ladder, Pullman car steward	57-62	14	18
87	Petrol Pumps on Stand	1	all red with *Essolube* or *Shell X100* motor oil on sign between 2 *Esso* pumps, plastic pipes, originally coded K16	56-60	8	12
88	Roadside Kiosks	4	*RAC*, telephone, enquiries and police kiosks, castings are slightly different from earlier ones****	58-61	20	25
89	Footbridge	1	2 sections of 6" paling fence (74 above) welded to cast floor section	58-62	8	12
90	Sheep	6	sheep from 11 above	60	12	18
92	Four Electric Signals	4	this consists of one each from 53, 54, 55 and 56 above	56-59	20	25
94	Bus and Coach Stops	4	London Transport design, 2 single flag bus stops, single flag coach stop with timetable, double flag coach + bus stop, (see 00 or K14 in other tables)	59-61	12	15
94	Bus and Coach Stops	4	London Transport design, 3 single flag bus stops, single flag coach stop	?	12	15
95	4 Road Signs	4	round double sided signs: *road up, no parking, open/closed, no entry*, from K9, K20 and K21	55-58	12	18
96	Left Luggage Office	1	long double fronted kiosk with door between, both signs say *Left Luggage*	58-61	20	30
96	Left Luggage Office	1	as above but both signs say *Parcels Office*	58-61	20	30
96	Left Luggage Office	1	as above but one sign says *Left Luggage,* the other *Parcels Office*	58-61	20	30
98	Scale Scenic Background	4	cardboard tube containing 4 sheets 20"x8", (see also '00' in lettered table)	61	15	20
97	Oil Storage Tanks	1	2 silver tanks mounted on a cradle, *Shell Petroleum Products* transfer on each tank	58-62	15	20
5800	Single Signal	1		?-61	10	15

** Identical to one sold by Trix and possibly supplied by B.J.Ward.
*** This appears to have been designed so that an alternative semaphore gantry could be made with the castings.
**** The police and enquiries boxes now have a light projection on top and the RAC and telephone boxes share a flat topped casting.

3.   **Presentation Sets**

1	Special Value Set	8	buffer stop, timetable, hoarding, 4 track signs, seat	52-54	NPG 40
2	Special Value Set	7	siding buffer, 2 track signs, 2 station lamps with adverts, timetable, seat	52-54	NPG 40
3	Special Value Set	8	2 timetables, 4 track signs, 2 hoardings	52-54	NPG 40
	Plastic Set	11	double lamp standard, 2 Belisha beacons, policeman, red woman, telephone kiosk, motorcycle, motorcyclist, news vendor, pillar box, bus stop	62?	NPG 15

The plastic set has been found with some parts in metal.

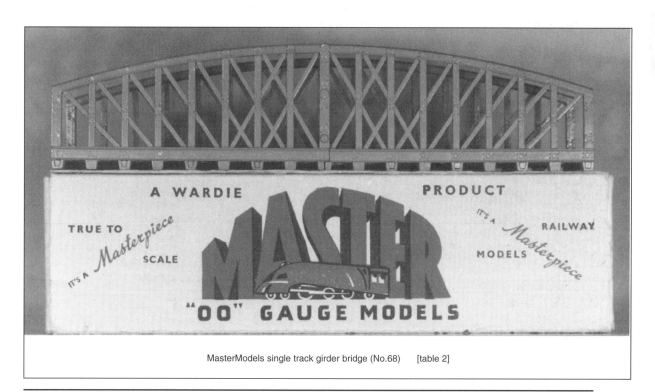

MasterModels single track girder bridge (No.68)   [table 2]

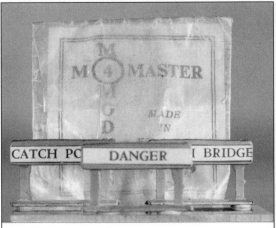

MasterModels track signs set A
[table 1]
showing translucent paper packaging.

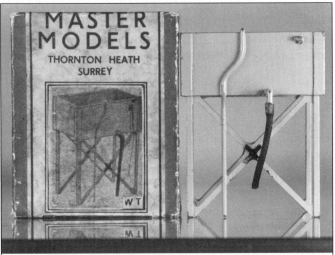

MasterModels water tower (WT1) [table 1] – one of several types.

MasterModels Ye Old Smugglers Inn (BR/13) [table 1] – made of wood blocks covered in paper.

Replica

History

When General Mills decided to cease toy production in Europe, Dapol acquired the stock, intellectual assets and the former Airfix tooling from Palitoy. The tools for Palitoy's own Mainline Railways belonged to Kader of Hong Kong, their manufacturer.

Godfrey Hayes of Railwayania sold Mainline models and spares and ran a sideline of repaints, transfers and detailing components under the name of Replica Railways. Discovering that the Mainline tools belonged to Kader, Hayes approached them in 1984 with a view to taking over the distribution of models made by them. In May 1985 Hayes was invited to Hong Kong to discuss the project

A production plan was worked out and in the autumn of 1985, the first sample wagons arrived. Advertisements were placed in the model railway press to launch the new range. Dapol, who owned the intellectual assets of the Mainline system were unhappy with the arrangement and a court case followed. Replica, however, weathered the storm, and more wagons and some coaches were available by Christmas. A steady stream of models appeared over the next few years.

Godfrey Hayes set very high quality standards and every item brought in from the Far East was unpacked and inspected. After testing for running qualities and finish the models were repackaged in the green Replica boxes and rejects were returned to Kader.

In 1987, Kader took over the American toy company of Bachmann, for whom they were a primary manufacturer and this effectively signalled the end of the Replica range. In order to expand into Europe, Kader formed Bachmann Industries Europe and the former Mainline range became the core of their products for the British market. Kader could not

Milestones

1984	Hayes approaches Kader regarding use of the Mainline tools.
1985	Hayes goes to Hong Kong to visit Kader and work out a production plan.
1987	First catalogue released.
1987	B1 model is released.
1987	Kader buys Bachmann.
1989	Bachmann Industries Europe Ltd is formed.
1990	The Modified Hall is released.
1990	Bachmann Branchlines launched in UK initially using former Mainline tools which are no longer available to Replica Railways.

manufacture for their new European company while at the same time produce models for a rival and so further access to the Mainline tools was denied Replica.

Further Reading

There has been a series of articles by Graham Smith-Thompson, in Model Railway Collector magazine (formerly Model Railway Enthusiast), profiling the Airfix and Mainline ranges and other systems that later used the tools. There were three parts devoted specifically to Replica Railways published in the December 1999 and January and February 2000 issues of the magazine.

Dates – As there were only two Replica catalogues, we have depended on press advertising to determine when models reached the shops. A single date has been given because Replica models were produced in batches. Generally there was only an initial batch of models which, when sold-out, was not repeated.

Listing – As Replica adopted a catalogue numbering system that was designed to keep like models together, we have listed the models below in catalogue numerical order for easy reference.

Replica GWR Collett Goods 0-6-0 2203 (11042)   [table 4]

Locomotives

1. Class 57XX Pannier Tank 0-6-0PT (ex-Mainline model)

11001	7768	green	*GWR*, shirt button logo	86	27	30
11002	7843	black	BRc	88	27	30
11003	7752	green	*G W R*	88	27	30

2. Class B1 4-6-0 (partly ex-Mainline model)
This was in an advanced stage of tooling when Mainline collapsed and so the Replica models were the first to be produced from these tools. The resulting model reflected original Mainline quality and style rather than later production under the Bachmann label

11011	61026 'Ourebi'	black	BRb	87	44	48
11011U	As 11011, unnamed, unnumbered	black	BRb	?	NPG	NPG
11012	1000 'Springbok'	green	*LNER*	87	44	48
11013	1059	black	*LNER* lined	90	42	45
11014	61132	black	BRb lined	90	42	45

3. Class 03 Diesel Shunter 0-6-0DS (ex-Mainline model)

11021	D2083	green	BRc	87	26	30
11022	03189	blue	BRe	87	26	30

4. GWR Collett Goods 0-6-0 (ex-Mainline model with Manor tender)

11041	2244	green	*G W R*	89	30	35
11042	2203	black	BRb	89	30	35

5. Class 45/1 Diesel-Electric 1Co-Co1 (ex-Mainline model)
Manufacture of the Replica model reflected original Mainline quality and style rather than later production under the Bachmann label.

11501	45128	blue	BRe	89	27	30
11501U	As 11501, unnamed, unnumbered	blue	BRe		NPG	NPG
11502	45106	green	BRc	89	27	30

6. BR Standard Class 4 4-6-0 (ex-Mainline model)
This has a separate chimney moulding and finer printing than the Mainline model. It also had a completely redesigned chassis with a can motor.

11031	75019	black	BRb lined, Ltd Edn 750	90	75	100
11032	75024	green	BRc lined, Ltd Edn 24 only!	90	200	250
11033	75037	black	BRc lined, Ltd Edn 750	90	75	100

7. GWR Modified Hall Class 4-6-0 (a Mainline/Replica model)
Production had reached the test-shot stage when Replica took it over. It was much improved by Replica and the tender completely retooled.

11151	6976 'Graythwaite Hall'	green	*G*(crest)*W*	90	43	48
11152	7911 'Lady Margaret Hall'	green	BRc	90	43	48
11153	6998 'Burton Agnes Hall'	green	*G*(crest)*W*, as preserved	90	43	48

Coaches
Initially these reflected Mainline types but with different liveries and Commonwealth bogies on Mk1s. There were reruns of Collett and LMS 57' and 50' types but all had different fleet/stock numbers New types produced included Mk1 corridor composites and first opens with BGs (full brakes) in various liveries. The last of these were pure Replica products. The prices vary but the higher quality of Replica coaches is respected and they generally sell at higher prices than those from the Airfix and Mainline ranges (£10-£20).

Wagons
Without a catalogue or check list, these are going to cause confusion in future years when they turn up unboxed. Chassis are to Airfix style with brakes in-line with the wheels. Prices are generally around the £5 mark.

Replica
Class 57XX
GWR 7752 (11003)

[table 1]

(Replica Railways)

Replica
Class 03
diesel shunter
03189 (11022)

[table 3]

(Replica Railways)

Replica
Class 45/1 1Co-Co1
45106
(11502)

[table 5]

(Replica Railways)

Tri-ang Hornby locomotives:

row 1: Class 37 (R751) [table 24], 'Albert Hall' (R759) [table 26],
row 2: Class 81 (R753) [table 25], Class 35 (R758) [table 27], Class M7 (R754) [table 28],
row 3: 'Flying Scotsman' (R850) [table 29], Class 9F (R861) [table 31],
row 4: Hall Class (R759G) [table 26], Class A3 (R855) [table 29],
row 5: B12 (R866S) [table 20], Princess Royal Class (R258) [table 1],
row 6: Battle of Britain Class (R869S) [table 17], Class 3F Jinty (R52R) [table 3],
row 7: Class M7 (R868) [table 28], Princess Coronation Class (R864) [table 30],
row 8: Princess Coronation Class (R871) [table 30] and Class 57XX (R51S) [table 32].

Rovex – Tri-ang – Hornby

This section includes the model railway range started by *Rovex* in 1950, renamed *Tri-ang Railways* in 1952, again renamed in 1965 as *Tri-ang Hornby*, becoming *Hornby Railways* in 1972 and finally just *Hornby* around 1997. While the name changed several times, it remained one continuous system being made first at Richmond, then at Margate and now in China. It does not include Hornby Trains (0 gauge) or Hornby-Dublo both of which were made in Liverpool by Meccano Ltd until train production there ceased in 1964.

History

Rovex Plastics Ltd was founded in 1946 by Alexander Venetzian who made toys for Marks & Spencer's. Venetzian was asked to produce an electric train set based on the LMS express locomotive 'Princess Elizabeth'. Needing more space for this project the Company was moved from Chelsea to a disused brewery in Richmond. The train set was delivered in time for Christmas 1950 but financial limitations prevented further development.

Meanwhile, the giant toy manufacturer Lines Bros. Ltd, who traded under the name 'Tri-ang', was wanting to get into the post war model railway market. In 1951, Rovex Plastics Ltd. became a wholly owned member of the Lines Bros. Group. The trains would now be called Tri-ang Railways and the Company renamed Rovex Scale Models Ltd. To aid development of the system, a brand new factory was built at Margate, in Kent, and production moved there in the Summer of 1954.

Demand from the public for new models was so great that in 1951 Rovex bought the tools of a goods train set made by Pyramid Toys Ltd. which they were selling under the name Trackmaster. This gave them an 0-6-2 tank engine and two wagons.

By farming out work to outside designers and tool makers progress was made. The Jinty 0-6-0T and a range of station buildings came in 1952 and a guards van and other wagons in 1953.

Almost immediately there was pressure on the young firm to produce for the export market and a range of Transcontinental models, primarily for North America, was released in 1954.

Under constant pressure, the system expanded fast. 1955 saw the first real Tri-ang Railways retail catalogue - soon to be the best in the market place. By 1956 there were 10 locomotives available and a good range of rolling stock and lineside buildings etc. As if the existing pressure was not enough, in 1957 Rovex were

Milestones

1946	Venetzian founds Rovex Plastics Ltd.
1949	Trackmaster wagons and loco available.
1950	First Rovex train set in an M&S store.
1951	Lines Bros buy Rovex Plastics Ltd.
1951	Trackmaster tools purchased by Lines.
1952	Tri-ang Railways launched in May.
1953	Renamed Rovex Scale Models Ltd.
1954	Move to purpose-built factory in Margate.
1954	Launch of Transcontinental Series.
1955	Production starts up in South Africa.
1956	First New Zealand made models in shops.
1956	Polystyrene replaces cellulose acetate.
1957	Australian production starts at Moldex Ltd.
1957	Launch of Tri-ang TT.
1959	Tension-lock couplings introduced.
1961	Tri-ang factory opens in Calais.
1961	Walter Lines retires.
1962	Major expansion of range inc. Super 4 track.
1963	Rovex take over Real Estate kits and re-launch as Model-Land.
1964	Lines Bros. take-over Meccano Ltd.
1964	Lines turn down LoneStar buyout invite.
1965	Tri-ang Railways becomes Tri-ang Hornby.
1966	Lines Bros. turn down Trix buyout invite.
1966	Tri-ang Big Big 0 gauge trains launched.
1966	Rovex take-over Frog kit production.
1967	First models made for US market.
1967	Internal mergers form Rovex Industries Ltd.
1967	Minic motorway absorbed by Rovex.
1969	Name changed again to Rovex Tri-ang Ltd.
1970	Finer scale adopted for track and wheels.
1971	Lines Bros. in receivership.
1972	Rovex bought by Dunbee-Combex-Marx.
1972	Tri-ang Hornby became Hornby Railways
1972	Death of Walter Lines.
1974	Tampo printing started at Margate.
1976	Rovex International formed.
1976	Hornby Hobbies name first used.
1976	Hornby face Airfix/Mainline challenge .
1977	Frog and Big Big tools to Russia.
1979	H&M purchased and absorbed.
1979	Hornby live-steam 'Rocket' in shops.
1980	DCM goes under. Rovex in receivership.
1980	Paint finish adopted throughout range.
1980	Renamed Hornby Hobbies Ltd.
1981	Management buyout by Wiltminster Ltd.
1986	Hornby Group plc floatation.
1995	First model made by Sandakan in China arrives.
1996	Hornby buy tools from Dapol Ltd.
1997	First former Aifix/Dapol model in shops.
1997	Hornby Collectors Club formed.
1998	Hornby Collectors Centres established.
1999	Last model made in the Margate factory.
2000	Hornby plc. invite take-over.
2000	Rebuilt Merchant Navy released.

pressed by Lines Bros. to start a TT gauge model railway system. A completely new 00 track system called Series 3 also arrived that year.

At around this time, in order to overcome trade tariffs, Lines Bros. Ltd. were expanding toy production overseas and Tri-ang Railways was soon being made in South Africa, Australia and New Zealand; in each case for local markets but creating interesting variations for future collectors. 1962 was a high water mark in the development of Tri-ang Railways. That year another new track system called Super 4 was introduced and along with it an extensive new series of station buildings.

There were now 25 locomotives to choose from (including two historical subjects), an extensive range of British and Transcontinental rolling stock, new scale length coaches had just been added, there was a catenary system, locos had Magnadhesion and smoke and the famous railway artist, Terence Cuneo, had been engaged to show how you could 'weather' your Tri-ang models.

Much of this growth was at the expense of other manufacturers and the two main rival systems, Trix and Hornby-Dublo, were feeling the draught. The former had already changed hands twice and in 1964, Meccano Ltd, the manufacturers of Hornby-Dublo invited Lines Bros. Ltd to buy them out. Meccano Ltd. joined the Lines Bros. Group.

By this time, production of Hornby-Dublo had already ceased but there were large stocks to clear. Under public pressure it was agreed to retain the Hornby name by renaming Tri-ang Railways, 'Tri-ang Hornby'. This was presented at the time as an amalgamation of the two systems but the only additions this brought to the Tri-ang system were the E3000 (after extensive modification) and, for a brief period, the terminus station kit.

It is interesting to note that Lines Bros. were also invited to buy both Trix and Lone Star Trebl-o-lectric! On both occasions they declined.

Another subsidiary of Lines Bros., G&R Wrenn Ltd., put in a bid for the Hornby-Dublo tools and these were used to launch Tri-ang Wrenn in 1967. They also took over remaining stocks of Hornby-Dublo and Tri-ang Railways TT. Lines Bros. Ltd were under pressure to get into N gauge but chose instead to import the Lima system which they marketed through G&R Wrenn Ltd.

The Tri-ang Hornby period will be best remembered for the change to blue liveries for modern stock, the introduction of pre-Nationalisation liveries for steam locomotives, the disappearance of the Transcontinental range, the appearance of Battle Space and the introduction of exhaust noise. Memorable locomotives of this period include E3000, Hymek, Class 37, M7, Hall, 'Flying Scotsman', Coronation and, of course, 'Evening Star'. Around 1970 Tri-ang Hornby went 'finescale' with a new track system and re-profiled wheels.

In 1967, Rovex Scale Models Ltd. had become the core of Rovex Industries Ltd. which was called the 'model division' and included Minic Ltd., Minimodels Ltd., Spot-On Ltd., Pedigree Dolls Ltd. and IMA Ltd. (Frog). It also had under its wing G&R Wrenn Ltd which was not a fully owned company. The division was renamed Rovex Tri-ang Ltd. in 1969.

Amongst other things, losses overseas saw the giant Lines Bros. Group in trouble. At their peak they had 40 companies world-wide. In 1971 the crash came when Lines Bros. Ltd called in the Receiver. The Group was broken up and sold off. The profitable Rovex Tri-ang Ltd was for a brief period called Pocket Money Toys Ltd and then sold as Rovex Ltd, with its factories at Margate and Canterbury, to Dunbee Combex Marx Ltd. (DCM). At this point it parted company with G&R Wrenn which had bought itself free and renamed its system Wrenn Railways. The name Tri-ang had been sold with one of the other companies and so a new name was required for the Tri-ang Hornby system. Hornby Railways was chosen and this took effect from January 1972.

The 1970s saw new challenges come from Airfix and Palitoy who both launched model railway systems that offered finer scale models. This and pressure from Lima forced Rovex Ltd to raise its standards. There was steady development of new locomotives (over 20 in all) including the A4, Footballer, King, Patriot and Duchess. New diesels included the HST which was to become a major money spinner. There was also a new range of regional coaches as well as BR Mk3s and these would serve the system for many years.

In 1980 DCM were in trouble and the ball was in the air once again. Hornby Hobbies Ltd., as it was now called, became an independent company through a management buyout, with the help of venture capital. On 29 October 1986, Hornby Group plc was floated on the Unlisted Securities Market and became a public company. By now both the GMR (Airfix) and Mainline (Palitoy) systems had ceased to be produced and this led to a new player, Dapol, entering the field and Lima getting a stronger toehold.

Changes taking place on British Railways brought new liveries thus offering more subjects to model. The demand for higher standards of modelling lead to a number of models being retooled and a search for ways to improve printing on models. In 1996, Hornby Hobbies purchased a number of tools from Dapol including several formerly used for the Airfix GMR system.

Today, the privatised railways have brought a further rash of new liveries. Hornby Hobbies now has its models made by Sandakan in China and is gradually upgrading its range. Competition comes from Bachmann, using upgraded Mainline tools as well as new quality tooling, and from Lima who have concentrated on the lucrative modern image market. Hornby Hobbies recognises the important collectors' market and have established the Hornby Collectors Club and a chain of Collectors Centres. Now called just 'Hornby', it justifiably retains the position it has held for the last 40 years as Britain's leading model railway system.

Further Reading
If you are interested in further study of this model railway system, we recommend that you read 'The Rovex Story' by Pat Hammond. So far, two volumes have been published by New Cavendish Books. These are 'Volume 1 - Tri-ang Railways' (ISBN 0 904568 57 1), which covers the story from 1950 to 1965, and 'Volume 2 - Tri-ang Hornby' (ISBN 1 872727 58 1) which covers the period 1965 to 1971. 'Volume 3 - Hornby Railways' is currently in preparation and will take the story from 1972 until 1996.

Collectors Clubs
We would also like to recommend the Tri-ang Society which caters for collectors of a wide range of Tri-ang toy products. The Society has a quarterly newsletter, called Tri-ang Telegraph, which contains a number of original articles by well known collectors. Details of the Tri-ang Society may be obtained from the Miles Rowland on Tel: 0161 9765059.

Tri-ang Railways and Tri-ang Hornby are also usually well covered in the magazine of the Train Collectors Society (details at the front of the book).

Hornby Hobbies sponsor their own Collectors Club which publishes a full colour bimonthly magazine, called The Hornby Collector, which includes news of latest releases and regular profiles of models from the past. Further information about this organisation may be obtained from Fiona Baulard-Cato on Tel: 01223 208308 or from the Hornby Web site at http//www.hornby.co.uk

Spanning 50 years and worlds apart! The 1951 Tri-ang 'Princess Elizabeth' (R50) [table 1] and the 2000 Hornby 'Clan Line' (R2169) [table 89].

Loco Search

In order to help you find your Rovex – Tri-ang – Hornby locomotive, we have listed below, in the left column, the numbers that appear on the side of models (running numbers) and, in the right column, the table in the following locomotive list where you will find the model.

Loco No.	Table	Loco No.	Table	Loco No.	Table	Loco No.	Table	Loco No.	Table	Loco No.	Table
06003	65	21C166	17	1203	70	3775	10	6200	62	25052	40
06005	65	21C170	17	1226	58	3821	57	6201	1	25054	40
06008	65	23	42	1241	58	3824	57	6201	62	25071	40
08096	5b	23	70	1247	58	3825	57	6204	1	25078	40
08201	5b	27	14	1404	T3	3828	57	6206	62	25218	40
08500	5b	34	42	1421	74	3830	57	6208	62	25241	40
08523	5b	36	42	1427	74	3980	58	6210	1	25247	40
08531	5b	40	70	1444	74	4008	T3	6210	62	25550	14
08633	5b	43	70	1458	74	4466	45	6211	62	25555	26
08661	5b	45	42	1470	74	4468	45	6212	1	27000	16
08673	5b	61	29	1472	74	4469	45	6220	30	27002	16
08828	5b	99	42	1520	5a	4472	29	6221	30	27006	16
08896	5b	100	46	1542	T1	4476	29	6222	30	29561	2
08933	5b	101	42	1757	12	4482	45	6224	30	30027	28
08938	5b	101	46	1863	P3	4485	45	6228	30	30111	28
1	5b	101	T7	1863	P5	4498	45	6229	88	30902	54
1	42	102	46	2021	3	4657	33	6233	39	30908	54
1	45	103	29	2300	50	4718	P4	6234	39	30911	54
1	P7	103	46	2301	50	4830	T2	6237	30	30912	54
2	42	104	46	2309	50	4902	45	6241	30	30925	54
2	P8	105	42	2312	50	4903	45	6244	30	30927	54
3	8	112	49	2335	T1	4916	26	6245	30	30935	54
3	49	123	23	2345	50	4930	26	6253	39	31018	T7
4	42	157	80	2468	83	4983	26	6922	26	31757	12
4	49	205	49	2505	29	5004	75	7005	T4	32636	79
4	65	222	56	2509	45	5007	T4	7025	75	32670	79
4	P7	245	28	2512	45	5007	T5	7178	14	34029	17
4	P8	249	28	2526	83	5042	75	7321	P3	34051	17
5	8	254	P6	2571	P3	5053	75	7476	20	34054	17
5	53	256	P6	2579	83	5069	75	7503	T6	34076	17
5	70	270	49	2744	53	5097	75	7553	T4	34085	17
5	P7	300	66	2747	53	5112	33	7606	3	35005	89
5	P8	302	65	2753	56	5138	33	7744	P3	35023	89
6	14	303	T7	2776	53	5156	33	8006	80	35028	89
6	42	313	49	2783	53	5158	33	8027	66	37042	24
6	49	328	28	2788	53	5241	33	8035	66	37047	24
6	65	359	56	2821	69	5379	33	8118	66	37063	24
6	P7	501	T7	2844	69	5514	48	8193	66	37071	24
7	14	503	T7	2848	51	5533	48	8233	66	37072	24
7	42	579	84	2857	51	5539	48	8400	4	37073	24
7	49	627	49	2857	69	5541	48	8473	37	37130	24
7	49	644	84	2859	51	5771	P4	8477	37	37166	24
7	70	645	84	2859	69	5934	26	8479	20	37167	24
7	P7	690	34	2862	51	5955	26	8481	37	37198	24
8	14	748	6	2864	51	6000	44	8509	20	37202	24
8	32	795	38	2866	51	6005	44	8537	20	37203	24
8	42	900	54	2869	69	6006	44	8578	20	37207	24
8	49	903	54	2918	63	6008	44	8579	20	37293	24
8	65	905	54	2920	63	6009	44	8733	32	37371	24
8	P7	907	54	2927	63	6010	44	8751	32	37424	24
9	14	914	54	2937	63	6013	44	9003	T7	37518	24
9	70	921	54	3000	T4	6014	44	11232	78	37677	24
9	42	926	54	3015	73	6018	44	11250	78	37885	24
11	79	928	54	3016	73	6024	44	13002	5a	40610	84
17	5b	930	54	3021	73	6026	44	13005	5a	40634	84
21	42	934	54	3022	73	6027	44	13012	5b	41043	55
21C101	17	936	54	3046	15	6042	P3	14010	23	42202	19
21C119	17	1000	55	3111	58	6113	86	16020	49	42308	50
21C151	17	1004	76	3211	72	6124	43	16023	49	42363	50
21C155	17	1006	76	3212	72	6142	43	16030	49	43003	41
21C164	17	1015	76	3219	73	6147	86	16031	49	43046	41
21C165	17	1022	76	3400	T7	6150	86	16032	49	43050	41
21C165	17	1029	76	3403	T7	6200	1	16440	4	43051	41

Loco No.	Table	Loco No.	Table	Loco No.	Table	Loco No.	Table	Loco No.	Table	Loco No.	Table
43058	41	47285	35	56109	82	68080	80	91004	68	D6110	43
43059	41	47301	35	56118	82	68463	37	91009	68	D6119	43
43063	41	47311	35	56119	82	68472	37	91011	68	D6130	43
43063	41	47345	35	56123	82	68474	37	91014	68	D6713	24
43066	41	47353	35	56127	82	68846	58	91019	68	D6721	24
43072	41	47376	35	57317	85	69546	87	91022	68	D6736	24
43080	41	47378	35	57325	85	69506	87	91025	68	D6796	24
43086	41	47406	35	57344	85	70000	13	91026	68	D6830	24
43093	41	47409	35	58001	61	70004	13	91031	68	D7063	27
43102	41	47421	35	58006	61	70006	13	92000	31	D7093	27
43117	41	47458	4	58007	61	70010	13	92001	31	D7097	27
43118	41	47480	4	58021	61	70013	13	92009	71	D7568	40
43124	41	47483	35	58023	61	70014	13	92020	71	D7571	40
43128	41	47487	35	58025	61	70021	13	92022	71	D7581	40
43154	41	47541	35	58030	61	70023	13	92026	71	D7596	40
43193	41	47549	35	58033	61	70028	13	92045	71	D7596	40
43620	10	47556	4	58034	61	70030	13	92099	31	D7597	40
43775	10	47568	35	58039	61	70032	13	92108	31	E112	29
44313	81	47573	35	58042	61	70034	13	92158	31	E1664	51
44331	81	47576	35	58044	61	70038	13	92166	31	E3001	25
44523	81	47579	35	58047	61	70040	13	92200	31	E27000	16
44808	33	47583	35	58048	61	70042	13	92203	31	E51812	60
44871	33	47586	35	58050	61	70046	13	92207	31	E51815	60
44932	33	47606	3	58051	61	70047	13	92212	31	E51816	60
44932	33	47613	35	60006	45	70050	13	92220	31	E51819	60
45021	33	47620	35	60010	45	78327	77	92222	31	E51824	60
45156	33	47711	35	60012	45	78351	77	92231	31	E51827	60
45158	33	47712	35	60014	45	82004	4	92241	31	E51829	60
45192	33	47716	35	60019	45	86102	59			E51832	60
45292	33	47808	35	60020	45	86210	59	142013	64	E51844	60
45422	33	47814	35	60021	45	86218	59	142015	64	E51846	60
45519	48	47822	35	60022	45	86219	59	142020	64	E52066	60
45537	48	47844	35	60028	45	86220	59	142023	64	E52073	60
46200	1	47845	35	60029	45	86228	59	142048	64	E52078	60
46201	1	48141	66	60030	45	86235	59	142065	64	E52080	60
46201	62	48142	T4	60034	45	86243	59	142069	64	E52085	60
46204	62	48278	66	60046	29	86246	59	142074	64	E59695	60
46205	1	48705	66	60048	29	86255	59	155317	85	E59707	60
46208	62	48758	66	60052	29	86261	59	155325	85	E59708	60
46209	62	48774	66	60061	29	86401	59	155344	85	E59814	60
46210	62	51218	78	60071	29	86405	59	253001	41	E59816	60
46225	39	51222	78	60075	29	86414	59	253005	41	GM12	T10
46226	39	51235	78	60080	29	86417	59	253028	41	H2000	49
46230	39	52317	85	60085	29	86417	59	370001	52	L90	32
46231	39	52325	85	60103	29	86419	59	370002	52	M79079	9
46232	39	52344	85	61520	20	86419	59	466016	77	M79628	9
46236	39	55554	64	61553	20	86431	59	A5	65	M79629	9
46237	39	55556	64	61572	20	86504	59	D1008	47	M79632	9
46239	39	55564	64	61649	51	90001	67	D1013	47	S1052S	7
46247	39	55589	64	61650	51	90012	67	D1035	47	S1057S	7
46247	39	55604	64	61651	51	90014	67	D1039	47	T336	T4
46248	39	55606	64	61654	51	90015	67	D1058	47	TR20071	8
46250	39	55614	64	61656	51	90018	67	D1062	47	W2	79
46251	39	55639	64	61662	51	90020	67	D1670	35	W11	79
46252	39	55715	64	61663	51	90028	67	D1738	35	W12	79
46255	39	55761	64	61663	51	90030	67	D2412	65	W60095	21
46400	36	55742	64	61664	51	90033	67	D2424	65	W60747	21
46521	36	55770	64	61665	51	90034	67	D2428	65		
47079	35	56010	49	61672	51	90037	67	D2907	18		
47085	35	56025	49	62700	56	90040	67	D3010	5b		
47124	35	56038	49	62750	56	90042	67	D3035	5a		
47156	35	56047	82	62758	56	90131	67	D5177	40		
47170	35	56049	82	64875	77	90135	67	D5200	40		
47207	35	56058	82	64899	77	91001	68	D5206	40		
47231	35	56066	82	64899	77	91001	68	D5572	19		
47234	35	56100	82	68049	80	91003	68	D5578	19		
47270	35	56105	82	68062	80	91003	68	D6103	43		

Locomotives

Overseas Models – Many Tri-ang models were made in Australia, New Zealand and South Africa for local distribution but only British made models are listed here.

'R' Numbers – These are catalogue numbers. The additional ones are for the tender (steam engines) or dummy unit (multiple units) when sold separately. In the early 1970s, with the introduction of computers, it became necessary to bring 'R' numbers up to three digits and this was done by adding one or two noughts before those numbers less than '100'. Thus, R52 became R052.

'Noise' – refers to a tender fitted device which created a 'chuff-chuff' sound.

Code 3 Models – There are a number of excellently renumbered and renamed Hornby models which have

been done for shops, in batches, professionally, outside the factory. These normally have etched metal nameplates but have been included in this list.

Dates
– Wherever possible we have given you the years in which we know the models were in production bit it is difficult to be completely accurate as we do not have the production detail for every year. Models often appeared in the catalogue to clear slow moving stock after production had ceased. The dates given should, therefore, be treated only as a guide.

Listing – The model types are arranged in the order we believe they were available to the public. Because of the large range of some of the types (e.g. A1/3s, A4s, Class 47s) the variations have been grouped according to colour or livery rather than in chronological order. This should make it easier to trace the one you are looking for if you know its appearance.

R.No.	Name / Number	Colour	Details	Years	£	£

1. 'Princess' Royal Class (Short) 4-6-2 (for scale Princess see 62)
gl = gold BRb logo on tender   tl = transfer logo   t+l = transfers and lining   lf = lacquer finish

R.No.	Name / Number	Colour	Details	Years	£	£
R50+R30	46201 'Princess Elizabeth'	black	gl, roller pick-ups	50	2000	N/A
R50+R30	46201 'Princess Elizabeth'	black	gl, plunger pick-ups	50-52	20	50
R50+R30	46201 'Princess Elizabeth'	black	gl	52-55	15	50
R50+R30	46201 'Princess Elizabeth'	black	BRb, tl	55	30	65
R50+R30	46201 'Princess Elizabeth'	black	BRb, t+l	55-58	20	45
R50+R30	46201 'Princess Elizabeth'	black	BRb, tl, red letters on black nameplate	58	80	95
R50+R30	46205 'Princess Victoria'	black	BRc, t+l	59-62	20	35
R050	46205 'Princess Victoria'	black	gl, mail order model	74	25	40
R53+R31	46201 'Princess Elizabeth'	olive	BRb, gl	53	30	45
R53+R31	46201 'Princess Elizabeth'	olive	BRb, tl	54	45	60
R53+R31	46201 'Princess Elizabeth'	olive	BRb, t+l	54-56	30	45
R53+R31	46201 'Princess Elizabeth'	green	BRb, t+l	56-57	20	35
R53+R31	46201 'Princess Elizabeth'	green	BRc, t+l, lf	58-61	25	40
R386	46201 'Princess Elizabeth'	green	BRc, CKD kit	62-69	N/A	70
R050	46205 'Princess Victoria'	green	gl, mail order model	74	25	40
R258+R34	46200 'The Princess Royal'	maroon	BRc, t+l	59-64,69	25	45
R258	6200 'The Princess Royal'	maroon	*LMS*, CKD kit	70	N/A	150
R258	6201 'Princess Elizabeth'	maroon	*LMS*	70-74	25	35
R258, R258NS	6204 'Princess Louise', 6210 'Lady Patricia', 6212 'Duchess of Kent'	maroon	*LMS*, + alternative names	70-72	40	60
R***	46205 'Princess Victoria'	maroon	gl, mail order model	74	100	NPG
R***	46205 'Princess Victoria'	blue	gl	74	150	NPG
R260	?	?	Sp Edn 100	73	NPG	NPG

This model was also made in New Zealand and Australia using the earliest tools.

2. Class N2 Tank 0-6-2T (former Trackmaster model)

R.No.	Name / Number	Colour	Details	Years	£	£
Trackmaster	29561	black	BRa	49-51	35	45
R51	29561	black	BRa	51-53	45	75
R51	29561	black	BRb	53-54	55	85

The original Trackmaster model was sold in its own packaging by Pyramid Toys.

3a. Class 3F 'Jinty' Tank 0-6-0T   s-tw = see-through wheels (gaps between spokes)

R.No.	Name / Number	Colour	Details	Years	£	£
R52	-	black	BRa, unlined	52	100	150

R52	47606	black	BRb, unlined	52-57	10	30
R52	47606	black	BRb, lined	57-59	20	35
R52	47606	black	BRc, lined	59-64	15	35
R52/R52S	47606	black	BRc, s-tw, lined	64-75	20	35
R52/R52S	47606	black	BRc, cream logos, s-tw, lined	72	30	40
R757	2021	black	s-tw, lined	73	25	30*
R52RS/						
R52AS	7606	maroon	*LMS*, s-tw, with smoke unit	70-73	25	35
R452	7606	maroon	*LMS*, s-tw	73-74	25	35
R377S	-	brown	*GN&SR*, s-tw from Lt Edn			
			'The Railway Children' set (RS615)	70-73	35	40*
R558S	-	khaki	Battle Space, s-tw	66-67	30	35*

This model was also made in New Zealand and Australia from a different body tool. This usually has a lamp mounted on the smokebox.

3b. Class 3F 'Jinty' Tank 0-6-0T (new body with cab interior)   npf = non-paint finish

R052	16440	maroon	LMS npf	78-79	25	30
R301	16440	maroon	LMS	80-84 88-89	30	35
R058	47458	black	BRc	78-79	25	30
R302	47480	black	BRc	80-82	30	35
R053	47556	black	BRc	88-91	35	40
R130	8400	green	*LNER*	88-89	30	35*

4. Class 3 Standard Tank 2-6-2T

R59	82004	black	BRb	56-58	30	75
R59	82004	black	BRc	59	30	75
R59	82004	green	BRc	60	30	55
R59	82004	green	BRc, see-thru wheels	61-66 69-72	25	55

5a. Class 08 Diesel Shunter 0-6-0DS

R152	13002	black	BRb	56	50	65
R152	13005	black	BRb	56-58	20	30
R154	13005	black	BRb c/w	57-58	80	100
R256	-	black	*TR* c/w	57?	80	100
R317	Devious Diesel	black	face on front	87-88	45	60
R152	13005	olive	BRb	56?	50	65
R152	D3035	green	BRb	58-68	25	40
R256	-	maroon	*TR* c/w	57-58	40	55
R152	D3035	blue	BRe	69-75	25	35
R316	-	blue	*VR*, made for Australia	74	60	80
R1520	1520	bt.blue	made for Canada	71	60	90

This model was also made in New Zealand and Australia with a different body tool. This has a higher cab roof.

Tri-ang Class N2 tank formerly a Trackmaster model. Clockwork only. (R51).   [table 2]

Tri-ang Class 3F Jinty (R52).   [table 3]

Tri-ang Class 3 Standard tank (R590).   [table 4]

Tri-ang Class S saddle tank , clockwork (R151).   [table 6]

Tri-ang Class 08 diesel shunter (R152).   [table 5a]

Tri-ang EMU (R156+R225).   [table 7]

Tri-ang Class 101 DMU (R157+R158).   [table 9]

Tri-ang
Steeple Cab
electric locomotive (R254).

[11]

R.No.	Name / Number	Colour	Details	Years	£	£

5b. Class 08 Diesel Shunter 0-6-0DS (new body)   arc = automatic rear coupling   ladders = metal ladders up sides of radiator

R.No.	Name / Number	Colour	Details	Years	£	£
R156	13012	green	BRc, arc, ladders	76-79	20	25
R354	D3010	green	BRc paint finish, arc, ladders	80-81	25	30
R2157A/B	08531, 08096	green	BRc	00	30	38
R339	17	green	*WD*, arc, ladders	82-84	25	50
R780	08201	blue	BRe black wheels, arc, ladders	81-85	25	30
R780	08201	blue	BRe red wheels, ladders	87-88	20	25
R2007	08523	vio blue	*Mainline* Set R1002	97-98	25	30*
R803	08938	grey	*ED* Engineering Department, ladders	86-88	25	40
R054	08673 'Piccadilly'	grey	BRe	88-92	30	40
R272	08933	grey	BRe Railfreight	95-96	25	40
R2008	08661 'Europa'	grey	*Railfreight Distribution.*	97-98	30	40
R050	08633 'The Sorter'	red+blk	Express Parcels	93-94	30	45
R165	-	maroon	NSWR (made for Australia), arc, ladders	77-78	40	65
R2111	08896 'Stephen Dent'	maroon	*EWS*	99	25	30
R2163	08828	maroon	*EWS*	00	30	38
R2123	08500 'Thomas 1'	maroon	York Wagon Depot loco	99-00	25	30

6. Class S Saddle Tank 0-6-0ST

R.No.	Name / Number	Colour	Details	Years	£	£
R153	748	black	BRb	56-58	30	40
R151	748	black	BRb c/w	57-58	35	45
R153	748	black	BRc	59-61	25	35
R255	-	blk+grn	*TR* c/w	59-58	30	40

7. Class 4SUB EMU

R.No.	Name / Number	Colour	Details	Years	£	£
R156+R225	S1052S/S1057S	green	BRb, 2-car	57-58	55	85
R156+R225	S1052S/S1057S	green	BRc, 2-car	59-62	45	90
R156+R225	S1052S/S1057S	yell/grn	BRc, 2-car	62-64	75	110

Most of the British sets are a bluegreen but those produced towards the end were a yellow-green.
Tools went to New Zealand in 1965 where a similar but slightly different model was made.

8. Dock Shunter/Yard Switcher 0-4-0DS

R.No.	Name / Number	Colour	Details	Years	£	£
R253	5	black	*Dock Authority*, early coupling	57-61	20	55
R253	3	black	*Dock Authority*	72-78	20	30
R353	-	yellow	*TR*, no buffers	60-62	25	40
R253	3 or 5	red	*Dock Authority*	62-71	20	35
R253	TR20071	red	*TR*, no buffers	63-65	20	65*
R655	-	red	*TR*, no buffers	65?	35	65*

Some bodies were printed in New Zealand and these include ones with 'TR' but no shield.

9. Class 101 DMU

R.No.	Name / Number	Colour	Details	Years	£	£
R157+R158	M79628/M79629	green	BRb, 2-car	58	30	65
R157+R158	M79628/M79629	green	BRc, 2-car	59-61	20	35
R157+R158	M79079/M79632	green	BRc + yell panel, 2-car	62-67	25	40
R157	M79079/M79632	green	BRc illuminated, 2-car	74-78	35	45
R157C	M79079/M79632	blue	BRe + yell panel, 2-car	70-71	50	75

10. Class 3F (Deeley/Johnson) 0-6-0

R.No.	Name / Number	Colour	Details	Years	£	£
R251+R33	43775	black	BRc	58-66	30	40
R661S	43775	black	BRc weathered	65	70	100*
R251	3775	maroon	MR	66-67	30	40

11. Steeple Cab Electric 0-4-0

R.No.	Name / Number	Colour	Details	Years	£	£
R254	N/A	green	BRc	59-64	35	65
R254	N/A	green	*TR*	61-63	65	75
R252	N/A	maroon	*TR* dummy pantograph	59-62	40	75

12. Class L1 4-4-0

R.No.	Name / Number	Colour	Details	Years	£	£
R350+R36	31757	green	BRc	60-67	45	70
R350	1757	dk green	*Southern*	72	45	70

13. 'Britannia' Class 7P6F 4-6-2

sd = super detail version   nsd = no smoke deflectors   sn = sticker nameplates   ul = no lining on loco or tender

R.No.	Name / Number	Colour	Details	Years	£	£
R259+R35	70000 'Britannia'	green	BRc, metal nameplates	60-70	25	55
R259SF	70000 'Britannia'	green	BRc, Acho couplings	67-70	90	150
R259NS	70000 'Britannia'	green	BRc, sn	71-72	35	50
R259NS	70006 'Robert Burns', 70013 'Oliver 'Cromwell', 70010 'Owen Glendower'	green	BRc, with alternative names for R259NS, sn	71-72	55	N/A

R056	70047 'Iron Duke' **	green	BRc, sn, ul, nsd	75-76	35	40*
R056	70047 'Iron Duke' **	green	BRb, sn, ul, nsd	75?	120	150*
R056	70014 'Iron Duke' **	green	BRc, sn, ul, nsd	75-76	40	45*
R056	70014 'Iron Duke' **	green	BRc, sn, ul, smoke deflectors fitted (about 50 made)	76?	80	150*
R552	70013 'Oliver Cromwell'	green	BRc, sn	73-75	35	50
R063	70000 'Britannia'	green	BRc, sn	76-79	35	50
R033	70021 'Morning Star'	green	BRc	81-82	45	65
R033	70028 'Royal Star', 70034 'Thomas Hardy', 70038 'Robin Hood'	green	BRc, with alternative names for R033	81-83	50	N/A
R329	70004 'William Shakespear'	green	BRc	90-91	40	55
R190	70000 'Britannia'	green	BRb	92-93	35	65
R507	70000 'Britannia'	green	BRb, Ltd Edn 2000, Royal Duties (white cab roof)	92-93	50	90
R378	70032 'Tennyson'	green	BRc, Sp Edn 2000 (Kays)	91	55	120
R242	70006 'Robert Burns'	green	BRb, Sp Edn 2000 (Kays)	96	45	90
R2031	70023 'Venus'	green	BRb, train pack with 3 coaches, Ltd Edn 3000	97	70	110
R2010	70042 'Lord Roberts'	green	BRb, Ltd Edn 1000	98	45	85
R2091	70028 'Royal Star'	green	BRb, Ltd Edn 777	99	70	100
X****	70012 'John of Gaunt'	green	BRc, in set R1021 (Kays)	99	55	65*
R2103	70050 'Firth of Clyde'	green	BRc, late tender	99	40	75
R2142	70038 'Robin Hood'	green	BRc, Sp Edn 1000 (A.B.Gee)	99	50	70
R2180	70040 'Clive of India'	green	BRc, sd	00	60	80
R2177	70046 'ANZAC'	green	BRc, sd, late tender, Ltd Edn 1000	00	NPG	NPG

** Cheap mail order model
Many Hornby Britannias have been renumbered/renamed after leaving the factory. These may be listed in the Code 3 section of this book.

14. Industrial Tank 0-4-0T

R355B	6 or 7 'Nellie'	blue		60-68	20	35
R355	6, 7 or 9 'Connie'	blue		60-62?	35	50
R355B	6 'Connie'	blue	deeper blue (in sets)	72	35	45*
R355B	7 'Nellie'	blue	deeper blue	71-72	30	40
R255	7178	blue	S&D gold or yellow lining	76-78	20	30
R255	7178	blue	S&D white lining	76?	40	NPG
R355Y	6 or 8 'Connie'	yellow		63-65	50	75
R355R	6 or 9 'Polly'	red		63-70	25	45
R455	25550	red	silver dome	73-75	25	35
R455	25550	red	no silver dome	73-75	30	40
R355G	27	green	shades of green	70-72	20	30

15. Dean Single 4-2-2

R354+R37	3046 'Lord of the Isles'	green	*Great O Western*, matt	61-65,67	25	85
R354	3046 'Lord of the Isles'	green	*Great O Western*, gloss	70-72	30	75
R49	3046 'Lord of the Isles'	green	*Great O Western*, tampo printed splasher, + 3 coaches	81	65	100

16. Class EM2 Electric Co-Co

R351	27000 'Electra'	green	BRc	61-65	55	100
R388	27000 'Electra', 27002 'Aurora', 27006 'Pandora'	green	BRc, CKD kit with choice of names	65	N/A	100
R351	27000 'Electra'	blue	BRc, electric blue	66-68	50	125
R388	27000 'Electra', 27002 'Aurora', 27006 'Pandora'	blue	BRc, electric blue, CKD kit with choice of names	66-67	N/A	125
R388	27000 'Electra', 27002 'Aurora', 27006 'Pandora'	blue	BRe, electric blue, assembly pack with choice of names	68	N/A	125
R351	27000 'Electra'	blue	BRe, rail blue	69-71	60	100
R388	27000 'Electra', 27002 'Aurora', 27006 'Pandora'	blue	BRe, rail blue, assembly pack with choice of names	69-70	N/A	100
R351	E27000 'Electra'	blue	BRe, rail blue	71	75	100

17. Class BB/WC 'Battle of Britain' and 'West Country' 4-6-2

R356+R38	34051 'Winston Churchill'	green	BRc	61-69	45	75
R356+R38	34051 'Winston Churchill'	green	BRc, in Tri-ang Railways box	61-69	45	100
R074	34076 '41 Squadron'	green	BRb	85-86	80	120
R310	34054 'Lord Beaverbrook'	green	BRc	95-97	45	55

R.No.	Name / Number	Colour	Details	Years	£	£
R646	34085 '501 Squadron'	green	BRb *Golden Arrow*, Sp Edn 1000 (Beatties)	96	80	120
R869S	21C151 'Winston Churchill'	brt green	*Southern* with red shading	69	80	NPG
R869S	21C151 'Winston Churchill'	brt green	*Southern* with black shading, gloss	69-72	30	45
R869S	21C157'Biggin Hill', 21C164 'Fighter Command', 21C165'Hurricane'	brt green	*Southern*, gloss, alternative names for R869S	69-72	40	N/A
R374	21C166 'Spitfire'	malachite	*Southern*, matt	81-82	45	70
R374	21C155 'Fighter Pilot', 21C165 'Hurricane', 21C170 'Manston'	malachite	*Southern*, matt alternative names for R374	81-82	50	N/A
R866	21C155 'Fighter Pilot'	malachite	*Southern*, matt	86?	50	60
R866	21C155 'Fighter Pilot'	malachite	*Southern*, Golden Arrow	87-89	45	55
R368	21C101 'Exeter'	malachite	*Southern*, matt, Ltd Edn 4000	95	50	60
R265	21C119 'Bideford'	malachite	*Southern* matt	96-97	45	55

18. North British Diesel Shunter 0-4-0DS

R.No.	Name / Number	Colour	Details	Years	£	£
R557	-	blue	BRc c/w	62-65	15	55
R559	D2907	green	BRc	63-67	25	55
R557?	-	green	BRc c/w	68?	30	35*
R756	-	red	BRc c/w	66	30	35*
R***	-	red	Battle Space	66-67	35	40*
R654	-	blue	BRc	64-65	25	30*
R557?	-	violet	c/w	68?	40	45*
R***	-	black	c/w	65	40	45*

19. Class 31 Diesel (Brush Type 2) A1A-A1A

R.No.	Name / Number	Colour	Details	Years	£	£
R357(G)	D5572	green	BRc, dull	63-67	15	25
R357(G)	D5578	green	BRc, dull	63-67	55	70
R357	D5572	green	BRc, gloss	72-76	15	25
R357	D5578	exp. blue	BRc, pale blue window surrounds	62	50	95
R357B	D5578	exp. blue	BRc, with white lines and roof	65-66	30	65
R357	D5572	elec.blue	BRe	68	20	30
R357	D5572	rail blue	BRe	69-71	15	25
R307	42202	maroon	NSWR, made for Australia	74-76	50	70

20. Class B12 4-6-0

R.No.	Name / Number	Colour	Details	Years	£	£
R150S	61572	black	BRc, with smoke	63-69	25	35
R150SF	61572	black	BRc, with smoke, Acho couplings	67-70	70	120
R359S	61572	black	BRc, with smoke, assembly Pack	68-69	N/A	90
R150NS	61572	black	BRc, with smoke + noise	70-71	30	50
R2102A/B	61553, 61520	black	BRb, fully lined	99	37	45
R150	7476	black	*NE*	76-78	30	45
R866S	8509	green	*LNER*, with smoke, gloss	70	30	55
R359S	8509	green	*LNER*, with smoke, assembly pack, gloss	70-71	N/A	120
R866NS/ R866AS	8509	green	*LNER*, with smoke + noise	71-74	25	40
R866	8509	green	*LNER*, matt + noise	78-79	25	45
R284	8579	green	*LNER*, fully lined + noise	96-00	35	45
R2156A/B	8537, 8578	green	*LNER*, fully lined + noise	00	40	50

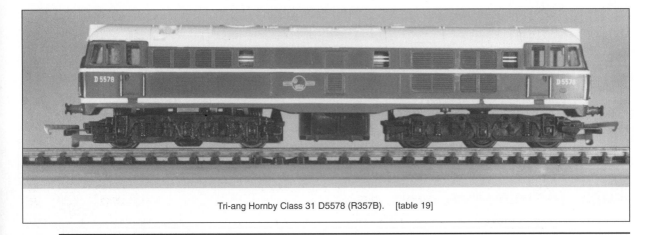

Tri-ang Hornby Class 31 D5578 (R357B).   [table 19]

21. 'Blue Pullman' DMU

R555+R556	-	blu+wht	BR *Pullman*, crest on front	63-67	25	45
R555+R556	-	blu+wht	BR *Pullman*, yellow front	68	35	50
R538	-	blu+wht	BR *Pullman*,	74	40	45*
R555C	W60095/W60747	gry+blu	BR *Pullman*	69-72	30	65

22. 'Rocket' 0-2-2

R651S+R652	'Rocket'	yellow	L&MR, + smoke, + 1 coach	63-66	45	80
R651+R652	'Rocket'	yellow	L&MR, no smoke, + 3 coaches	68-69	65	125
R796	'Rocket'	yellow	L&MR + 3 coaches, presentation pack	82	80	120

23. 'Caledonian Single' 4-2-2

R553+R554	123	blue	*CR*, matt	63-66	55	100
R553	123	blue	*CR*, gloss	71,73-74	60	85
R763	14010	maroon	LMS	83	40	65
R765	14010	maroon	LMS, Sp Edn 340 (Grattans)	83	40	90

24. Class 37 Diesel (English Electric Type 3) Co-Co   scb = split code box on cab front   npf = non-painted finish

R751	D6830	green	BRc, npf	66-67	15	30
R347	D6736	green	BRc, scb	86-87	20	30
R284	D6721, D6713, D6796	green	BRc, scb, alternative numbers	88-90	25	35
R2128	Eddie Stobart Ltd.	green	Sp Edn 1000 (Eddie Stobart Club/Trafford Model Centre)	99	40	60
R365	37072	bt.green	BReLL	82	18	25
R359	37071	bt.blue	BReLL	82-83	18	25*
R751,R751A	D6830	blue	BRe, npf	68-76	12	22
R751	37130	blue	BRe, npf	77-79	15	25
R369	37073	blue	BRe	80-83	18	28
R402	37207 'William Cookworthy'	blue	BRe	84-86	20	35
R285	37202, 37166, 37***	blue	BRe, alternative numbers	88-90	20	30
R871	37***	blue	BRe, choice of numbers	96	20	40
R348	37063	grey	BReLL *Railfreight*, scb	86-89	25	40
R286	37677,37518,37***	grey	BReLL *Railfreight*, alternative numbers	88-90	23	45
R243	37885	grey	BRe, Railfreight Metals	95	25	45
R327	37424	grey	'*T*' (Transrail)	96-97	25	40
R2012A/B/C	37371, 37203, 37198	vio blue	*Mainline*	97	30	45
R2027	37042	maroon	*EWS*, scb	97-98	28	32*
R2060A/B/C	37427, 37688, 37415	maroon	*EW&S*	98	30	40

25. Class 81 (AL1) Electric

R753	E3001	electric blue	BRd with 2 pantographs	66	70	125
R753	E3001	electric blue	BRd with 1 pantograph	67	50	100
R753	E3001	electric blue	BRe with 1 pantograph	68	50	80
R753	E3001	rail blue	BRe with 1 pantograph	69-70	60	90

26. Class 49XX 'Hall' 4-6-0

R759	4983 'Albert Hall'	green	BRc	66-69	35	60
R759G, R759N, R759A	4983 'Albert Hall'	green	*Great* (crest) *Western*, gloss, with alternative names, with or without exhaust noise or nickel wheels	70-72	25	50
R759G, R759N, R759A	4916 'Crumlin Hall', 6922 'Burton' Hall', 5955 'Garth Hall'	green	*Great* (crest) *Western*, gloss or matt, the alternative names for R759G	70-72	45	N/A
R759	4983 'Albert Hall'	green	*Great* (crest) *Western*, gloss	73-77	25	40
R761	5934 'Kneller Hall'	green	*Great* (crest) *Western*	78-79	28	45
R313	4930 'Hagley Hall'	green	*Great* (crest) *Western*	80-83	30	50
R765	25555 'Lord Westwood'	bt.red		73-74	25	45

27. Class 35 Hymek Diesel Hydraulic B-B   npf = non-painted finish

R758	D7063	green	BRc, npf	67	15	30
R074	D7063	green	BRc, npf	77-78	15	25
R335	D7097	green	BRc	79-82	25	35
R758	D7063	electric blue	BRe, npf	68	12	25
R396	D7063	electric blue	BRe, npf, assembly pack	68	N/A	80
R758	D7063	blue	BRe, npf	70-76	10	25
R396	D7063	blue	BRe, npf, assembly pack	69-70	N/A	80
R122	D7093	blue	BRe white window frames	94-95	25	45
R768	-	orange	*CIE*	76-78	45	80

28. Class M7 Tank 0-4-4T   npf = non-painted finish

R.No.	Name / Number	Colour	Details	Years	£	£
R754	30027	black	BRc, npf, fire glow	67-70	40	55
R862	30111	black	BRc	87-88	55	75
R868	328	bt. green	*Southern*, npf, fire glow	69-70	25	40
R868	328	bt. green	*Southern*, npf	71	25	40
R868	245	dk.green	*Southern*, npf	72-75	35	55
R103	249	olive	*Southern*	85-86	55	75

29. Class A1/A3 4-6-2

sd = super detailed version   GN = Great Northern style tender (with rails round top)   ct = corridor tender   nct = non-corridor tender
gsd = German smoke deflectors   npf = non-paint finish   +n = 'chuff-chuff' sound from tender   bd = banjo dome   fsw = fine scale wheels

R.No.	Name / Number	Colour	Details	Years	£	£
R855	4472 'Flying Scotsman'	lt. green	*LNER*, ct, npf, bd	68-70	18	30
R855N	4472 'Flying Scotsman'	lt. green	*LNER*, +n, ct, npf, bd	71-77	20	35
R845	4472 'Flying Scotsman'	lt. green	*LNER*, ct, npf, bd, fsw, improved lining	78-79	30	40
R322	4472 'Flying Scotsman'	lt. green	*LNER*, +n, ct, npf, bd, fsw, crew	80	30	40
R398	4472 'Flying Scotsman'	lt. green	*LNER*, ct	81-95	22	40
R398	4472 'Flying Scotsman'	lt. green	*LNER*, ct, silver hinges + handles	96-00	25	45
R387	4472 'Flying Scotsman'	lt. green	*LNER*, special	82-83	20	45
R074	4472 'Flying Scotsman'	lt. green	*LNER*, GN	93-94	30	55
R075	4472 'Flying Scotsman'	lt. green	*LNER*, 2 tenders (both green)	93	60	150
R098	4472 'Flying Scotsman'	lt. green	*LNER*, 2 tenders (one blue/grey), Ltd Edn 5000	95	50	90
R2146	103 'Flying Scotsman'	lt. green	*LNER*, sd, nct, gold metalwork, Ltd Edn 2000	99-00	120	150
R2147	4472 'Flying Scotsman'	lt. green	*LNER*, double chimney, Ltd Edn 500	00	60	80
R375	61 'Pretty Polly'	lt. green	*LNER*, GN, Sp Edn 1000 (Beatties)	95	45	80
R042	4476 'Royal Lancer'	lt. green	*LNER*, ct	89-91	45	90
R2103	2505 'Cameronian'	lt. green	*LNER*, sd, GN	99-00	50	90
R2168	E112 'St Simon'	lt. green	BRa, GN, sd, train pack with 3 coaches	00	-	-
R850	60103 'Flying Scotsman'	green	BRc, nct, npf, bd, red nameplate	68	30	45
R850	60103 'Flying Scotsman'	green	BRc, nct, npf, bd, blk. nameplate	69-70	25	40
R850	60103 'Flying Scotsman'	green	BRc, ct, npf, bd	69-70	30	45
R078	60103 'Flying Scotsman'	green	BRc, nct, gst	93-97	35	60
R059	60061 'Pretty Polly'	green	BRb, GN, gst, Sp Edn 1000 (Beatties)	94	45	85
R295	60080 'Dick Turpin'	green	BRb, GN	95-97	45	80
R2020	60103 'Flying Scotsman'	green	BRb	97-98	40	75
R2054	60103 'Flying Scotsman'	green	BRc, sd, nct	98-00	60	80
R2126	60046 'Diamond Jubilee'	green	BRc, sd, nct, Ltd Edn 500	99	80	100
R2140	60048 'Doncaster'	green	BRc, sd, GN, Sp Edn 1000 (A.B.Gee)	99	60	80
R2152	60085 'Manna'	green	BRc, GN, gsd, sd	00	60	80
R146	60052 'Prince Palatine'	blue	BRb, GN	94-95	40	70
R129	60061 'Pretty Polly'	blue	BRb, GN, Sp Edn 1000 (Beatties)	95	45	80
R140	60071 'Tranquil'	blue	BRa, GN, Sp Edn 1500 (Littlewoods)	96	50	90
R2036	60075 'St Frusquin'	blue	BRa, GN, Sp Edn 1500 (Kays)	96	45	90

Many Hornby A3s have been renumbered/renamed after leaving the factory. These may be listed in the Code 3 section of this book.

30. Princess 'Coronation' Class 4-6-2 (for scale length model see 88)

R.No.	Name / Number	Colour	Details	Years	£	£
R864	6220 'Coronation'	blue	*LMS* gloss	70-72	30	45
R864	6221 'Queen Elizabeth', 6222 'Queen Mary', 6224 'Princess Alexandra'	blue	*LMS* gloss, alternative names for R864	70-72	35	N/A
R685	6220 'Coronation'	blue	*LMS* matt	83-85 92-93	40	50
R834	6222 'Queen Mary'	blue	*LMS* matt	86-87	50	80
R871	6244 'King George IV'	maroon	*LMS* gloss	71-74	35	50
R871	6221 'Queen Elizabeth', 6228 'Duchess of Rutland', 6241 'City of Edinburgh'	maroon	*LMS* gloss, alternative names for R871	71-72	35	N/A
R072	6237 'City of Bristol'	maroon	*LMS* matt	85-86	50	80
R767	6244 'King George IV'	maroon	*LMS* matt, Sp Edn 500 (Beatties)	83	55	80
R2092	6245 'City of London'	black	*LMS* matt, Ltd Edn 1000	98	60	90

31. Class 9F 2-10-0   wh = wire handrails   sd = super detail   npf = non-paint finish   lt = large tender

R.No.	Name / Number	Colour	Details	Years	£	£
R861	92220 'Evening Star'	green	BRc, npf, gloss, separate cab handrails	71	40	60
R861	92220 'Evening Star'	green	BRc, npf, gloss	71-74	25	40
R065	92220 'Evening Star'	green	BRc, npf, matt	77-79	30	45
R303	92220 'Evening Star'	green	BRc	80-82	30	45
R373	92220 'Evening Star'	green	BRc, wh	88-91	35	50
R301	92220 'Evening Star'	green	BRb Sp Edn (NRM)	?	35	70
R330	92220 'Evening Star'	green	BRc Sp Edn 125 (NRM)	83	30	70
R2187	92220 'Evening Star'	black	BRc, sd, lt	00	60	80

R550	92166	black	BRb, 2900 made	73	35	50
R264	92200	black	BRc	82-83	30	45
R330	92207, 92231, 92222	black	BRc, wh	90-92	35	50
R864	92241	black	BRc, wh	96	40	55
R2016	92001	black	BRC, wh	97	40	55
R2057	92212	black	BRc, wh	98	40	50
R2105A	92108	black	BRc, sd, lt	99	50	70
R2105C	92158	black	BRc, sd, lt	00	-	-
R2137	92203 'Black Prince'	black	BRc, sd	99	50	70
R2139	92099	black	BRc, sd, + 5 vans, train pack, Sp Edn 1000 (A.B.Gee)	00	NPG	100

32. Class 57XX Pannier Tank 0-6-0PT (for Class 2721 Pannier see 52)   npf + non-painted finish

R51S/R051	8751	green	*GWR*, npf, smoke	71-72	18	25
R041	8751	green	*GWR*, npf, without smoke	75-79	18	28
R300	8733	green	*GWR*	80-81	22	35
R048	L90	bt.red	*London Transport*, from set	78	30	40*
R382	8 ('Duck' in Thomas series)	bt.green	*GWR*, face on front	86-91 95-00	25	35

33. 'Black 5' Class 4-6-0   ovg = old valve gear   nb = new body

R859	45192	black	BRc, ovg, + alternative numbers and names	73-75	25	45
R859	45158 'Glasgow Yeomanry', 45156 'Ayrshire Yeomanry'	black	BRc, ovg, alternative names/numbers for R859	73-75	30	N/A
R068	45021	black	BRc, Ltd Edn 2500	84	40	60
R314	44808, 44871,44932	black	BRc, nb	90-91	30	40
R292	45422	black	BRc fully lined, nb	96-98	35	45
R2081	45292	black	BRa fully lined, nb, Ltd Edn 1500 (Littlewoods)	98	45	80
R347	44932	green	BRc, nb, Sp Edn 1500 (Kays)	92	45	90
R061	5112	black	*LMS*, ovg, + alternative numbers and names	76	25	35
R061	5158 'Glasgow Yeomanry', 5156 'Ayrshire Yeomanry'	black	*LMS*, ovg, alternative names/numbers for R061	76	30	N/A
R840	5112	black	*LMS*, + alternative names/numbers	77-78	30	40
R840	5158 'Glasgow Yeomanry', 5156 'Ayrshire Yeomanry'	black	*LMS*, alternative names/numbers for R840	77-78	35	N/A
R320	5138	black	*LMS*	81-82,84	30	40
R858	5241	black	*LMS*, nb	87-89	35	45
R2083M	5379	black	*LMS*, nb, Sp Edn 1500 (Kays)	98	50	80
R842	4657	maroon	*LMS*	78-79	30	40

Hornby
Class 25
D7596 (R2121).

[table 40]

R.No.	Name / Number	Colour	Details	Years	£	£

34. Class 2P 4-4-0 (ex-Tri-ang L1) (for scale Class 2P see 84)

R.No.	Name / Number	Colour	Details	Years	£	£
R450	690	black	*LMS* lined	73-75	25	45

35. Class 47 Diesel Co-Co   **SC = self-coloured (i.e., not with a paint finish)**

R.No.	Name / Number	Colour	Details	Years	£	£
R863	D1738	green	BRc, SC	75	15	25
R060	D1520	green	BRc, SC	76	15	25
R073	D1670 'Mammoth'	green	BRc, SC	79	18	30
R328	D1670 'Mammoth'	green	BRc	80-81	20	30
R075	47421	blue	BRe, SC	77-78	15	25
R316	47712 'Lady Diana Spencer'	blue	BReLL	81	20	30
R307	47170 'County of Norfolk'	blue	BReLL	82-83	20	30
R769	47480 'Robin Hood'	blue	BRe, Sp Edn 480 (Beatties)	83	35	60
R319	47541 'The Queen Mother'	blue	BRe	83-84	25	35
R329	47541 'The Queen Mother'	blue	BRe, Sp Edn 187 (Grattans)	83	NPG	NPG
R404	47568	blue	BRe	84-87	18	30
R354	47406 'Rail Riders'	blue	BRe	85	30	40
R287	47409, 47353, 47124	blue	BRe	88-89	25	40
R876	47573 'The London Standard'	brt blue	BRe NSE	87-88	23	40
R219	47583 'County of Hereford', 47576 'King's Lynn', 47579 'James Nightingale GC'	brt blue	BRe NSE, choice of names/ numbers	89-93	25	40
R802	47487	grey	BRe *InterCity*	86-87	23	40
R886	47711 'Greyfrier's Bobby'	grey	BRe *ScotRail*	88	25	35
R887	47716 'The Duke of Edinburgh's Award'	grey	BRe *ScotRail*	88	25	35
R288	47620 'Windsor Castle', 47613 'North Star', 47549 'Royal Mail'	grey	BRe *InterCity*, choice of names/ numbers	88-90	25	40
R587	47586 'Northamptonshire'	grey	*InterCity* Swallow	91-92	25	35
R898	47378, 47285	grey	BReLL *Railfreight* General	88	25	40
R245	47231 'The Silcock Express', 47207 'Bulmers of Hereford', 47311 'Warrington Yard'	grey	BRe Railfreight Distribution, choice of names/numbers	89-92 96	25	40
R342	47079	grey	BRe Railfreight Construction	90-92	25	30*
R116	47234	grey	*Railfreight Distribution*	94	28	45
R416	47156 'REPTA 1893-1993'	grey	*Railfreight Distribution*	94?	30	45
R416	47085 'REPTA 1893-1993'	grey	*Railfreight Distribution*	94?	25	35
R2013	47376 'Freightliner 1995', 47270, 47301	grey	*Freightliner*	97	25	40
R2080	47345	grey	*Freightliner*, train pack with 3 wagons	98	50	75
R717	47808	red	BRe Parcels	95-96	30	38*
R2061A/ B/C	47844, 47814 'Totnes Castle', 47845 'County of Kent'	red+blk	*Virgin*	98	25	40
X****	47822 'Pride of Shrewsbury'	red+blk	*Virgin*, in R1022 set, (Kays)	99-00	25	35*

Hornby Class N15 Southern 795 'Sir Dinadan' (R154).   [table 38]

36. Class 2 'Ivatt' 2-6-0

R857	46400	black	BRc	75-77	35	45
R852	46521	green	BRc	78-80	30	40

37. Class J83 0-6-0T

R252	8477	green	*LNER*	76-78	18	25
R316	8473	green	*LNER*	94-98	25	35
R2164A/B	8481, 8477	green	*LNER*	00	22	30
R722	68472	green	BRa	95-96	23	28*
R2155A/B	68474, 68463	black	BRb	00	22	30

38. Class N15 'King Arthur' 4-6-0

R154	795 'Sir Dinadan'	green	*Southern*, gloss or matt	76-78	40	65

39. Princess Coronation Class 'Duchess' 4-6-2

npf = non paint finish   bnp = black nameplate   rnp = red nameplate   RD = presentation pack with Royal Doulton plate.

R066	6233 'Duchess of Sutherland'	maroon	*LMS*, npf	77-79	30	45
R305	6234 'Duchess of Abercorn'	maroon	*LMS*	80-81	35	60
R459	6253 'City of St Albans'	black	*LMS*, RD, Ltd Edn 3000	96	50	100
R262	46231 'Duchess of Athol'	green	BRb with alternative names	82-84	35	60
	46232 'Duchess of Montrose', 46230 'Duchess of Buccleugh'	green	BRb, alternative names for R262	82-84	35	NA
R102	46250 'City of Lichfield'	green	BRc, Sp Edn 2000 (Kays)	91	50	100
R221	46252 'City of Leicester'	green	BRc	92-93	40	75
R2015	46255 'City of Hereford'	green	BRb	97	40	50*
R2112	46237 'City of Bristol'	green	BRc, + 3 coaches, train pack	99	70	90
X****	46236 'City of Bradford'	green	BRc, R1004 set	99	40	45*
R577	46251 'City of Nottingham'	maroon	BRc	91-93	40	80
R194	46247 'City of Liverpool'	maroon	BRc, bnp, Sp Edn 1500 (Kays)	94	50	90
R134	46226 'Duchess of Norfolk'	maroon	BRc	94-95	45	90
R2041	46247 'City of Liverpool'	maroon	BRb, rnp, Sp Edn 1000 (Hattons)	97	40	80
R2023	46225 'Duchess of Gloucester'	maroon	BRc	97-98	35	70
R2078	46248 'City of Leeds'	maroon	BRc, + 3 coaches, train pack	98	70	90
R372	46231 'Duchess of Athol'	blue	BRb, Sp Edn 1500 (Kays)	92	50	100
R208	46239 'City of Chester'	blue	BRb	94-95	50	60*

Many Hornby Duchesses have been renumbered/renamed after leaving the factory. These may be listed in the Code 3 section of this book.

40. Class 25 Diesel Bo-Bo   npf = non paint finish   wbl = with blue line   wgl = with grey line

R072	D7596	green	BRc, wbl, npf	77-79	20	30
R327	D7571	green	BRc, wbl	80-81	20	30
R878	D5177, D5200, D5206, D7568, D7597	green	BRc, wbl, alt. number transfers	87-88	25	35
R253	D5206	green	BRc, wbl	95-97	30	45
R2121	D7596	green	BRc, wgl	99	35	45
R2121A	D7581	green	BRc, wgl	00	35	45
R068	25247	blue	BRe	77-79	20	30
R326	25241	blue	BRe	80-84	20	30
R877	25218, 25071, 25078, 25052, 25054	blue	BRe, alt. number transfers	87-90	25	35

41. Class 43 'HST 125'   neb = no exhaust baffle on cab roof

R069/070	253 001	blue	BRe *Inter-City 125*, 2 car, neb	77-79	20	30
R332	253 005	blue	BRe *Inter-City 125*, 3 car, neb	80-83	20	35
R401	253 028	grey	BRe *Inter-City 125*, 3 car, neb	84-87	25	40
R397	43072/43051	grey	*Inter-City* Swallow, 3 car pack	88-89	30	45
R?	43051 'Armada 400' / 43072	grey	*Inter-City* Swallow, Sp Edn 3 car pack	88-89?	100	130
R336	43046/43080/ 43066/43050	dk.grey	*Inter-City* Swallow, 3 car pack	90-96	25	40
R897	43154 'Intercity'/43193	dk.grey	*Inter-City* Swallow from 2 car set, Ltd Edn. 5000	96	35	40*
R901	43102/43086	dk.grey	*Inter-City* Swallow from 4 car set	97	50	55*
R2000	43117/43118	navy	*GNER*, 4 car pack	97-98	40	60
R2116	?	navy	*GNER*, 4 car pack	99-00	40	60
R2046	43058 'Midland Pride'/43059	blue/grn	*Midland Mainline*, 4 car pack	97-98	40	60
R2045	43063 'Maiden Voyager'/ 43093 'Lady in Red '	red	*Virgin*, 4 car pack	97-00	40	60
R2114	43063/43003	red	*Virgin*, 4 car pack	99-00	40	60
R2115	43128/43124	grn+ivry	*Great Western*, 4 car pack	99-00	40	60
R696	-	silver	*Intercity XPT*, 3 car pack, neb	83-84	70	100

42. Class 101 Holden Tank 0-4-0   pf = paint finish   npf = non paint finish

R.No.	Name / Number	Colour	Details	Years	£	£
R77	101	green	*Great Western*	78-79	10	18
R099	99	green	CIE	77-79	40	50*
R2130	9	green	CIE	99-00	18	22
R333	101	green	*Great Western*	80-81	15	25
R173	101	green	*1835 (GWR 150) 1985*	85	25	35
R794	4	green	*H.A.R.Wood*	91-92	20	25
R758	6 'Northern Nellie'	blue		83	20	25
R796	2	blue	*Crewe & District*	91-92	20	25
R759	7 'Southern Connie'	yellow		83	18	25
R759?	7 'Connie'	yellow		84	20	25
R155	21	yellow	*Colman's*, npf	84-85	18	23*
R155	21	yellow	*Colman's*, pf	?	25	30*
R760	8 'Polly'	red		83-84	18	25
R336	36 'Roger'	red		83-84	20	25*
R766	1 'Super S'	red		84-85	20	25*
R2129	105	red		99-00	15	22
R781	34 'Terry'	orange		83	15	22
R163	45	white	*Ford*	84-85	20	30
R153	1	grey	*Tolgus Tin Co*	86-88	20	25
R795	6	black	*Lion Works*	91-92	25	28
R854	23 'Sentinel'	maroon		96-98	20	25

A blue 'Forest of Pendle MRS' Holden 0-4-0T is Code 3, the transfers having been put on an R796 tank by the Society. 150 were made.

43. Class 29 Diesel Bo-Bo   npf = non paint finish

R.No.	Name / Number	Colour	Details	Years	£	£
R080	D6110	green	BRc, npf	78-79	20	25
R338	D6103	green	BRc	80-81	22	30
R2122	D6130	green	BRc, 2 tone green	99	30	40
R2122A	D6119	green	BRc, 2 tone green	00	30	40
R084	6124	blue	BRe	78-79	15	20
R337	6142	blue	BRe	80-82	20	25
R318	?	?	Sp Edn (Beatties)	82	NPG	NPG

44. 'King' Class 6000 4-6-0   npf = non paint finish   dc = double chimney
RD = presentation pack with Royal Doulton plate   bm = black metalwork

R.No.	Name / Number	Colour	Details	Years	£	£
R78	6024 'King Edward I'	green	*Great* (crest) *Western*, npf	78-79	25	35
R349	6013 'King Henry VIII'	green	*Great* (crest) *Western*	80-84	30	40
R70	6000 'King George V'	green	*Great* (crest) *Western*, in GWR 150 set	85	35	40*
R292	6027 'King Richard I'	green	*Great* (crest) *Western*	88-90	40	50
R82	6008 'King James II'	green	*Great* (crest) *Western*	93-94	40	50
R650	6018 'King Henry VI'	green	*Great* (crest) *Western*, RD, Ltd Edn 3000	96	45	60
R2022	6006 'King George I'	green	*Great* (crest) *Western*	97-98	40	50
R2119	6014 'King Henry VII'	green	*Great* (crest) *Western*	97-99	40	50
R303	6005 'King George II'	green	BRc, dc	95-96	40	50
R845	6010 'King Charles I'	green	BRc, in set, dc	96-97	45	50*
R2077	6026 'King John'	green	BRc, + 3 coaches, train pack	98	70	90
R2084	6009 'King Charles II'	green	BRa, train pack, Sp Edn 1500 (Kays)	98	45	100
R737	6000 'King George V'	blue	BRb, bell	96-97	45	55

Some Hornby Kings have been renumbered/renamed after leaving the factory. These may be listed in the Code 3 section of this book.

45. Class A4 4-6-2
sd = super detailed version   ct = corridor tender   nct = non-corridor tender
v = with valances down over the wheels   nv = no valances down over the wheels
ebn = etched brass nameplate   pq = with plaque   npq = no plaque
npf = non-paint finish   RD = presentation pack with Royal Doulton plate

R.No.	Name / Number	Colour	Details	Years	£	£
R350	60022 'Mallard'	green	BRc, ct, pq, nv, npf	79	40	50
R309	60022 'Mallard'	green	BRc, ct, pq, nv	80-83 89-93	30	45
R353	60006 'Sir Ralph Wedgewood'	green	BRc, nct, nv, Ltd Edn 3000	94	50	80
	'Sir Ralph Wedgewood'		3 locos in presentation box	94	N/A	250
R144	60010 'Dominion of Canada'	green	BRc, ct, nv	94-95	40	60
R204	60019 'Bittern'	green	BRb, nct, nv	94-95	45	50*
R286	60021 'Wild Swan'	green	BRc, ct, nv, L.Edn 1000	96-97	40	60
R2032	60020 'Guillemot'	green	BRc, nct, nv, + 3 coaches, train pack	97	70	90
R2089	60014 'Silver Link'	green	BRb, sd, ct, nv, + 3 coaches, train pack	99	70	90
R2136	60012					
	'Commonwealth of Australia'	green	BRb, sd, ct, nv, ebn, Sp Edn 500	99	100	140
R2101	60030 'Golden Fleece'	green	BRc, sd, ct, nv	99	60	75

R294	60028 'Walter K. Whigham'	dp blue	BRa, ct, nv	95	40	60
R2037	60029 'Woodcock'	dp blue	BRa, ct, nv	97	45	70
R372	4902 'Seagull'	blue	*LNER*, ct, v	81-82	45	60
R077	4468 'Mallard'	blue	*LNER*, ct, pq, v	84-85, 91	40	50
R327	4468 'Mallard'	blue	*LNER*, ct, npq, v	88-89	35	45
R304	4468 'Mallard'	blue	*LNER*, nct, pq, v	93-94 96-98	40	55
R2059	4468 'Mallard'	blue	*LNER*, sd, nct, npq, v	98-00	50	80
R888	4498 'Sir Nigel Gresley'	blue	*LNER*, ct, v	87-88	50	70
R528	4498 'Sir Nigel Gresley'	blue	*LNER*, ct, nv, Ltd Edn 2000	92	60	100
R328	4469 'Sir Ralph Wedgewood'	blue	*LNER*, nct, v, Ltd Edn 3000	94	50	80
R304	4469 'Gadwall'	blue	*LNER*, nct, v, Sp Edn 1500 (Kays)	95	70	110
R649	1 'Sir Ronald Matthews'	blue	*LNER*, nct, nv, RD, Ltd Edn 3000	96	50	100
R2127	4903 'Peregrine'	blue	*LNER*, sd, nct v Ltd Edn 500	98-99	90	130
R2154	4485 'Kestrel'	blue	*LNER*, sd, ct, v	00	60	80
R376	60022 'Mallard'	blue	BRa, ct, pq, nv, Sp Edn 1000 (Kays)	90	80	120
R2167	60034 'Lord Farringdon'	blue	BRa, sd, ct, nv, + 3 coaches, train pack, Ltd Ed 2000	00	NPG	100
R099	2512 'Silver Fox'	silver	*LNER*, ct, v	85-89	60	85
R312	2509 'Silver Link'	silver	*LNER*, ct, v	90-93	55	75
R313	4482 'Golden Eagle'	green	*LNER*, ct ,v	90-94	45	70
R341	4466 'Sir Ralph Wedgewood'	black	*NE*, nct, nv, Ltd Edn 3000	94	50	80
R099	4466 'Herring Gull'	black	*LNER*, nct, nv, Sp Edn 1000 (Littlewoods)	95	120	180

Many Hornby A4s have been renumbered/renamed after leaving the factory. These may be listed in the Code 3 section of this book.

46. Class E2 0-6-0T   npf = non paint finish

R353	100	brown	*LBSC* npf	79	30	45
R315	100	brown	*LBSC*	80	25	40
R261	104, (101, 102, 103)	olive	*Southern*, alternative numbers	82-84	40	50
R157	103	black	*Southern*	85	50	60

47. Class 52 'Western' Diesel Hydraulic C-C   npf = non paint finish

R352	D1062 'Western Courier'	maroon	BRc, npf	79	25	35
R368	D1062 'Western Courier'	maroon	BRc	80-81	20	30
R101	D1039 'Western King'	maroon	BRc	94-95	30	38
R319	D1035 'Western Yeoman'	green	BRc	92-93	30	40
R778	D1008 'Western Harrier'	blue	BRe	81-82	30	40
R348	D1058 'Western Nobleman'	blue	BRe	96-97	28	37
R2158	D1013 'Western Ranger'	blue	BRe	00	28	34

48. 'Patriot' Class 4-6-0   npf = non paint finish

R357	5541 'Duke of Sutherland'	maroon	*LMS*, npf	79	32	40
R311	5541 'Duke of Sutherland'	maroon	*LMS*	80	35	50
R308	5533 'Lord Rathmore'	maroon	*LMS*	95-97	35	45
R2182A/B	5539 'E.C.Trench', 5514 'Holyhead'	maroon	*LMS*	00	50	68
R324	45519 'Lady Godiva'	black	BRa	83	40	55
R578	45537 'Private Sykes VC '	green	BRb	91-92	35	50

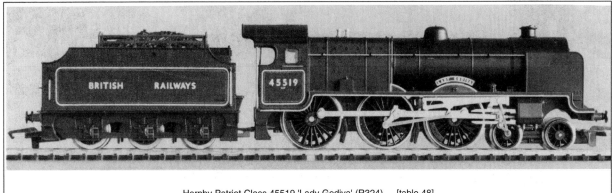

Hornby Patriot Class 45519 'Lady Godiva' (R324).   [table 48]

Hornby Class 0F Caledonian Pug LMS 16032 (R770).   [table 49]

Hornby Class 4P tank LMS 2309 (R299).   [table 50]

Hornby Class 2721 Pannier tank GWR 2730 (R760B).   [table 53]

Hornby Class 38XX GWR 3828 'County of Hereford' (R392).   [table 57]

Hornby Class V Schools Southern 907 'Dulwich' (R2124).   [table 54]

Hornby Class J13 saddle tank GNR 1226 (R2186B).   [table 58]

49. Class 0F 'Caledonian Pug' 0-4-0ST (for L&Y Pug see 78)

R.No.	Name / Number	Colour	Details	Years	£	£
R057	270	blue	*CR* Caledonian Railway	80-81	15	25
R255	8 'Loch Ness'	blue	*Highland Railway*	88-92	15	22
R072	6 'Ben-Y-Gloe'	blue	*Highland Railway*	94,97-00	15	20
R161	3	blue	*William Mansfield*	86-87	20	25*
R214	7	lt blue	*Powergen*	94-97	15	20
R782	56025 'Smokey Joe'	black	BR	83-98	12	20
R150	627	black	*Lancashire Yorkshire*	86-92	18	25
R300	16023	black	*LMS*	92-98	15	20
R770	16032	black	*LMS*, Sp Edn 480 (Beatties)	83	30	45
R266	16020 'Monty'	black	*LMS*	90	22	28
R337	16030	black	*LMS*	95-98	17	22
R2049	56038	black	BRa, Sp Edn (Hornby Collector's Club)	97	18	25
X****	56010	black	BRc, in R1017 set	99-00	15	20*
R159	313 'Robbie Burns'	maroon	*MR*, from sets	86-87	18	20*
R152	16031	maroon	*LMS*, from sets	90-93	20	25*
R2150	H2000	maroon	*Millenium Collectors Edition*	00	15	20
R779	7 'Desmond'	red		81-83	18	25
R752	205	brown	*Stewart & Lloyds*	83-85	20	28
R750	205	brown	*Stewart & Lloyds*, Sp Edn 260 (Grattans)	83	NPG	NPG
R174	4	brown	*Huntley & Palmer*	85	25	30
R162	112	yellow	*NCB*	84	20	28

50. Class 4P Tank 2-6-4T

R.No.	Name / Number	Colour	Details	Years	£	£
R055	2300	maroon	*LMS*	80-81	30	35
R505	2312	maroon	*LMS*	92	35	40
R261	2301	maroon	*LMS*	94-95	30	35
R299	2309	maroon	*LMS*	96-97	30	35
R088	2345	black	*LMS*	84-85	50	65
R062	42308	black	BRc	82-84	35	45
R239	42363	black	BRb	92-97	35	45

51. Class B17/4 4-6-0

R.No.	Name / Number	Colour	Details	Years	£	£
R053	2862 'Manchester United'	green	*LNER*	80-81	30	65
R053	2864 'Liverpool', 2848 'Arsenal', 2866 'Nottingham Forest'	green	*LNER*, alternative names for R053	80-82	40	N/A
R188	2848 'Arsenal'	green	*LNER*	92-93	30	50
X3558						
X3607	2862 'Manchester United'	green	*LNER*, green cylinders, Sp Ed 1500 (Kays)	97	40	50*
R2056	2857 'Doncaster Rovers'	green	*LNER*	98	35	55
R2185	2859 'Norwich City'	green	*LNER*	00	-	-
R060	61656 'Leeds United'	green	BRb	82-83	30	65
R060	61663 'Everton', 61665 'Leicester City', 61672 'West Ham United'	green	BRb, alternative names for R060	82-85	40	N/A
R133	61663 'Everton'	green	BRc	94-95	35	55
R315	61662 'Manchester United'	green	BRc	96-97	35	55
R2038A	61650 'Grimsby Town'	green	BRb, Sp Edn 250 (Rails)	97	75	100
R2038B	61654 'Sunderland'	green	BRb, Sp Edn 250 (Rails)	97	75	100
R2038C	61651 'Derby County'	green	BRb, Sp Edn 250 (Rails)	97	75	100
R2038D	61649 'Sheffield United'	green	BRb, Sp Edn 250 (Rails)	97	75	100
R2014	61664 'Liverpool'	green	BRc, Ltd Edn 1000	97	45	55
R2044	E1664 'Liverpool'	black	BRa, in train pack with 3 coaches, Sp Edn 1500 (Kays)	97	55	120

52. Class 370 APT

R.No.	Name / Number	Colour	Details	Years	£	£
R543	370 001/2 'City of Derby'	grey	BRe, *InterCity APT*, all yellow front, 5 car from set	80	55	65*
R794	370 001/2 'City of Derby'	grey	BRe, *InterCity APT*, yell + black front, 5 pack	81-85	65	95

53. Class 2721 0-6-0PT (open cab) (for Class 57XX Pannier see 32)

R.No.	Name / Number	Colour	Details	Years	£	£
R59	2744	green	*Great Western*	81-82,84	20	25
R165	2783	green	*Great Western*	89-93,95	20	25
R760	2776	green	*Great Western*	96-98	20	25
R760A	2783	green	*Great Western*	99	25	30
R2006	2788	green	*Great Western* in set R1000	96-00	20	25*
R158	2747	black	*Great Western*	85-88	35	50
R073	No5	red	coat of arms	93	25	35

54. Class V 'Schools' 4-4-0   RD = presentation pack with Royal Dalton plate.

R380	928 'Stowe'	malachite	*Southern*	81-82	50	65
R583	921 'Shrewsbury'	malachite	*Southern*	91-92	40	55
R648	905 'Tonbridge'	malachite	*Southern*, RD, Ltd Edn 3000	96	50	100
R2018	930 'Radley'	malachite	*Southern*	97-98	40	50
R2124	907 'Dulwich'	malachite	*Southern*	99-00	45	60
R2144	914 'Eastbourne'	malachite	*Southern*, Ltd Edn 1000	00	45	60
R683	926 'Repton'	olive	*Southern*	83-84	55	70
R817	900 'Eton'	olive	*Southern*, sometimes without smoke deflectors	86-87	45	60
R057	903 'Charterhouse'	olive	*Southern*	89-90	40	55
R533	934 'St. Lawrence'	olive	*Southern*, Ltd Edn 2000	92	65	85
R132	936 'Cranleigh'	olive	*Southern*	94-95	40	55
R25730	911 'Dover'	green	BRc	82-83	70	110
R31730	908 'Westminster'	green	BRc	96	45	60
(R2082)	30902 'Wellington'	green	BRc, + 3 coaches, train pack, Sp Edn 1500 (Kays)	98	70	100
R2181	30935 'Sevenoaks'	green	BRc	00	60	75
R08430	927 'Clifton'	black	BRb	84-85	55	80
R2039	30925 'Cheltenham'	black	BRb Sp Edn 1000 (Cheltenham Model Centre)	97	40	50
R2079	30912 'Downside'	black	BRc in train pack with 3 Pulman cars, Ltd Edn 2000,	98	90	120

Many Hornby Schools have been renumbered/renamed after leaving the factory. These may be listed in the Code 3 section of this book.

55. Class 4P Compound 4-4-0

R376	1000	maroon	*LMS*	81-82	40	55
R755	?	?	*LMS*, Sp Edn 300	82	-	-
R355	1000	maroon	MR	83-85	50	70
R175	41043	black	BRa	86-87	40	60

56. Class D49/1 'Shire/Hunt' 4-4-0

R378	2753 'Cheshire'	green	*LNER*	81-82	40	55
R859	359 'The Fitzwilliam'	green	*LNER*	87-89	40	55
R123	222 'The Berkeley'	green	*LNER*	94-95	40	55
R259	62700 'Yorkshire'	black	BRb	83-84	55	70
R860	62750 'The Pytchley'	black	BRb	87-89	40	50
R2021	62758 'The Cattistock'	black	BRc	97-98	45	60

57. Class 38XX 'Churchward County' 4-4-0

R392	3821 'County of Bedford'	green	*Great O Western*	81-83	30	45
R390	3830 'County of Oxford'	green	*Great O Western*	84-85	45	65
R584	3825 'County of Denbigh'	green	*Great* (crest) *Western*	91-92	30	45
R298	3828 'County of Hereford'	green	*Great O Western*, Ltd Edn. 2000	91	75	100
R125	3824 'County of Cornwall'	green	*Great O Western*	94-95	35	50

Hornby –
two versions of the
APT (R794).

[table 52]

(Miles Rowland)

58. Class J13/J52 0-6-0ST

R.No.	Name / Number	Colour	Details	Years	£	£
R396	1247	green	*GNR*	81-82,84	30	45
R2186A/B	1241, 1226	green	*GNR*	00	28	33
R861	3980	black	*LNER*	87-88	35	55
R504	3111	black	*LNER*	92-93	35	50
R186	68846	black	BRc	92-94	30	45

59. Class 86/2 Electric

R.No.	Name / Number	Colour	Details	Years	£	£
R360	86219 'Phoenix'	blue	BRe	81-83	25	35
R367	86243 'The Boy's Brigade'	blue	BRe	83-84	35	55
R2120	86218 'NHS 50'	blue	*Anglia*	99	38	45
R2160	86235 'Crown Point'	blue	*Anglia*	00	40	50
R368	86401	brt blue	BRe NSE	88-89	35	50
R800	86246 'Royal Anglian Regiment'	grey	BRe InterCity	86-87	30	35
R289	86417 'The Kingsman', 86255 'Penrith Beacon', 86228 'Vulcan Heritage'	grey	BRe InterCity, alternative names	88-89	35	50
R388	86414 'Frank Hornby'	grey	BRe InterCity, Ltd Edn	88-89	35	50
R333	86405, 86419, 86431	grey	*InterCity*, alt. nos.	90-92	30	45
R335	86504 'Halley's Comet'	grey	BRe Railfreight General	90-94	30	45
R589	86419 'Post Haste'	red	BRe Parcels	91-94	30	50
R322	86417	red	BRe RES	96-97	35	50
R301	86210 'C.I.T 75th Anniv'	red	BRe RES Sp Edn 1000 (CIT)	96	35	40
R2159	86261 'The Rail Charter Partnership'	maroon	*EWS*	00	40	50

60. Class 110 DMU

alt. nos. = a sheet with two sets of alternative numbers is provided in the pack
dest. = a choice of three destination blinds is provided

R.No.	Name / Number	Colour	Details	Years	£	£
R698	E51816/E59707/E51832	white	BRe, 3 car set, dest. (2 sets)	82-83	35	45
R377	E52073/E59816/E51846	white	BRe, 3 car set, dest.	96-97	35	45
R687	E51824/E59708/E51844	green	BRc, 3 car set, dest.(2 sets)	83-84	40	50
R369	E51829/E59695/E51812	green	BRc, 3 car set, dest.	92-98	40	50
R267	E51819/E51846	blue	BRe, 2 car set, alt. nos., dest.	89-91	25	30
R403	E51815/E59814/E52078	blu+grey	BRe, 3 car set, alt. nos., dest.	84-85	35	45
R2073	E51827/E59808/E52080	blu+grey	BRe, 3 car set, dest.	98	40	55
R2073A	E52066/E59696/E52085	blu+grey	BRe, 3 car set, dest.	99-00	40	55

61. Class 58 Diesel

R.No.	Name / Number	Colour	Details	Years	£	£
R332	58007	grey	BRe, number at both ends	82	30	40
R250	58007	grey	BRe, number at one end *Railfreight*	83	25	35
R250	58001	grey	BRe *Railfreight*	84-91	20	25
R887	58048	grey	BRe *Railfreight*	94	30	35*
R283	58034 'Bassetlaw'	grey	BRe *Railfreight*	88-89	35	50
R705	58050 'Toton Traction Depot'	grey	BRe Railfreight Coal Sector	88-89	30	45

Hornby Class 86/2 Anglia Railways 86218 'NHS 150' (R2120).   [table 59]

R332	58044, 58006, 58025	grey	BRe Railfreight Coal Sector	90-94	30	47
R358	58050 'Toton Traction Depot'	blue	*Mainline*	96	40	55
R2011A	58023 'Peterborough Depot'	blue	*Mainline*	97-98	35	45
R2011B/C	58021 'Hither Green Depot', 58042 'Petrolea'	blue	*Mainline*	97	40	50
R2034	58033	maroon	*EW&S*	97-98	35	45
R2125A/B	58030, 58039	maroon	*EWS*	99	35	45
R2125C	58047	maroon	*EWS*	00	35	45

62. 'Princess' Class 4-6-2 (scale model) (for non-scale model see 1)

R050	6200 'The Princess Royal'	maroon	*LMS*, Fowler tender	84-86	45	60
R832	6201 'Princess Elizabeth'	maroon	*LMS*, maroon tender chassis	86-88	40	55
R084	6201 'Princess Elizabeth'	maroon	*LMS*, black tender chassis	93-94	40	55
R375	6210 'Lady Patricia'	maroon	*LMS*, Sp Edn 1000 (Kays)	90	50	65
R2033	6208 'Princess Helena Victoria'	maroon	*LMS*, + 3 coaches, train pack, Ltd Edn 3000	97	70	90
R2052	6211 'Queen Maud'	maroon	*LMS*, Sp Edn 1000 (A.B.Gee)	98	50	75
R2051	6206 'Princess Marie Louise'	black	*LMS*, Sp Edn 1000 (A.B.Gee)	98	50	75
R037	46210 'Lady Patricia'	blue	*BRb*	89-91	45	65
R138	46208 'Princess Helena Victoria'	blue	*BRb*	94-95	45	65
R080	46201 'Princess Elizabeth'	green	*BRb*	84-85	40	60
R196	46209 'Princess Beatrice'	green	*BRb*	92-93	45	65
R2070	46204 'Princess Louise'	green	*BRb*, Sp Edn 1000 (A.B.Gee)	98	50	75

Some Hornby Princesses have been renumbered/renamed after leaving the factory. These may be listed in the Code 3 section of this book.

63. Class 29XX 'Saint' 4-6-0 (adapted from the Tri-ang Hornby Hall)

R830	2920 'Saint David'	green	*Great* (crest) *Western*	86-87	40	55
R141	2918 'Saint Catherine'	green	*Great* (crest) *Western*	94-95	45	60
R2019	2927 'Saint Patrick'	green	*G* (crest) *W*	97-98	40	55
R380	2937 'Clevedon Court'	black	*BRb*	88-91	50	65

64. Class 142 'Pacer' DMU

R867	142048 (55589/55639)	blue	BRe Provincial Sector	87-92	28	35
R297	142013 (55554/55604)	orange	BRe Manchester PTE	88-90	45	65
R326	142015 (55556/55606)	brown/ cream	BRe Western England	92-93	50	70
R103	142023 (55564/55614)	grey	BRe *Regional Railways*	94-95	35	55
R451	142069 (55589/55639)	grey	BRe *Regional Railways*	96-97	35	55
R***	142020 (55589/55639)	yellow	BRe *Regional Railways* Tyne&Wear PTE	95-96	40	48*
X****	142065 (55715/55761)	blue	*Northern Spirit*, Sp Edn (Kays)	99	30	45*
R2161	142074 (55742/55770)	blue	*Northern Spirit*	00	40	55

65. Class 06 Diesel Shunter 0-4-0DS

R875	D2428	green	BRc	87-89	25	35
R136	D2424	green	BRc	95-96	25	35
R****	D2412	green	BRc, for HCC members	00	-	-
R051	6	green	*Redland*	93-94	25	35
R874	06005	blue	BRe	87-91	20	35
R2009	8	blue	*ECC*	97-98	22	30
R2003	06008	grey	BRe Set R1003	97-98	28	30*
R2184	06003	grey	Rf Distribution	00	22	27
R799	4	grey	*CEGB*	91-93	22	30
R801	302	yellow	*Tilbury Refineries*	91-93	22	30
R061	302	yellow	*Hornby Railways*	93-98	15	25
R234	A5	cream	*Robert Horne*	95-97	20	30

66. Class 8F 2-8-0

R315	8193	black	*LMS*	88-89	40	60
R325	8193	black	*LMS*	90	45	65
R325	8027	black	*LMS*	90-92	50	70
R325	8118	black	*LMS*	90-92	50	70
R325	8233	black	*LMS*	90-92	50	70
R297	8035	black	*LMS*	96-97	40	60
R322	48758	black	*BRb*	88-89	40	60
R324	48774	black	*BRb*	90-93	50	70
R324	48141	black	*BRb*	90-93	50	70
R324	48278	black	*BRb*	90-93	50	70
R2055	48705	black	*BRc*	98	45	65
R2043	300	grey	*WD*, Sp Edn 500 (Much Ado About Toys)	97	130	200

Hornby
Class 110 DMU
(R2073)

[table 60]

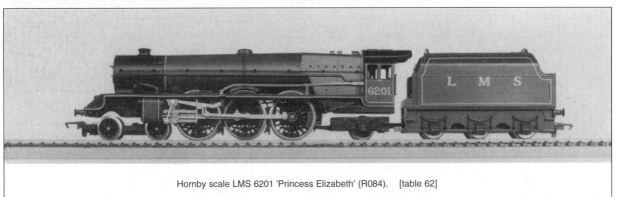

Hornby scale LMS 6201 'Princess Elizabeth' (R084).   [table 62]

Hornby
Class 142
Northern Spirit Pacer
(R2161)

[table 64]

Hornby Class 06 0-4-0DS Engineer's Dept. 06008 (R2003).   [table 65]

Hornby Class 8F 48705 (R2055).   [table 66]

Hornby
Class 90 Virgin
90015 (R2109A)

[table 67]

67. Class 90 Electric

R.No.	Name / Number	Colour	Details	Years	£	£
R242	90001	grey	*Intercity* Swallow	88-90	35	45
R***	90028	grey	BRe InterCity	?	50	60
R593	90030, 90033, 90034	grey	BRe	91-92	40	50
R586	90042, 90040, 90037	grey	BRe Railfreight Distribution	91-94	40	50
R270	90131	grey	*Railfreight Distribution*	95-96	35	45
R2005	90135	grey	*Railfreight Distribution*	97	35	45
R595	90020	red	BRe Parcels/ dummy pantograph	91-93	45	50*
R062	90018	red	BRe Res	93-94	45	55
R2048	90002 'Mission Impossible'	red+blk	*Virgin*, Sp Edn of 500 (Model Rail)	97	60	85
R2067	90912 'British Transport Police'	red+blk	*Virgin*	98	35	45
R2109A	90015 'The International Brigade Spain 1936-1939'	red+blk	*Virgin*	99-00	35	45
R2019B	90014	red+blk	*Virgin*	99-00	35	45
R2110	90020 'Sir Michael Heron'	maroon	*EWS*	99-00	35	45

68. Class 91 Electric

R.No.	Name / Number	Colour	Details	Years	£	£
R240	91001	grey	*InterCity* Swallow	88-92	30	40
R269	91014	grey	*InterCity* Swallow, dummy pantograph	91-97	30	38*
R585	91004 'The Red Arrows'	grey	*InterCity* Swallow	91-92	45	60
R585	91011 'Terence Cuneo'	grey	*InterCity* Swallow	91-92	45	60
R585	91001 'Swallow'	grey	*InterCity* Swallow	91-92	45	60
R392	91025 'BBC Radio 1 FM'	grey	*InterCity* Swallow	93	45	60
R***	91025 'BBC Radio One FM'	grey	*InterCity* Swallow, Sp Edn	92?	90	120
R356	91003 'The Scotsman'	grey	*InterCity* Swallow	94	40	50
R293	91009 'Saint Nicholas'	grey	*InterCity* Swallow	95	40	50
R367	91031 'Henry Royce'	grey	*InterCity* Swallow	96-97	35	45
R2069	91022 'Robert Adley'	grey	*InterCity* Swallow	98-99	35	45
X3554	91019 'Scottish Enterprise'	navy	*GNER* train pack	97-00	50	75
X****	91003	navy	*GNER*	98	35	45

69. Class 2800 2-8-0

R.No.	Name / Number	Colour	Details	Years	£	£
R532	2859	green	*Great Western*	91-93	55	70
R2053	2844	green	*GWR* (button)	98	45	60
R2153A/B	2821, 2869	green	*GWR*	00	60	74
R143	2857	black	BRc	94-97	50	65

70. Class D 0-4-0T

R.No.	Name / Number	Colour	Details	Years	£	£
R531	40 'King George V'	red		91-92	12	18
R863	43 'Queen Mary'	red		92-96	10	15*
R058		red	*Hornby*	93-98	10	15*
R153	5	red	*ER*	94, 97-00	15	20
R069	23	blue	*Hensall Sand*	93-94	15	20
R2058	7	blue	*BRb*	98	20	25
R2131	1203	blue	*CR*	99-00	15	20
R068	5	grey	*NCB*	93-94	15	20
R066		grey	*Hornby*	93-94?	20	N/A
R856	9	green	*BRa*	96-98	10	15*
R368	40 'King George V'	green		95-97	12	18
R066		yellow	*Hornby*	93-98	10	15

71. Class 92 Electric

R.No.	Name / Number	Colour	Details	Years	£	£
R289	92009 'Elgar'	grey	BRe Tunnel *Railfreight Distribution*	95-97	35	50*
R374	92020 'Milton'	grey	*EPS* Tunnel	96	45	65
R855	92022 'Charles Dickens'	grey	BRe Tunnel *Railfreight Distribution*, from R825 train set	96-97	35	55*
R2004	92026 'Britten'	grey	BRe Tunnel	97-98	40	55
R2035	92045 'Chaucer'	grey	*EPS* Tunnel	97	45	60

72. Class 373 'Eurostar' (Jouef) (H0 scale model)

R.No.	Name / Number	Colour	Details	Years	£	£
R543	3211/3212	grey	E Tunnel, (*Jouef* on under side)	95	30	50

73. Class 373 Eurostar (Hornby)

R.No.	Name / Number	Colour	Details	Years	£	£
R665 Eur 3021/X	3015/3016	grey	Tunnel, train pack	96-97	35	50
Eur 3022/X	3021/3022	grey	Tunnel from train set	96-97	35	45*
R665A	****/****	grey	Tunnel train pack	99	35	50
X****	3219/****	grey	Tunnel from train set	99-00	35	45*

74. Class 14XX 0-4-2T (ex-Airfix model)

R2026	1458	green	*GWR*	97-98	25	35
R2026A	1472	green	*GWR*	98	25	35
R2026B/C	1427, 1444	green	*GWR*	00	25	35
R2095A/B	1421, 1470	green	BRc	99-00	30	35
R2173	?	green	BR?, train pack with 2 coaches, Ltd + Sp Edn 1000?	00	NPG	73

75. Class 4073 'Castle' 4-6-0 (ex-Dapol model)

R2028	5042 'Winchester Castle'	green	BRb, train pack with 3 coaches	97-98	70	90
R2086	5053 'Earl Cairns'	green	BRb	98-00	50	60
R2088	5097 'Sarum Castle'	green	BRa, Sp Edn 1000 (Beatties)	98	60	80
R2090	5004 'Llanstephen Castle'	green	BRb, train pack with 3 coaches, Ltd Edn 2000	99	70	90
R2133M	7025 'Sudeley Castle'	green	BRb, train pack with 3 coaches, Sp Edn 1000 (Kays)	99	80	100
R2141	5069 'Isambard Kingdom Brunel'	green	BRb Sp Edn 1000 (A.B.Gee)	99	60	80

Some Hornby Castles have been renumbered/renamed after leaving the factory. These may be listed in the Code 3 section of this book.

76. Class 1000 'Hawksworth County' 4-6-0 (ex-Dapol model)

R2029	1004 'County of Somerset'	green	G(crest)W, train pack with 3 coaches	97-98	70	110
R2085	1029 'County of Worcester'	green	G(crest)W	98	55	70
R2166	1006 'County of Cornwall'	green	BRc, train pack with 3 coaches	00	NPG	100
R2097	1015 'County of Gloucester'	black	BRb	99-00	60	70
R2174	1022 'County of Northampton'	green	BRb, Sp Edn 1000?	00	NPG	75

77. 'Networker' DMU

R2001	466*** (64899/78351)	white	NSE, *Kent Link Networker*	97-98	55	80
R2001A	466016 (64875/78327)	white	NSE, *Kent Link Networker*	99-00	50	70

78. 'L&Y Pug' 0-4-0ST (ex-Dapol model)

R2065	11232	black	*LMS*	98-99	25	30
R2065A	11250	black	*LMS*	00	25	30
R2093A/B	51218, 51222	black	BRb	99	25	30
R2093C	51235	black	BRb	00	25	30

79. Class A1X 'Terrier' Tank 0-6-0T (ex-Dapol model)

R2063	W2 'Freshwater'	green	*Southern*	98	35	45
R2100A	W11	green	*Southern*	99	30	40
R2100B	W12	green	*Southern*	00	30	40
R2156A/B	32670, 32636	black	BRc	00	32	40
R2192	54 'Waddon'	pl. brown	LBSC, Ltd Edn 1000	00	NPG	40

80. Class J94 'Austerity' 0-6-0ST (ex-Dapol model)

R2062	8006	black	*LNER*	98	30	40
R2094A/B	68049, 68062	black	BRc	99	30	40
R2094C	68080	black	BRc	00	30	40
R2151	157	blue	*LMR*	99-00	30	40
R2096	'Harry'	red	NCB	99-00	30	40

Hornby Collectors Club

Join the official Hornby Collectors Club and keep up to date with the latest news and model releases. Benefits include:

- 6 bi-monthly full colour A4 magazines packed full of useful Hornby information and reader offers during your subscription year
- Membership card entitling you to discount on your Hornby purchases from many Hornby Service Dealers
- the chance to win fantastic prizes through club competitions
- FREE annual Club model. The Year 2000 model, available until the end of December 2000 is the Class 06, 0-4-0 diesel locomotive in BR green
- the opportunity to purchase selected Hornby releases through Hornby's direct sales outlet.

The Year 2000 subscription is £14 (UK); £16 (Europe); £18 (RoW). Send your application and remittance (cheques drawn on a British bank and payable to Hornby Hobbies Ltd) to Hornby Collectors Club, PO Box 35, Royston, Herts., UK, SG8 5XR. Visa/Mastercard accepted with valid expiry date. Please ring for details of the Club model and subscriptions payable in 2001/2002.

Tel/Fax: (01223) 208308. Website: www.hornby.com   Please quote the John Ramsay Guide when responding.

R.No.	Name / Number	Colour	Details	Years	£	£

81. Class 4F 0-6-0 (ex-Airfix model)

R.No.	Name / Number	Colour	Details	Years	£	£
R2066	44331	black	BRc	98	35	45
R2135M	44313	black	BRc yellow stripe	99-00	40	60
R2138	44523	black	BRb train pack with 6 wagons, 1000 (A.B.Gee)	99	60	90
R2148	?	blue	S&DJR, Ltd Edn 1000	00	NPG	NPG

82. Class 56 Diesel Co-Co (ex-Mainline model)

R.No.	Name / Number	Colour	Details	Years	£	£
R2074/B	56100, 56109	black	*Loadhaul*	98, 00	30	50
R2074A	56118	black	*Loadhaul* Ltd Edn 500	98	50	70
R2075	56058	maroon	*EW&S*	98	30	45
R2075A	56105	maroon	*EW&S* Ltd Edn 500	98	50	70
R2107A/B/C	56119, 56127, 56123 'Drax Power Station'	grey	BRe *Transrail*	99	30	50
R2107D	56066	grey	BRe *Transrail*	00	30	50
R2106	56049	gry+yell	*Transrail* Dutch	99	30	50
R2106A	56047	gry+yell	*Transrail* Dutch	00	30	50

83. Class 2361 'Dean Goods' 0-6-0 (ex-Airfix model)

R.No.	Name / Number	Colour	Details	Years	£	£
R2064A	2468	green	*Great Western*	98-00	35	45
R2064B	2526	green	*Great Western*, Ltd Edn 500	99	50	60
R2064C	2579	green	*Great Western*	00	35	45

84. Class 2P 4-4-0 (ex-Mainline)(for earlier non-scale 2P model see 34)

R.No.	Name / Number	Colour	Details	Years	£	£
R2099A/B	579, 645	black	*LMS*	99	35	40
R2099C	644	black	*LMS*	00	35	40
R2183A/B	40610, 40634	black	BRa	00	40	54
R2172	634	black	LMS, train pack with 3 coaches, Sp Edn 1000?	00	NPG	100

85. Class 155 Super Sprinter DMU (ex-Dapol model)

R.No.	Name / Number	Colour	Details	Years	£	£
R2108	155344(57344/52344)	maroon	Metro, 2 car set	99-00	45	60
R2162A/B	155325(57325/52325) 155317(57317/52317)	grey+blu	Provincial, 2 car set	00	45	60

86. Class 61XX Prairie Tank 2-6-2T (ex-Airfix model)

R.No.	Name / Number	Colour	Details	Years	£	£
R2098	6113	green	*Great Western*	99	35	47
R2098A	6147	green	*Great Western*	00	35	47
R2143	6150	green	*Great Western*, Ltd Edn 1000	99	40	50

87. Class N2 Tank 0-6-2T (ex-Airfix model)

R.No.	Name / Number	Colour	Details	Years	£	£
R2178A/B	69546, 69506	black	BRc, lined	00	35	47

88. 'Coronation' Class 4-6-2 (scale model) (for non-scale model see 30)

R.No.	Name / Number	Colour	Details	Years	£	£
R2179	6229 'Duchess of Hamilton'	green	*LMS*, sd	00	-	

Some Hornby Coronations have been renumbered/renamed after leaving the factory. These may be listed in the Code 3 section of this book.

89. 'Merchant Navy' Class (Rebuilt) 4-6-2

R.No.	Name / Number	Colour	Details	Years	£	£
R2169	35028 'Clan Line'	green	BRc, sd	00	70	90
R2170	35023 'Holland-Afrika Line'	green	BRb, sd	00	70	90
R2171	35005 'Canadian Pacific'	blue	BRb, sd	00	-	-

Some Hornby Merchant Navys have been renumbered/renamed after leaving the factory. These may be listed in the Code 3 section of this book.

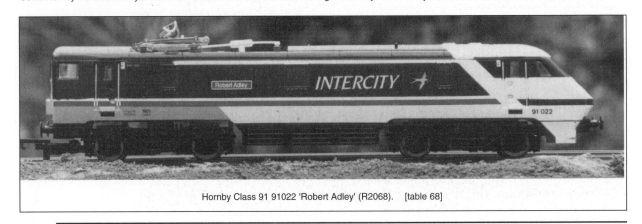

Hornby Class 91 91022 'Robert Adley' (R2068).   [table 68]

Hornby Class 2800 GWR 2839 (R2153B).   [table 69]

Hornby Class D 0-4-0 (R2058).   [table 70]

Hornby
Castle Class 5069
'Isambard Kingdom Brunel'
(R2141)

[table 75]

PLAY LOCOMOTIVES

P1. Top Tank 0-4-0T

Cat.No.	Name / Number	Colour	Details	Years	£	£
R657	-	black	also R659, R659	63-67	3	8
R660	-	brt blue		66?	4	10
R660	-	mid blue		66?	8	15
R660	-	yellow		67	4	10
R660	-	dk.green		68	5	12

0-4-0 Diesel Shunter (see 20. 0-4-0DS North British Shunter)

P2. Barclay 0-4-0DS

Cat.No.	Name / Number	Colour	Details	Years	£	£
R858	-	blue		69-71?	25	30*
R858	-	red		?	35	40*

P3. Continental Tank 0-4-0T

Cat.No.	Name / Number	Colour	Details	Years	£	£
R852	7744	blue		68-74	12	15*
R852	7744	black		?68	10	15
R852T	7744	black	NMRA couplings	?68	10	15
R852CN	Chugga	yellow		69-71	40	80
R854		red	c/w	69?-79	5	7*
R854	1863	red	c/w	71?	25	30*
R854		maroon	c/w	69?-79	8	10*
R854		green	c/w	71	10	12*
R854	7321	bt green	c/w	71-72	12	15*
R854	7321	dk green	c/w	?	8	10*
R854	7321	red	c/w	?	10	12*
R854	7321	black	c/w	73-82	10	15
R854T	?	?	NMRA couplings	?	30	60
R755	6042	black	c/w	73-74	10	12*
R?	Timmy	red	c/w	83-87	12	15*
T121	Peter	yell	c/w	83-84	12	15*
T118	Adam, Michael, Simon, Robert	red	c/w	84-90?	12	15*
T118	Edward, Douglas	blue	c/w	84-90?	12	15*
T118	Henry	green	c/w	84-90?	12	15*
T118	Ivor	red	c/w	91-?	14	17*
T774	Postman Pat	red	c/w T107 set	?-87	20	25*
T868	2571	red	c/w	88-94	7	10
T113	Pound Puppies	yell	c/w T113 set	?-87	20	25*

P4. Swedish Diesel 0-4-0

Cat.No.	Name / Number	Colour	Details	Years	£	£
R853	?	blue		69	25	30*
R853	5771	yellow		69-71	20	25*
R853	4718	red		69-71	20	25*

P5. Wild West 0-4-0

Cat.No.	Name / Number	Colour	Details	Years	£	£
R873	1863	red	tender	71	80	100*

P6. International Tank 0-4-0T

Cat.No.	Name / Number	Colour	Details	Years	£	£
R254	254	black		75-76	15	20
R256	256	black		76-77	12	17
R256	256	red		77	12	17
R257	256	green		77	15	20
R256	Bulldog	green		83	20	25
R164	Iron Horse	grey		84-85	20	25

P7. Thomas the Tank Engine and Friends

Cat.No.	Name / Number	Colour	Details	Years	£	£
R251	1 (Thomas)	blue	chassis 0-6-0T, push along	88-92 95-?	5	7*
R352 /R9005	1 (Thomas)	blue	chassis 0-4-0T, clockwork	86-98	8	13
R354	1 (Thomas)	blue	chassis 0-4-0T, electric	95-98	10	12*
R9034	1 (Thomas)	blue	chassis 0-6-0T, clockwork	99	5	8
R350	6 (Percy)	green	chassis 0-4-0ST, electric	85-99	15	20
R810/R4004	6 (Percy)	green	chassis 0-4-0ST, clockwork	87-98	8	13
R9035	6 (Percy)	green	chassis 0-4-0ST, clockwork	99	5	8
R351	1 (Thomas)	blue	chassis 0-6-0T, electric	85-99	20	30
R383	4 (Gordon)	blue	chassis 4-6-2, electric	86-92, 95-99	35	55

Tri-ang Railways
Class B12 BR 61572
(R150)
[table 20]

Tri-ang Railways
Princess Royal 46200
'The Princess Royal'
(R258)
[table 1]

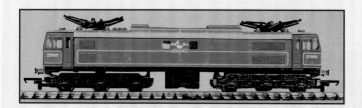

Tri-ang Hornby
Class EM2 27000
(R351)
[table 16]

Tri-ang Hornby
Class BB 34051
'Winston Churchill'
(R356)
[table 17]

Tri-ang Railways
Class 3F MR 3775
(R251)
[table 10]

Tri-ang Hornby
Class 9F 92220
'Evening Star'
(R861)
[table 31]

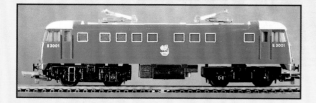

Tri-ang Hornby
Class AL1 E3001
(R753)
[table 25]

Hornby ex-Caledonian Pug as LMS 16032 (R770) [table 49] and Hornby Class 47 BR 47480 'Robin Hood' (R769) [table 35]
Beatties received 480 of each in 1983

Hornby LMS streamlined Princess Coronation as 6244 'King George VI' (R767) [table 30]
500 were supplied to Beatties in 1983

Hornby BR Class A4 as 60022 'Mallard' in LNER garter blue (R376) [table 45]
1000 were made for Kays in 1990

Hornby LMS Princess Royal as 6210 'Lady Patricia' (R375) [table 62]
1000 were made for Kays in 1990

Hornby GWR Class 38XX as 3828 'County of Hereford' (R298) [table 57]
2000 were made in 1991

Hornby BR Britannia as 70032 'Tennyson' (R378) [table 13]
2000 were made for Kays in 1991

Hornby BR Princess Coronation as 46250 'City of Litchfield' (R102) [table 39]
2000 were made for Kays in 1991

Hornby LNER Class A4 as 4498 'Sir Nigel Gresley' (as preserved) (R528) [table 45]
2000 were made in 1992

Hornby BR 70000 'Britannia (on royal train duties) (R507) [table 13]
2000 were made in 1992

Hornby BR blue Princess Coronation as 46231 'Duchess of Atholl' (R372) [table 39]
1500 were made for Kays in 1992

Hornby Schools Class as 934 'St. Lawrence' (R533) [table 54]
2000 were made in 1992

Hornby Black 5 in green as 44932 (R347) [table 33]
1500 were made for Kays in 1992

BRITANNIA'S

TMC131 70037 **Hereward The Wake**
TMC132 70029 **Shooting Star**
TMC133 70017 **Arrow**
TMC134 70010 **Owen Glendown**
TMC135 70000 **Britannia**
TMC174 70040 **Clive Of India**
Price £94.99 + £3 P&P

The above TMC exclusive limited editions are based on the new
Hornby 'Super Detail' Britannia model featuring:- Midland
region smoke deflectors with hand rails replaced by grab holes,
blackened finish valve gear, wheels, hand rails
& fitted etched brass nameplates.
Limited to **250** of each model, accompanied by uniquely
numbered certificate.

THE SPANISH ARMADA

This is our first release consisting of a pair of **Bachmann Jubilee's**.
45679 **Armada** with Fowler tender and late crest.
45670 **Howard of Effingham** with Stanier tender and early crest.
31-150Y   **£175 + P&P**

THE RAINHILL TRIALS

This is our second release consisting of a pair of **Bachmann Jubilee's**.
45732 **Sanspareil** with Stanier tender and late crest.
45733 **Novelty** with Stanier tender and early crest.
31-150Z   **£175 + P&P**

The above exclusives are limited to only **250** of each pair and
come complete with certificate and wooden presentation case,
along with a brief history of each locomotive.
(Etched nameplates are included and features sprung buffers.)

TMC EXCLUSIVES

A wide range of models not otherwise available.
We make what our research shows you want. *'Listening to your suggestions'*
All liveries are ex-factory finish (*Standard*).

Due to Popular demand our TMC range of Exclusive Limited Editions continues to grow and currently stands at:-

32 Variations of Gresley's A3 Class	28 Variations of BR Britannia Class	28 Variations of Maunsells Schools Class
30 Variations of Gresley's A4 Class	29 Variations of Staniers Duchess Class	3 Variations of BR Castles with Hawksworth Tenders
1 King Class	9 Variations of WD Austerity Class	5 Variations of Hornby Streamlined Duchess Class
2 Princess Class	1 BR Evening Star STD Class	6 Variations of Hornby Merchant Navy Class

Model range increasing all the time.

EDDIE STOBART LTD
HORNBY CURTAIN SIDED WAGON

TMC together with Eddie Stobart Ltd commission various
models, please phone for details.

Ref. R6101 3rd model in the series.

R382	8 (Duck)	green	chassis 0-6-0PT, electric	86-91, 95-99	25	35
R317	(Devious Diesel)	black	chassis 0-6-0DS, electric	87-88	45	60
R852	5 (James)	red	chassis 0-4-0T, electric	88-99	30	50
R90	(Bertie the Bus)	maroon	clockwork	88-92 95-98	15	18*
R9024	Bill	yellow	chassis 0-4-0ST, clockwork	99	5	8
R9025	7 (Toby)	brown	Tram, clockwork	99	5	8
R9026	Ben	yellow	chassis 0-4-0ST, clockwork	99	5	8

P8. Push-Along Models 0-4-0T

T123	Gordon	blue	push along	84	3	5*
T123	Percy	green	push along	84	3	5*
T123	Thomas	blue	push along	84	3	5*
T123	James	red	push along	84	3	5*
T119	4 Dixie	red	push along	83	3	5*
T120	2 Pixie	blue	push along	83	3	5*
T116	My First Train	red	push along	91-?	5	8*
T106	5 Postman Pat	red	push along	84	5	8*

TRANSCONTINENTAL (produced with overseas markets in mind)

T1. Class 23 TC Pacific (Hiawatha) 4-6-2   8wt = 8 wheel tender   6wt = A3 6 wheel tender

R54+R32	2335	black	8wt		54-61	20	40
R54+R32	2335 Hiawatha	black	8wt		62-69	30	50
R54+R32	2335 Hiawatha	black	8wt number in yellow		?	40	70
R54S	2335 Hiawatha	black	8wt, with smoke		68	40	60
R54S	2335 Hiawatha	black	Acho couplings		68	50	100
R54S+R32L	2335 Hiawatha	black	Lima couplings		68	90	150
R?	2335 Hiawatha	black	6wt		70?	40	60
various	1542	black	6wt		70-73	30	50
various	2335	black	*Canadian Pacific*		69-73	70	120

The model was also sent out to Australia and New Zealand for finishing and sale in local packaging.

T2. Class Wab Baltic Tank 4-6-4T   (lamps front and back)

R56	4830	black		55-60	20	75
R56	4830	maroon		61	100	150

The model was also made in Australia, New Zealand and South Africa.

T3. Class F7 A+B Units ('Single Ended Diesel')

R55	4008 (A unit)	silv+red	TR, silver cabs	55-57	15	40
R57	4008 (dummy A unit)	silv+red	TR, silver cabs	55-57	10	30
R56	4008 (B unit)	silv+red	no cabs	56-60	15	40
R56	4008 (B unit)	silv+red	no cabs, number both ends	56	30	50
R56	4009 (B unit)	silv+red	no cabs	?	50	90
R55	4008 (A unit)	silv+red	TR, red cabs	58-61	12	30
R57	4008 (dummy A unit)	silv+red	TR, red cabs	58-61	8	20
R55	4008 (A unit)	silv+red	*Transcontinental*	62-64	20	55
R55	4008 (A unit)	silv+red	two motors	63	50	90
R55	4008 (A unit)	silv+red	*TransAustralia*	66-66,70	90	120
R0551	4008 (A unit)	blk+red	*CN*	65-66 69-73	12	30
R0552*	4008 (A unit)	gry+mrn	*Canadian Pacific*	67-69	80	120
R0553*	1404 (A unit)	red	*CPRail*	70-73	20	30
R0550*	1404 (A unit)	red	*Transcontinental*	71-72	15	18*

*Also found with other 'R' numbers
The model was also sent out to Australia and New Zealand for finishing and sale in local packaging.

T4. RS2 Switcher Bo-Bo

R155	5007	maroon	TR	57	50	125
R155	5007	green	TR	57	50	150
R155	5007	yellow	TR	57	50	100
R155	5007	yellow	TR, dazzle stripes	58-60	15	30
R155	7005	yellow	TR, dazzle stripes	61	20	40
R155	7005	yellow	*Transcontinental*	62-64	20	40
R1550	7005	yellow	*TransAustralia*	65-67	50	100
R1551	3000	black	*CN*	65-72	25	45
R1552	3000	grey	*Canadian Pacific*	69	100	150

Cat.No.	Name / Number	Colour	Details	Years	£	£
R1553	7553	red	*CPRail*	71-73	20	40
R308	48142	maroon	NSWR	74-76	45	70
R763	T336	blue	*VR*	76	45	70

T5. B-60 'Double Ended Diesel'

Cat.No.	Name / Number	Colour	Details	Years	£	£
R159	5007	blue+yell	*Tri-ang Railways*	58-61	10	20
R250	5007 (dummy unit)	blue+yell	*Tri-ang Railways*	58-61	10	20
R159	5007	blue+yell	*TR* shield	62-69	15	30
R159	5007	greeny blue+yell	*TR* shield	68, 70	30	50
R159	5007	bt. blue+yell	*TR* or *VR* on front, no name or shield on sides	70-76	35	60
R?	5007	grn+yell	*Tri-ang Railways*	60?	90	150

The model was also made in Australia and New Zealand and in different liveries.

T6. TC Electric Loco (same body tool as 'Double Ended Diesel')

Cat.No.	Name / Number	Colour	Details	Years	£	£
R257	7503	grn+org	*Tri-ang Railways*	59-60	50	80
R257	7503	2 x green	*Tri-ang Railways*	61	90	140
R257	7503	2 x green	*TR* shield	62-64	75	100

Yard Switcher (see 8. DOCK SHUNTER)

T7. Budd RDC-2

Cat.No.	Name / Number	Colour	Details	Years	£	£
R352	31018	silv+red	*Transcontinental*	61-67	50	90
R232	31018	silv+red	*Transcontinental*, dummy	61-67	90	150
R352CN	101	silv+blk	*CN*	65-71	40	50
R232CN	101	silv+blk	*CN*, dummy	65-71	40	50
R829	303	silver	*Northern Pacific*	68	45	60
R825	303	silver	*Northern Pacific*, dummy	68	45	60
R830	3400, 3403	silver	*Santa Fe*	68	45	60
R826	3400, 3403	silver	*Santa Fe*, dummy	68	45	60
R831	9003	silver	*C&O*	68	45	60
R827	9003	silver	*C&O*, dummy	68	45	60
R832	501, 503	silver	*Reading Lines*	68	45	60
R828	501, 503	silver	*Reading Lines*, dummy	68	45	60
R352A	31018	silv+red	*TransAustralia*	65-67	90	150

T8. Davy Crockett 2-6-0

Cat.No.	Name / Number	Colour	Details	Years	£	£
R358/R233	1863 'Davy Crockett'	red+yell	also R358S, *TTR*	62-65	40	95
R358SL	1863 'Davy Crockett'	red+yell	Lima couplings, *TTR*	62-65	90	150

T9. Continental Prairie 2-6-2T

Cat.No.	Name / Number	Colour	Details	Years	£	£
R653	-	black	single dome	63-65	50	100
R653	-	blk+red	double dome	69	70	120

NSWR Suburban Electric (made only in Australia and so not included here.)

T10. S Class GM Co-Co

Cat.No.	Name / Number	Colour	Details	Years	£	£
R317	S311	blue+yell	*VR*	77-79	35	55
R317	'Sir Ferdinand Muller'	blue+yell	*VR*	77-79	60	75
R317	'Sir Charles Gavin Duffy'	blue+yell	*VR*	77-79	60	75
R318	GM12	maroon	*Commonwealth Railways*	77-79	50	70

The range of Hornby electric locomotives in the Thomas series.   [table P7]

Tri-ang Hornby 'Swedish' 0-4-0DS (R853) [table P4], Barclay 0-4-0DS (R858) [table P2] and Continental 0-4-0 tank (R852), [table P3]

Coaches

British

Tri-ang Railways, Tri-ang Hornby and Hornby Railways coaches are always plastic and marked on the underside with 'Tri-ang', 'Tri-ang Hornby', 'Hornby Railways' or 'Hornby'. On some, the name 'Tri-ang' has been erased on the mould but the words 'Built in Britain' remain.

The wheels changed over the years roughly according to the following order: split axle, plain wheels on steel axle, white rims, metal tyres, white rims, plain (sometimes a bronze colour). Soon after the white rims were seen first time round, the wheels and axle became a single plastic moulding.

The original Rovex coaches were approximately 6" long and the first Tri-ang ones, 7" in length. These were all replaced by a large range of 9" long coaches based on the standard Mk1s plus a Southern utility van, Pullman car, DMU centre car, some suburban stock and a TPO.

The first serious attempt at scale main line coaches came in 1961 when the Mk1 sleeping car was

released, followed in 1962 by four more Mk1s. For their time they were very good and were produced in their hundreds of thousands. Most authentic liveries were used as well as non-authentic LMS, SR and GWR versions. They also formed the basis of some Caledonian and LNER Thompson stock - the former also appearing in strange liveries. The tools for the Mk1 coaches are still in use today although the coaches now have flush glazing and excellent printing.

Other well known coaches from the 1960s were the GWR clerestory stock, which have also appeared in LNER and MR livery amongst others, the four wheeled coaches for Rocket and a pair of Mk2s. Scale Pullmans and a 4-wheel coach arrived in the 1970s and a series of Mk3 coaches in 1977.

With competition from Airfix and Mainline in the 1970s, Hornby also introduced a range of what they called 'Regional Coaches' in 1977. These represented Collett (GWR), Maunsell (SR), Stanier (LMS) and Gresley (LNER) types and many of them later appeared also in BR liveries. These coaches are still made today. There is also a Collett restaurant car, a Gresley sleeper, a TPO and the Southern utility van of the 1950s has returned in a higher quality finish. In 1982 a pair of scale clerestory coaches were added to the range and Mk4 stock arrived in 1990 together with a DVT and, in 1996, Eurostar stock.

From 1997 the Hornby coach range was again enhanced with the addition of a number of the former Airfix models as the result of their purchasing tools from Dapol. The only ones missing were the former Airfix LMS coaches. The most recent development has been the introduction of some excellent scale length Mk3 coaches to replace the 1977 ones.

So vast has been the range of coaches produced by this manufacturer over the years that it is impossible to provide full guidance on values in the space available. Instead we suggest that the following models are more interesting than the others. The prices in brackets are for mint boxed examples:

6" and 7" coaches with a Tri-ang transfer on the underside (£20), brown short TPO (very rare) (£50), 9" coaches in a yellow-green (£17) rather than the usual blue-green (especially the suburbans (£18)), Rocket coaches (£20), short clerestory coaches with a crest on the side, clerestory Engineer's coaches (£20), maroon and white clerestory coach (£25), teak LNER clerestory coaches (£22), blue utility vans (1960s) (£22), green utility van with red doors (£25), Pullman car as a blue continental sleeper (£30), any unmade coach kits (£40), Caledonian coaches with white roofs (£20), blue Pullman DMU centre cars (£25), Class 101 DMU centre cars (£20), Irish Mk2s (£40), Royal Train Sleeper/Power (£25), Network South East Mk2a (£22), QPV breakdown crew coach (£20), Regional Railways Mk2a open (£20), Thompson red breakdown coach (£20), blue Golden Arrow Pullman cars (£20), Hoverspeed coach (£18), Maunsell BR green coaches (£20), Silver Jubilee coaches (£18), blue LMS Coronation coaches (£20), 1980 BR TPO set (£20) and 1985 GWR TPO set (£25).

Transcontinental
In addition to the British range of coaches there were two series of Transcontinental (TC) passenger cars, an American style mail car (£10) and an old time coach (£15). The first series of TC coaches were shorter and toy-like (£5). The scarcest of these are the dining cars (£10) and vista dome coaches with unusual colour schemes in the dome (£8). The second series were attractive models and were available in green (£30), silver (£12) or blue (£10). They were also released abroad in Australian (£25), Canadian (£18) and American liveries (£30). The old time coach was also released in two American liveries (£35).

Wagons

British
If the range of coaches was large, that of wagons was huge. The development of wheels followed that of the coaches and the wagons, too, are usually well marked with the manufacturer's name, except for those from the late 1960s. Early wagons chassis underwent constant development.

Couplings provide a useful way of dating stock. The first couplings had a large triangular hook and a bar fixed at only one end (Mk.IIa). In 1954 a skid-like lump was put on the downward projection from the coupling to make the MkIIb. In 1959 this coupling was replaced by the tension-lock coupling (MkIII) which had the bar fixed at both ends and a finer hook which actually gripped the bar of the adjoining coupling.

Chassis were metal until 1963, after which nearly all were plastic. The only exceptions were where extra weight was required as in the case of cranes and the unloading hopper wagon. A few wagon bogies remained metal until quite late for the same reason, for example the rocket launcher and helicopter car.

Over the years there have been about 100 wagon types and in the case of at least one of these there have been over 100 variations! This makes it impossible to list them here but the following are worth looking out for:

CIE long van (£25), CIE and SLNC 5-plank wagons (£15 each), Scottish private owner wagons from Harburn Hobbies (£5-£15), blue ICI bogie tankers (£20), cable drum wagons with open drums (especially those with thick cables (£10)) or with drums coloured other than green (£8), black bogie bolster with rail load (£20), dropside wagons in colours other than red-maroon (£10-£15), UD tank wagon with 'UD' outlined but no number (£10), Peters Milk (£15), sheep wagon in black plastic (£8), sheep wagon grey SR (£8), yellow mineral wagon 'Beatties' (£10), Trestrol with girder load (£20), flat wagon with white Lyons Maid container (£50), flat wagon with Rice Krispies container (£45), liner train container wagon with: 3 x CN (£20), 3 x BP (transfers) (£20), 3 x ACT (£20), 3 x Santa Fe (£35), 3 x Flexi-van (£35), 2 x CP (£30), 2 x Sea Containers Inc. (£30), 3 x Yellow Pages (£25), BR(ER) brake van VR or NSWR (£10), BR Cartic articulated car carrier (with cars still in individual boxes) (£30), Silcock car transporter with 16 Sunbeam Alpine cars (£30), Readymix cement wagon (£18), C&A open wagons

(£10), Murrell open wagon (£12), Ford or Fyffes ferry van (unboxed) (£18), Hull & Barnsley van as: Railmail, Redgates, Yorkshire Pudding, GW, SR banana van (all £10 each), Taylor & McKenna, Eastbourne Models (both £8 each), Cory mineral with transfers (intact) (£10), Monoblock tanks: CIG (£12), Think Tanker (£25), Norris (£12), Vedette & Sentinal (£20), girder flat with boat (£20), long van Yellow Pages (£15), either 6-wheeled van with paint finish (£12), LBSC brake van (£15), GLW van or OAA open wagon Speedlink Distribution promotion (£25 each), Australian Z brake van yellow (£15) maroon (£18), Refrigerator van Pendle Forest blue (£45) white (£35) and Yorkshire Dales Railway (£10).

Starter Set Wagons
These are mainly of little value but some starter sets contained unique container wagons which are now much sought after. These include, Tri-ang Toys, Scalextric, Frog and Coca Cola. These wagons unboxed can fetch (£25-£35) each.

Battle Space
In the battle space range, the most sought after model is the Q Car (£185) but also hard to find are multiple missile site (£175), Twin Missile Site (£175), Honest John Pad (£75), pack of commandos (£25) and Assault Tank (£75).

Transcontinental
The TC range contained some very attractive freight cars produced principally for the Canadian market. Ones to particularly lookout for are:

CN snow plough (£35), stock car in maroon, green or blue (£20 each), gondola in grey (£20), cement car in pale blue (£20), light blue depressed centre car with cable drums (£20), depressed centre car with low-loader and dozer (£30), flat car complete with side irons (£25), Fourgon (£30), blue CN oil tanker (£35), early Canadian Pacific long box car (£25), CN cement car (£25), pulp wood car in CPRail, Northern Pacific, L&N or Southern livery (£30) and CN flat car with logs (£25).

Accessories

Rovex, more than any other British manufacturer, supported their trains with plenty of lineside accessories so that a complete scene could be created. Once again it would be impossible to list them all here but the following are particularly sought after:

Water troughs (£75), pack of double space sleepers (£10), metal badge (£35), Pullman trainboards (£50), Golden Arrow coach stickers and headboard (£50), coach train boards (£20), railway sounds record (£25), former Hornby-Dublo covered station (£195), extension to covered station (£195), former H-D island platform (re-boxed) (£30), track packs (£10-£35), olive green foot bridge, river bridge or level crossing (£20 each), early foot bridges or station buildings with uncommon posters (£10), Arkitex Ultra Modern Station (£175), pack of unpainted passengers and staff (£15), brown large girder bridge (£150), orange-red small girder bridge (£10), orange-red catenary mast (£8), brick bridge with graffiti, (£15), freight depot (ex-Minic) (£20), home maintenance kit (£20), power cleaning brush (£20) and service boxes (£70).

Sets

Since 1952 about 500 sets have been released by this company. Most of these worth only as much as their contents but a few are worth more as sets. Here are some of them:
Original Rovex set (picture box £120, label box £100), No4 or No5 set (£100), Gamages Rovex set, (£200), Gamages Tri-ang set (£150), Blundells set (£120), Old Smoky set (£120), R6 Rich Uncle set (£180), RF EMU set (£100), R3P and R3Q sets (£80 each), RS36 Highwayman set (£450), RS38 Snow Rescue set (£120), RS37 The Frontiersman (£120), RS44 The Picador (£150), RS8 or RS28 large Lord of the Isles set (£250), RS30 Crash Train set (£100), RS47 Monster Double set (£250), RS38 Lord of the Isles set (£80), RS65 The Conqueror (£120), R346 Rocket presentation pack (£120), Dutch Primary sets (£120 each), Canadian assembled sets (£100-£200), Miniville sets (£80), RS74 export military set (£120), clockwork toy train wholesale sets (£80), RS7 unlisted set (£80), RS62 Car-a-Belle set (£100), RS105 Diesel Freight set (£80), RS602 Senior Freightliner set (£100), RS603 Local Diesel set (£90), RS606 Express Goods set (£80), RS615 The Railway Children set (£120), R346C Stephenson's Rocket set (£125) RS16 and RS17 Battle Space sets (£100 each), RMA, RMB, RMC (£450) and RMD Motorail sets (£95). This list is not exhaustive.

Trix Many-ways station, coal conveyor and longer tinplate coaches.

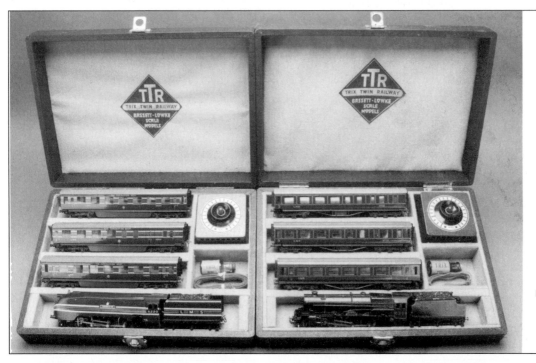

Trix 'Coronation' and 'Princess' presentation sets.

(Barry Potter Auctions)

Trix (British range, including Liliput UK)

History

The history of the Trix model railway system is very complicated and, with its twists and turns, it is a fascinating one to study. It started out as a 3-rail 14V AC coarse scale system and finished up 2-rail fine scale with 12V DC operation. At times its owners could not decide whether it was an 00 or an H0 scale and the confusion did nothing to improve sales. The company changed hands many times and the product was renamed on almost as many occasions. The story is further complicated by its links with the German Trix system and Liliput of Austria.

The Trix Twin Railway took its name from the fact that one could operate two trains on the same piece of track. This was achieved by having three rail track with the centre rail acting as a common return. The left-hand outer rail was then used by one locomotive to collect current and the right outer rail by another loco. When overhead catenary was introduced it became possible to run three trains on the same track!

Trix was a system invented and initially made in Germany but, soon afterwards, made in Britain through the involvement of W.J.Bassett-Lowke.

Stephan Bing left the famous family toy making firm and, in 1928, purchased the toy making business of Andreas Fortner. Bing brought to his new venture a number of colleagues including Siegfried Kahn who became his general manager and designer of his new range of toys. A construction toy, along the lines of Meccano, was launched in 1930 under the name of Trix and proved very successful. In order to make this system in Britain, Trix Ltd was formed in 1932.

The actual manufacture took place at Winteringham Ltd; an associate company of Bassett-Lowke Ltd. The MD at the factory was James Mackenzie and he had as his assistant Robert Bindon Blood, a keen model railway man who was responsible for the design of some of the finest locomotives made by Bassett-Lowke Ltd.

In 1932 Stephan Bing's son Franz emigrated to Britain and joined the fledgling company, organising sales. About this time Mettoy Ltd, another toy manufacturer who would later be remembered for Corgi toys and Playcraft model railways, started up in the basement of Winteringham Ltd with Winteringham doing the manufacturing for them. In 1935, a new 00 scale

model railway system called Trix Express was launched in Germany by Stephan Bing and, by the end of the year, was being imported to the UK by Trix Ltd. Initially it was sold here as 'Bassett-Lowke Twin-Train Table Railway' and production of a British version was soon started at Winteringham Ltd in Northampton and launched by Trix Ltd in time for Christmas 1936.

Like the German version, design was built around an 0-4-0 14V AC electric mechanism. The locomotives had diecast bodies while rolling stock was tinplate and wood was largely used for lineside buildings.

1937 saw considerable expansion of the Trix Twin Railway and, to keep the public informed, The TTR Gazette was published from late 1937. The first Pacific locomotives arrived in 1938 but this was the year the

Milestones

1928	Stephan Bing buys Andreas Fortner.
1930	Trix construction toy launched.
1932	Trix Ltd formed in UK. with W.J.Bassett-Lowke as a director.
1932	Franz Bing joins Trix Ltd.
1935	Trix Express is launched in Germany and imported and sold by Trix Ltd.
1936	Trix Twin, made by Winteringham Ltd, is launched by Trix Ltd.
1937	Wholesale expansion of Trix Twin on the back of early high volume sales.
1937	First issue of The TTR Gazette printed.
1938	First Pacific locomotives arrive.
1938	Launch of Hornby Dublo hits sales.
1940	Death of Stephan Bing.
1941	Trix Ltd and Winteringham Ltd form Precision Models Ltd.
1942	Trix Ltd take control of Precision Models Ltd.
1946	Post-war production starts.
1948	Models designed for the American market.
1950	BR liveries introduced.
1950	First post-war edition of The TTR Gazette.
1951	Winteringham Ltd wound up.
1952	German company sells its Trix Ltd shares.
1953	Death of W.J.Bassett-Lowke.
1955	The first 12V DC train set is produced.
1957	Ewart Holdings Ltd buy Trix.
1957	Fibre base track introduced.
1958	Ewart Holdings bankrupt and Trix and PML assets are acquired by Dufay Ltd.
1958	Trix Products Ltd formed.
1960	Trix production moved to Birmingham.
1961	Ernst Rozsa joins Trix Products Ltd.
1961	Production of Trix ceases.
1963	Trix sold to British Celanese Ltd and moved to Wrexham.
1965	Courtaulds offer Trix to Lines Bros..
1967	Production of British Minitrix starts at Wrexham.
1968	Trix sold to German Trix and production restarted at Wrexham through Thernglade Ltd.
1971	Decision taken to phase out Trix production.
1973	Thernglade factory closes. Rozsa acquires British Trix spares and stock, Liliput buy tooling.
1973	Rovex Ltd take over marketing of British outline Minitrix models as Hornby Minitrix.
1974	Rosza forms Liliput Model Railways (UK) Ltd.
1992	Ernst Rosza ceases production.
1993	Kader buy Liliput and thereby acquire Trix Trains tools.

rival Hornby Dublo system was launched with its better looking models.

Anti-Semitic legislation in Germany forced Stephan Bing and his partners to sell their German company. Their associate Ernst Voelk, who had also bought the Distler toy company in Nuremberg, purchased it. The partners and Kahn emigrated to Britain.

War halted production as Winteringham Ltd transferred its attention to the war effort. In 1941, Winteringham Ltd got together with Trix Ltd and formed Precision Models Ltd to take over the production of the Trix range. The following year, Trix Ltd took a controlling interest in Precision Models Ltd and effectively separated the former Winteringham factory from Bassett-Lowke's control.

The Trix trains were not to reappear until 1948 and by then had the Peco type automatic couplings fitted. It was at this time that the fateful decision was made to stick with 14V AC 3-rail operation and coarse wheels, for the sake of existing customers; a decision that was to condemn Trix to a very slow death and to bankrupt companies along the way.

Export was the first priority after the war and American outline models were produced. However, shortage of materials was the company's biggest problem. Ahead of their rivals, Trix adopted the new BR liveries in 1950 but the public wanted more realism in model design. They were getting it from Hornby Dublo and Tri-ang but not from Trix. In 1952 the German company decided it was time to pull out of its involvement with Trix Ltd and sold its shares. The following year W.J.Bassett-Lowke resigned from the boards of both Trix Ltd and Precision Models Ltd and soon after, died.

Trix Ltd limped along but with very low profits there was no money to invest in the new models needed to reform the system. They managed to produce a 12V DC junior train set in 1955 but a complete 12V DC system was needed. By the end of 1956 the financial problems peaked and there was no way out but to sell the company. In February 1957 the Trix group was bought by Ewart Holdings Ltd.

From 1957 both Trix Ltd and Precision Models Ltd had a completely new board of Directors and a fresh start was feasible. The conversion to 12V DC continued, fibre base track was introduced and an excellent range of new locomotives was designed. The only problem was: they were to be in the smaller H0 scale!

Furthermore, 3-rail operation was retained and so too were those horrible coarse wheels.

New models needed new capital and money was borrowed. With insufficient money coming in the financial position worsened and in 1958 Ewart Holdings collapsed. A major creditor was Dufay Ltd who in November 1958 acquired the assets of Trix Ltd and Precision Models Ltd. Trix Products Ltd took over the design and marketing of the Trix range and in 1960 Dufay moved Trix production to Birmingham.

In 1958 Ernst Rozsa had established a company to import Liliput models from Austria. His company was called Miniature Constructions and assembled some of the Austrian models in the UK. They persuaded Liliput to make an 00 model of the Class AL1 E3000 for them. Rozsa joined Trix in 1961 and took with him the E3000 model.

Poor sales in 1960 and 1961 lead to Dufay closing down Trix production in order to save damaging the rest of their group and Trix was prepared for sale. In 1962 the company was sold to Alvus Investments & Trading Ltd who planned to restart production of Trix in High Wycombe but only the coach moulding tools were made.

In April 1963 British Celanese (part of the Courtaulds Group) formed British Trix Ltd and purchased the goodwill and patents of Trix Products Ltd for £1 and a production base was set up at the British Celanese factory in Wrexham. Ernst Rozsa was placed in charge of design and development but later took full responsibility for production. The decision was taken to dump the stocks of tinplate and 14V AC models and they were buried in a large hole on the Wrexham factory site.

To swell the range quickly a lot of models were bought in from Continental manufacturers and repackaged. 1964 was a good year but by 1965 Courtaulds were inviting Lines Bros. to take Trix off their hands. Lines Bros. turned down the offer. Kit locomotives and rolling stock were introduced that year and sold well and in 1967 N gauge Minitrix models for the British market were being made in the Wrexham factory.

Despite a number of successes, the financial problems continued and at the end of 1967 the plug was once again pulled. Quickly the German Trix company acquired the assets of British Trix and a company called Thernglade Ltd was acquired to take over production. Rozsa was a Director of the new company and the product was renamed 'Trix Trains'. This period was famed for the excellent LNER Pacific locomotives they produced in 00 scale.

A number of German toy company ownership changes lead to a decision to phase out model railway production at Wrexham from 1971. The Minitrix tools were bought by the German Trix company and in 1973 Rovex Ltd became the importers of the range which was renamed Hornby Minitrix. Meanwhile Thernglade continued toy production until the factory closed in 1973.

Rozsa had salvaged the model railway side of the business and purchased stock and spares. He set up a mail order business under the name Berwyn Hobbies Supplies while Liliput of Austria purchased the British model tools owned by Trix of Germany. In 1974 Rozsa formed Liliput Model Railways (UK) Ltd and continued to assemble former British Trix models from parts supplied by Liliput. This continued until 1992 when the supply of parts finally dried up. Some parts and tools were acquired by Dapol Ltd and others were retained by Liliput which was bought by Kader in 1993. Kader, a Chinese company who owned the American Bachmann company, had established Bachmann Industries Europe Ltd in Britain to market British outline models made from the former Mainline Railways tools which it owned. With the Liliput tools now in their possession, the former British Trix A4 model formed the basis of the Class A4 models currently sold by Bachmann.

As we said at the beginning, Trix has a very complicated history!

Further Reading
The excellent book 'The History of Trix H0/00 Model Railways in Britain' by Tony Matthewman, which formed the basis of the above potted history, is strongly recommended to anyone wishing to study the subject. It was published by New Cavendish Books (ISBN 0-904568-76-8).

Collectors Clubs
The Trix Twin Railway Collectors Association (TTRCA) was founded in 1975 and caters for enthusiasts of Trix Twin, Trix Express, Trix Trains and the models of Liliput UK. It publishes a quarterly magazine called 'Trix Twin Gazette' and offers a spares service to its members. For enquiries concerning membership, telephone: 0116 271 5943.

Locomotives

Dates
Where a model was available with a variety of numbers, it is hard to say which numbers were being carried at any one time. The dates quoted in the following tables, therefore, normally apply to the model form and not the number.

Couplings
These provide a means of distinguishing between pre- and post-war models. The pre-war coupling (referred to as 'pwc' in the tables) was non-automatic and consisted of a cast (or tinplate) hook and a wire loop. The post-war couplings were the Peco style automatic ones also used by Meccano Ltd on Hornby Dublo stock.

White Numbers
A lot of people are mystified by white numbers printed on the underside of locomotives (and other electrical equipment) made after 1948. These numbers indicate the month and year that the model was made. The months were lettered 'A' for January, 'B' for February, and so on, while the year was represented by the last digit (sometimes last two digits). Thus 'C3' was March 1953. This provides us with a very useful way of dating much post-war Trix electrical equipment up until 1960 when the system was dropped. Incidentally the letter 'I' was not used and so September was 'J'.

A single 'R' on a chassis means that it went back to the factory at some time for a repair and 'M' was applied to chassis in 1948, indicating modification.

Voltage
The Trix Twin Railway system initially operated on a 14V AC power supply but later manufacturers used 12V DC as it was more controllable. Trix were tied to their AC system but eventually had to change over to 12V DC as the market demanded. The DC system was introduced in 1956. Some of the locomotives listed below were made only for an AC supply and some only for DC. Four models may be found with either AC or DC mechanisms and these are clearly marked in the respective tables. The models that were available only with AC mechanisms are those listed in tables 1-7, 12 and 13.

Trix Collett Class 5600   [table 20]

Locomotives

1.　0-4-0 with Tender
This was the first loco in the Trix range being originally released with 'Trix Express' on the tender.

pwc = pre-war couplings　　dlt = double lining on tender　　slt = single lining on tender

Cat.No.	Name / Number	Colour	Details	Years	£	£
	5391	green	*TRIX EXPRESS*, lined, disc wheels	36	500	NPG
	5391	black	*TRIX EXPRESS*, unlined, disc wheels	36	500	NPG
		green	*TRIX TWIN* on tender, unlined, demonstration model, pwc	46?	600	NPG
		black	*TRIX TWIN* on tender, unlined, demonstration model, pwc	46?	600	NPG
2/520	5647	maroon	*LMS* lined, pwc	36-39,46	80	100
2/520	5670	maroon	*LMS* lined, pwc	36-39,46	80	100
2/520	5724	maroon	*LMS* lined, pwc	36-39,46	80	100
2/520	6138	maroon	*LMS* lined, pwc	36-39,46	80	100
2/520	6200	maroon	*LMS* lined, pwc	36-39,46	80	100
2/520	5647	maroon	*LMS* lined	47-52	80	100
2/520	6138	v.dk.mrn	*LMS* lined	47-52	80	100
2/525	5049	black	*LMS* lined, pwc	36-39,46	60	80
2/525	6138	black	*LMS* lined, pwc	36-39,46	60	80
2/525	8046	black	*LMS* lined, pwc	36-39,46	60	80
2/525	8067	black	*LMS* lined, pwc	36-39,46	60	80
2/525	8209	black	*LMS* lined, pwc	36-39,46	60	80
2/525	6138	black	*LMS* lined front band and tender	47-52	40	60
2/525	8209	black	*LMS* lined front band and tender	47-52	40	60
2/525	6138	black	*LMS* lined front boiler band	47-52	40	60
2/525	5124	black	*LMS* unlined	47-52	40	60
2/525	8032	black	*LMS* unlined	47-52	30	50
4/520	2581	lt. green	*LNER* lined, pwc	36-39,46	80	100
4/520	4472	lt. green	*LNER* lined, pwc	36-39,46	60	80
4/520	2876	lt. green	*LNER* lined	47-52	80	100
4/520	2876	dk. green	*LNER* lined	47-52	80	100
4/520	693	lt. green	*LNER* lined, black cylinders	47-52	80	100
4/520	103	green	*LNER* lined	47-52	100	120
4/520	447	green	*LNER* lined	47-52	100	120
4/520	465	green	*LNER* lined	47-52	100	120
4/520	2876	green	*LNER* lined	47-52	80	100
4/525	2394	black	*LNER* lined, pwc	36-39,46	40	60
4/525	3451	black	*LNER* lined, pwc	36-39,46	40	60
4/525	4472	black	*LNER* lined, pwc	36-39,46	80	100
4/525	2394	black	*LNER* lined	47-52	40	60
4/525	3451	black	*LNER* lined	47-52	40	60
4/525	2394	black	*LNER* lined on tender only	47-52	40	60
4/525	3451	black	*LNER* lined on tender only	47-52	40	60

4/525	4472	black	*LNER* lined on tender only	47-52	80	100
4/525	103	black	*LNER* unlined	47-52	60	80
4/525	620	black	*LNER* unlined	47-52	60	80
4/525	693	black	*LNER* unlined	47-52	60	80
4/525	4472	black	*LNER* unlined	47-52	80	100
4/525	5124	black	*LNER* unlined	47-52	60	80
5/520	763	green	*Southern* lined, pwc	37-39,	200	250
5/525	498	black	*Southern* lined tender, pwc	37-39,46	180	250
5/520	763	green	*Southern* lined	48-50?	250	NPG
5/525	498	black	*Southern* lined tender	47-52	180	220
1/520	46231	light blue	BRb lined	50-51	100	120
1/520	46256	light blue	BRb lined	50-51	80	100
1/520	60100	light blue	BRb lined	50-51	80	100
1/520	46256	dark blue	BRb lined	51-52	80	100
1/520	60100	dark blue	BRb lined	51-52	80	100
1/520	30782	green	BRb lined, dlt, black cylinders	52-58	40	60
1/520	46256	green	BRb lined, dlt, black cylinders	52-58	40	60
1/520	46258	green	BRb lined, dlt, black cylinders	52-58	40	60
1/520	60089	green	BRb lined, dlt, black cylinders	52-58	40	60
1/520	60100	green	BRb lined, dlt, green cylinders	51-52	60	70
1/520	73029	green	BRb lined, dlt, green or black cylinders	52-53	60	70
1/520	30782	green	BRb lined, slt, black cylinders	52-58	40	60
1/520	46258	green	BRb lined, slt, black cylinders	52-58	30	50
1/520	60089	green	BRb lined, slt, black cylinders	52-58	40	60
1/525	48427	black	BRb lined front boiler band and cylinders	52-58	30	50
1/525	48152	black	BRb lined front boiler band only	52-58	30	50
1/525	2750	black	BRb unlined	50-58	30	50
1/525	6201	black	BRb unlined	50-58	30	50
1/525	30846	black	BRb unlined	50-58	25	40
1/525	31829	black	BRb unlined	50-58	25	40
1/525	46201	black	BRb unlined	50-58	50	70
1/525	48427	black	BRb unlined	50-58	30	50
1/525	63950	black	BRb unlined	50-58	25	40

2. 0-4-0 Tank Tank engines bearing the wording on the back of the bunker 'Patents TTR Pending' were made before mid-1937 while those with 'British TTR Patents 465168 469656 Patented Abroad' were made between 1937 and circa 1950. They were not to be found on BR models.
pwc = pre-war couplings

2/510	121	black	*LMS* lined or unlined, pwc	36-39,46	30	50
2/510	141	black	*LMS* lined, pwc	36-39,46	30	50
2/510	191	black	*LMS* lined, pwc	36-39,46	30	50
2/515	5	black	*LMS* unlined, pwc	36-39,46	30	50
2/515	20	black	*LMS* unlined, pwc	36-39,46	30	50
2/515	31	black	*LMS* unlined, pwc	36-39,46	30	50
2/515	39	black	*LMS* unlined, pwc	36-39,46	40	60
2/515	58	black	*LMS* lined or unlined, pwc	36-39,46	40	60
2/515	62	black	*LMS* unlined, pwc	36-39,46	40	60
2/515	91	black	*LMS* lined or unlined, pwc	36-39,46	30	50
2/515	5	black	*LMS* unlined	47-52	30	50
2/515	11	black	*LMS* unlined	47-52	30	50
2/515	20	black	*LMS* unlined	47-52	30	50
2/515	30	black	*LMS* unlined	47-52	40	60
2/515	31	black	*LMS* unlined	47-52	30	50
2/515	62	black	*LMS* unlined	47-52	40	60
2/515	63	black	*LMS* lined	47-52	40	50
2/515	68	black	*LMS* unlined	47-52	40	50
2/515	91	black	*LMS* lined or unlined	47-52	30	40
2/515	97	black	*LMS* unlined	47-52	25	35
2/515	98	black	*LMS* unlined	47-52	40	45
2/515	781	black	*LMS* unlined	47-52	35	40
2/515	914	black	*LMS* unlined	47-52	35	40
2/515	1109	black	*LMS* unlined	47-52	35	40
4/510	2901	black	*LNER* lined or unlined, pwc	36-39,46	50	70
4/510	9276	black	*LNER* lined, pwc	36-39,46	50	70
4/515	6178	black	*LNER* unlined, pwc	36-39,46	50	70
4/515	7693	black	*LNER* unlined, pwc	36-39,46	50	70
4/515	8403	black	*LNER* unlined, pwc	36-39,46	50	70
4/510	396	black	*LNER* lined	47-52	40	60
4/515	298	black	*LNER* unlined	47-52	40	60

Top: The Trix ubiquitous 0-4-0 tender engine [table 1].   2nd: Trix Hunt Class loco [table 9].
3rd: Trix Ruston Hornsby 0-6-0DS [table 16].   4th: Trix Standard V [table 18].   Bottom: Trix 'Britannia' [table 17].

Trix Class AL1 [table 23],

Western diesel hydraulic [table 25]

and Warship diesel hydraulic [table 21].

Trix layout with Class EM1 [table 19] and plastic coach.

Cat.No.	Name / Number	Colour	Details	Years	£	£
4/515	605	black	*LNER* unlined	47-52	40	60
4/515	7693	black	*LNER* unlined	47-52	40	60
4/515	8403	black	*LNER* unlined	47-52	40	60
5/510	520	green	*Southern* lined, pwc	37-39,46	150	200
5/515	951	black	*Southern* lined, pwc	37-39,46	150	200
5/510	1923	green	*Southern* lined	47-52	150	200
5/515	91	black	*Southern* lined or unlined	47-52	100	150
1/510	40	black	BRb lined	47-52	30	40
1/510	63	black	BRb lined or unlined	47-52	30	40
1/510	48	black	BRb lined	50-55	25	35
1/510	50	black	BRb lined	50-55	25	35
1/510	85	black	BRb lined	50-55	25	35

3. Southern EMU

This model was made in Germany with the exception of the tinplate body which was produced in the UK. Several shades of green may be found.

5/375	11081	green	Southern Railway 3-car set	37-39	400	700
5/530	11081	green	Southern Railway power car only	37-39	200	400

4.   LT 0-4-0 Electric   This was an adaptation from a German model with pantographs removed etc.

7/530	19	maroon	*London Transport*	37-38	350	450
7/530	17	maroon	*London Transport*	not made	NA	NA

5. Princess 4-6-2

The chassis were made in Germany. The tooling became damaged beyond economic repair and so the model was not reintroduced after the war.

2/540	6201 'Princess'	maroon	*LMS*	38-39	375	475
2/344	6201 'Princess'	maroon	*LMS* set in wooden presentation box with 3 coaches	38-39	525	1000

6.   A3 4-6-2   The chassis were made in Germany.   pwc = pre-war couplings   dlt = double lined tender

4/540	4472 'Scotsman'	green	*LNER*, pwc	38-39	600	800
4/344	4472 'Scotsman'	green	*LNER*, in wooden presentation box with 3 coaches, pwc	38-39	800	1000
4/540	4472 'Scotsman'	green	*LNER*, pwc, black cylinders	39	600	800
4/540	4472 'Scotsman'	black	*LNER*, pwc	c42?	NPG	2000
1/540	4472 'Scotsman'	dark blue	BRb, single lined tender	51-52	300	400
1/540	4472 'Scotsman'	green	BRb, single lined tender	52-53	300	375
1/540	4472 'Scotsman'	green	BRb, dlt, silver nameplate	53-54	300	375
1/540	4472 'Scotsman'	green	BRb, dlt, orange nameplate	55-58	300	375

7. Coronation 4-6-2

After the war, with the streamlining being removed from the real locomotives, the model was thought to be out of date and not worth reintroducing.

2/542	6220 'Coronation'	maroon	*LMS*	39	600	800
2/347	6220 'Coronation'	maroon	*LMS* set in wooden presentation box with 3 coaches	39	800	1500
2/347	6220 'Coronation'	maroon	*LMS* set in dark green wooden presentation box with 3 coaches	39	800	1500

8. Midland Compound 4-4-0

2/536	1168	maroon	*LMS* lined, pwc	39,46	250	350
2/536	1168	black	*LMS* lined, pwc	39,46	150	250
2/536	1168	maroon	*LMS* lined	47-52	300	400
2/536	1168	black	*LMS* lined, matt black	49-52	100	200
2/536	41062	black	BRb, double lining on tender	50-56	80	120
2/536	41128	black	BRb, double lining on tender	50-56	80	120
2/536	41135	black	BRb, double lining on tender	50-56	80	120
2/536	41162	black	BRb, double lining on tender	50-56	60	90
2/536	41128	black	BRb, single lining on tender	50-52?	80	120
2/536	41135	black	BRc, double lining on tender	56-58	80	120
2/536	41162	black	BRc, double lining on tender	56-58	60	90
2/536	41162	green	BRb, double lining on tender	53	400	600
2/536	62750	green	BRb, double lining on tender, factory mistake (only one)	53	NPG	NPG
F101	1168	black	BRc, 12V DC	59-60	120	150
F101	41168	black	BRc, 12V DC	59-60	120	150

9.   Hunt Class 4-4-0   dlt = double lining on tender   slt = single lining on tender

4/536	298 'Pytchley'	green	*LNER* lined, pwc, 14V AC	39	400	500
4/536	298 'Pytchley'	green	*LNER* lined, 14V AC	47-48	500	600
4/536	2750 'Pytchley'	green	*LNER* lined, 14V AC	48-52	500	600
4/536	2750 'Pytchley'	black	*LNER* lined, matt black, 14V AC	49-52	200	300
4/536	62750 'Pytchley'	green	BRb, dlt, 14V AC	53-58	80	100
4/536	62750 'Pytchley'	green	BRb, slt, 14V AC	53-58	80	100
4/536	62750 'Pytchley'	black	BRb, dlt, 14V AC	50	120	150

4/536	62750 'Pytchley'	black	BRb, slt , 14V AC	50	120	150
230	62750 'Pytchley'	green	BRc, 12V DC	57-60	80	100
235	62750 'Pytchley'	black	BRc, 12V DC	57-60	80	100

10. Schools Class 4-4-0
The Schools Class locomotive was planned for 1940 and an order placed but the war intervened. The project was then shelved until the late 1950s when it was released as a 12v DC model with a new casting.

5/536	911 'Dover'	green	Southern	not made	NA	NA
5/364	911 'Dover'	green	Southern set in wooden presentation box with 3 coaches	not made	NA	NA
F100	30911 'Dover'	green	BRc, 12V DC	59-60	200	300

11. 2-4-2 Tank   This was planned for 1940 based on the German 2-4-2 chassis but was dropped because of the war.

2/514			*LMS*	not made	NA	NA
4/514			*LNER*	not made	NA	NA
5/514			*Southern*	not made	NA	NA

12. American 0-4-0 with Tender
This looked similar to the next model but had a larger square backed tender and a hooded lamp in the centre of the smokebox door.

9/519	4638	black	*Trix Twin* on tender, no light	48-49	60	80
9/519	4762	black	*Trix Twin* on tender, no light	48-49	60	80
9/520	4826	black	*Trix Twin* on tender	48-49	60	80
9/520	4638	black	*Trix Twin* on tender	50-56	60	80
9/520	4762	black	*Trix Twin* on tender	50-56	60	80
9/520	5986	black	*Trix Twin* on tender	50-56	60	80
9/520	8612	black	*Trix Twin* on tender	50-56	60	80

13. American 0-4-0 Switcher with Tender
This looked similar to the last model but had a smaller tender with a sloping back and a lamp above the smokebox door. Both were produced as part of a post-war export drive.

9/524	3747	black	no light	48-49	60	80
9/524	3812	black	no light	48-49	60	80
9/524	5986	black	no light	48-49	60	80
9/524	8612	black	no light	48-49	60	80
9/525	2690	black		48-49	60	80
9/525	4681	black		48-49	60	80
9/525	3747	black		50-56	60	80
9/525	3812	black		50-56	60	80
9/525	4701	black		50-56	60	80
9/525	5647	black		50-56	60	80
9/525	5986	black		50-56	60	80
9/525	8612	black		50-56	60	80
81/50	-	-	kit for export with DC motor	51	100	160
81/51	-	-	kit without lamp	51	100	160

14. 0-4-0 Tank with Plastic Body

1/510	59	black	BRb lined, 14v AC	56-57	35	45
1/510	85	black	BRb lined, 14v AC	56-57	35	45
1/510	85	black	BRc lined, 14v AC	56-57	35	45
1/515	84	black	BRb unlined, 14v AC	56-57	35	45
1/515	98	black	BRc unlined, 14v AC	56-57	35	45
1/515	30951	black	BRc unlined, 14v AC	56-57	35	45
210	84	black	BRc unlined, 12v DC	55-61	25	35
210	30951	black	BRc unlined, 12v DC	58-61	25	35
210	41218	black	BRc unlined, 12v DC	58-61	25	35
210	67611	black	BRc unlined, 12v DC	58-61	40	60

15. Meteor Diesel Express

377	1394	red	3-car 14V AC	55-58	140	200
277	1394	red	3-car 12V DC	57-61	140	200
277	2602	red	3-car 12V DC	57-61	140	200
277	2602	blue	3-car 12V DC	58-61	160	220
277	2782	blue	3-car 12V DC	58-61	160	220

16. Ruston Hornsby 0-6-0DS + Shunter's Truck (H0)

| 244 | - | green | | 58-61 | 85 | 110 |

17. Britannia Class 4-6-2 (H0)

'Scale' wheels fitted from 1960 had smaller flanges so that they could run on 2-rail track but the wheels were still thick. Many, however, were converted to run on universal tack, after purchase.

Cat.No.	Name / Number	Colour	Details	Years	£	£
236	70000 'Britannia'	green	BRc, coarse wheels	59	60	90
236						
1109	70000 'Britannia'	green	BRc, 'scale' wheels 2/3-rail	60-65	60	90
1110	70000 'Britannia'	green	BRc, 'scale' wheels 3-rail	63	60	90
1111	70000 'Britannia'	green	BRc, 'scale' wheels 2-rail	63-65	60	90
2111	70000 'Britannia'	green	Footplateman construction kit	66, 69	60	90

18. Standard Class V 4-6-0 (H0)

'Scale' wheels fitted from 1960 had smaller flanges so that they could run on 2-rail track but the wheels were still thick. Many, however, were converted to run on universal tack, after purchase.

Cat.No.	Name / Number	Colour	Details	Years	£	£
237G	73000	green	BRc, coarse wheels	59	70	100
237G	73001	green	BRc, coarse wheels	59	100	150
237B	73000	black	BRc, coarse wheels	59	60	90
237G						
1115	73000	green	BRc, 'scale' wheels 2/3-rail	60-65	70	100
237B						
1112	73000	black	BRc, 'scale' wheels 2/3-rail	60-66	60	90
1117	73000	green	BRc, 'scale' wheels 2-rail	63-65	70	100
1114	73000	black	BRc, 'scale' wheels 2-rail	63-66	60	90
1113	73000	green	BRc, 'scale' wheels 3-rail	63-64	70	100
1116	73000	black	BRc, 'scale' wheels 3-rail	63-64	60	90
2113	73000	green	Footplateman construction kit	66, 69	NPG	110
2116	73000	black	Footplateman construction kit	66, 69	NPG	110

19. EM1 Bo-Bo (H0)

Cat.No.	Name / Number	Colour	Details	Years	£	£
F105B						
1122	26010	black	BRc, convertible wheels	59-63	100	160
F105B						
1123	26010	black	BRc, 2-rail 'scale' wheels	60-64	100	160
F105G	26056 'Triton'	green	BRc, convertible wheels	60-61	120	190
F105G	26056 'Triton'	green	BRc, 2-rail 'scale' wheels	60-61	120	190
F105G						
1125	26056	green	BRc, convertible wheels	62-63	120	190
F105G						
1125	26056	green	BRc, 2-rail 'scale' wheels	62-64	120	190

20. Collett Class 5600 0-6-2T (H0)   This was wrongly called a Class 66XX by Trix.

Cat.No.	Name / Number	Colour	Details	Years	£	£
F103B						
1101	6664	black	BRc, 3-rail convertible wheels	59-63	40	60
F103B	6664	black	BRc, 2-rail convertible wheels	59-60	45	60
F103B						
1102	6664	black	BRc, 2-rail 'scale' wheels	60-64	45	60
F103G						
1105	6664	green	BRc, 3-rail convertible wheels	59-63	50	75
F103G	6664	green	BRc, 2-rail convertible wheels	60	50	75
F103G						
1106	6664	green	BRc, 2-rail 'scale' wheels	60-64	50	75

21. Warship Type 4 Diesel Hydraulic B-B (H0)   'Vanguard' had red nameplates while the others had black ones.

Cat.No.	Name / Number	Colour	Details	Years	£	£
F106						
1119	D801 'Vanguard'	green	BRc, 2-rail convertible wheels	60-64	50	65
F106						
1120	D801 'Vanguard'	green	BRc, 2-rail 'scale' wheels	60-71	50	65
F106						
1118	D801 'Vanguard'	green	BRc, 3-rail 'scale' wheels	60-66	50	65
1120	D809 'Champion'	green	BRc, 2-rail 'scale' wheels	66-70	70	90
1118	D809 'Champion'	green	BRc, 3-rail 'scale' wheels	66	70	90
1120	D811 'Daring'	green	BRc, 2-rail 'scale' wheels	66-70	70	90
1118	D811 'Daring'	green	BRc, 3-rail 'scale' wheels	66	70	90
1120	D828 'Magnificent'	green	BRc, 2-rail 'scale' wheels	66-70	90	110
1118	D828 'Magnificent'	green	BRc, 3-rail 'scale' wheels	66	90	110
1120	D844 'Spartan'	green	BRc, 2-rail 'scale' wheels	66-70	70	90
1118	D844 'Spartan'	green	BRc, 3-rail 'scale' wheels	66	70	90
1122	D801 'Vanguard'	maroon	BRc, 2-rail 'scale' wheels	66-69	70	90
1119	D801 'Vanguard'	maroon	BRc, 3-rail 'scale' wheels	66	70	90

1122	D809 'Champion'	maroon	BRc, 2-rail 'scale' wheels	66-69	70	90
1119	D809 'Champion'	maroon	BRc, 3-rail 'scale' wheels	66	70	90
1122	D811 'Daring'	maroon	BRc, 2-rail 'scale' wheels	66-69	70	90
1119	D811 'Daring'	maroon	BRc, 3-rail 'scale' wheels	66	70	90
1122	D828 'Magnificent'	maroon	BRc, 2-rail 'scale' wheels	66-69	80	110
1119	D828 'Magnificent'	maroon	BRc, 3-rail 'scale' wheels	66	80	110
1122	D844 'Spartan'	maroon	BRc, 2-rail 'scale' wheels	66-69	70	90
1119	D844 'Spartan'	maroon	BRc, 3-rail 'scale' wheels	66	70	90
1123	D801 'Vanguard'	blue	BRc, 2-rail 'scale' wheels	67-71	70	90
1123	D809 'Champion'	blue	BRc, 2-rail 'scale' wheels	67-71	70	90
1123	D811 'Daring'	blue	BRc, 2-rail 'scale' wheels	67-71	70	90
1123	D828 'Magnificent'	blue	BRc, 2-rail 'scale' wheels	67-71	80	110
1123	D844 'Spartan'	blue	BRc, 2-rail 'scale' wheels	67-71	70	90

22. Class E2 0-6-0T (H0)

F107						
1107	32103	black	BRc, 2-rail	61-72	20	25
F107						
1108	32103	black	BRc, 3-rail	61-66	20	25

23. Class AL1 Bo-Bo Electric

This model was initially manufactured and partly finished by Liliput in Austria and imported by Miniature Construction Ltd who fitted the pantographs and put it on the market in 1960. In 1962, Trix bought the model from Miniature Construction Ltd to adapt and sell as a Trix product. From 1974 they were assembled and sold by Liliput Model Railways (UK) Ltd. After 1966, all models were 2-rail.

1128	E3001	blue	BRd (plastic moulding), 2-rail	63-64	100	150
1127	E3001	blue	BRd (plastic moulding), 3-rail	63-64	100	150
1128	E3001	blue	BRd (transfers), 2-rail, improved pantograph, yellow panels	64-72	100	150
1127	E3001	blue	BRd (transfers), 3-rail, improved pantograph, yellow panels	64-66	100	150
1130	E3001	blue	BRd (transfers), 2-rail, 2 motors	65-68	100	150
1129	E3001	blue	BRd (transfers), 3-rail, 2 motors	65-66	100	150
2128	E3001	blue	BRd, 2-rail, Footplateman kit	65-71	NA	120
2127	E3001	blue	BRd, 3-rail, Footplateman kit	65-66	NA	120
1128	E3001	blue	BRd, one pantograph	72	100	150
1001	E3001	blue	BRd, one pantograph	74-76	100	150
1002						
1001	E3001	blue	BRd, as 1001 but changing headlights	74-83	100	150
1003	E3001	blue	BRd, as 1001 but no lights	74-88	100	150
1004	E3001	blue	BRd, kit	not made	100	150
1002	E3001	blue	BRd, 2 motor bogies	76-82	100	150
1005	81007	blue	BRe, yellow front	77-88	100	150
1005	81014	blue	BRe, yellow front	77-88	100	150
1100	various	blue	models fitted with EMS train control	82-85	100	150
1001/0	E3001	blue	BRd, 2 pantographs	84-88	100	150
1001/0	E3012	blue	BRd, 2 pantographs	84-88	100	150
1001/0	E3018	blue	BRd, 2 pantographs	84-88	100	150
1001	E3001	blue	BRd, 1 pantograph	84-88	100	150
1001	E3012	blue	BRd, 1 pantograph	84-88	100	150
1001	E3018	blue	BRd, 1 pantograph	84-88	100	150

24. 0-4-0 Southern Tank   Illustrated in the 1964 catalogue but not made.

1165	-	black	2-rail	not made	NA	NA
1166	-	black	3-rail	not made	NA	NA

In 1965, a Royal Scot, a Black 5 and a 9F were planned but none of these came to fruition.

25. Western Diesel Hydraulic C-C (H0)

This model was developed and tooled by Liliput in Austria to a design by Ernst Rozsa. Route codes on these models vary as the model was supplied with a sheet of self-adhesive labels as well as yellow cab front panels (with earlier releases) for the purchaser to apply. All models made after 1966 were 2-rail. From 1974 these were Liliput UK models, manufactured in Austria and assembled in Wales.

1165	D1002 'Western Explorer'	green	BRc, 2-rail	65-73	30	60
1165	D1004 'Western Crusader'	green	BRc, 2-rail	65-73	30	60
1166	D1002 'Western Explorer'	green	BRc, 3-rail	65-66	30	60
1166	D1004 'Western Crusader'	green	BRc, 3-rail	65-66	30	60
1167	D1000 'Western Enterprise'	maroon	BRc, 2-rail	65-73	30	60
1167	D1038 'Western Sovereign'	maroon	BRc, 2-rail	65-73	30	60
1167	D1045 'Western Viscount'	maroon	BRc, 2-rail	65-73	30	60
1167	D1069 'Western Vanguard'	maroon	BRc, 2-rail	65-73	30	60

Cat.No.	Name / Number	Colour	Details	Years	£	£
1168	D1000 'Western Enterprise'	maroon	BRc, 3-rail	65-73	30	60
1168	D1038 'Western Sovereign'	maroon	BRc, 3-rail	65-68	30	60
1168	D1045 'Western Viscount'	maroon	BRc, 3-rail	65-68	30	60
1168	D1069 'Western Vanguard'	maroon	BRc, 3-rail	65-68	30	60
1169	D1000 'Western Enterprise'	maroon	BRc, 2-rail, 2 motor bogies	65-73	30	60
1169	D1038 'Western Sovereign'	maroon	BRc, 2-rail, 2 motor bogies	65-73	30	60
1169	D1045 'Western Viscount'	maroon	BRc, 2-rail, 2 motor bogies	65-73	30	60
1169	D1069 'Western Vanguard'	maroon	BRc, 2-rail, 2 motor bogies	65-73	30	60
1164	D1000 'Western Enterprise'	maroon	BRc, 3-rail, 2 motor bogies	65-66	30	60
1164	D1038 'Western Sovereign'	maroon	BRc, 3-rail, 2 motor bogies	65-66	30	60
1164	D1045 'Western Viscount'	maroon	BRc, 3-rail, 2 motor bogies	65-66	30	60
1164	D1067 'Western Vanguard'	maroon	BRc, 3-rail, 2 motor bogies	65-66	30	60
1163	D1002 'Western Explorer'	blue	BRe	67-73	30	60
1163	D1004 'Western Crusader'	blue	BRe	67-73	30	60
1163	D1000 'Western Enterprise'	blue	BRe	67-73	30	60
1163	D1038 'Western Sovereign'	blue	BRe	67-73	30	60
1163	D1045 'Western Viscount'	blue	BRe	67-73	30	60
1163	D1069 'Western Vanguard'	blue	BRe	67-73	30	60
1010	D1000 'Western Enterprise'	blue	BRe, yellow cab fronts	74-87	30	60
1010	D1002 'Western Explorer'	blue	BRe, yellow cab fronts	74-87	30	60
1010	D1004 'Western Crusader'	blue	BRe, yellow cab fronts	74-87	30	60
1010	D1038 'Western Sovereign'	blue	BRe, yellow cab fronts	74-87	30	60
1010	D1045 'Western Viscount'	blue	BRe, yellow cab fronts	74-87	30	60
1010	D1069 'Western Vanguard'	blue	BRe, yellow cab fronts	74-87	30	60
1012	D1000 'Western Enterprise'	maroon	BRc, yellow cab fronts	74-87	30	60
1011	D1002 'Western Explorer'	green	BRc, yellow cab fronts	74-87	30	60
1011	D1004 'Western Crusader'	green	BRc, yellow cab fronts	74-87	30	60
1012	D1038 'Western Sovereign'	maroon	BRc, yellow cab fronts	74-87	30	60
1012	D1045 'Western Viscount'	maroon	BRc, yellow cab fronts	74-87	30	60
1012	D1069 'Western Vanguard'	maroon	BRc, yellow cab fronts	74-87	30	60
1009	D1000 'Western Enterprise'	sand	BRc, changing lights	79-87	30	60
1014	various	blue	BRe, yellow cab fronts kit	74-76	30	60
1015	various	blue	BRe, yellow cab fronts, 2 motor bogies	74-81	30	60
1016	various	blue	BRe, yellow cab fronts, changing lights	75-77	30	60
1013	various	blue	BRe, yellow cab fronts, no lights	76-87	30	60
1013	D1002 'Western Explorer'	green	BRc, yellow cab fronts, no lights	77-87	30	60
1013	D1004 'Western Crusader'	green	BRc, yellow cab fronts, no lights	77-87	30	60
1013	various	maroon	BRc, yellow cab fronts, no lights	77-87	30	60
1017	D1002 'Western Explorer'	green	BRe, yellow cab fronts, 2 motor bogies	79-81	30	60
1017	D1004 'Western Crusader'	green	BRe, yellow cab fronts, 2 motor bogies	79-81	30	60
1017	various	maroon	BRe, yellow cab fronts, 2 motor bogies	79-81	30	60
1013	D1069 'Western Vanguard'	maroon	BRc, fitted with track cleaning device	82	30	60
1110	various	various	EMS equipment fitted	82-83	30	60

Many other variations were advertised but only those known to have been made are listed above.

26. Class 124 Trans-Pennine DMU (H0)

Based on BR 6-car units built at Swindon for the Hull-Manchester route, the model was partly tooled by Liliput of Austria with a German Trix motor bogie fitted. A choice of headcodes and front yellow panels were provided for the purchaser to attach. From 1974 the model was assembled and sold by Liliput UK and these models may be identified by grey (instead of cream) interiors. No 3-rail versions were made after 1970.

1178	NE51953/NE51954	green	BRc, 2-rail, 2 car set	66-73	70	95
1179	NE51953/NE51954	green	BRc, 3-rail, 2 car set	66-70	70	95
1174	51960/51960	blu+gry	BRe, 2-rail, 2 car, without lights	67-73	70	95
1175	NE51953/NE51954	green	BRc, 2-rail, 2 car, without lights	67-73	70	95
1176	NE51953/NE51954	green	BRc, 3-rail, 2 car, without lights	67-68	70	95
1177	51960/51960	blu+gry	BRe, 2-rail, 2 car, with lights	67-73	70	95
1173	51960/51960	blu+gry	BRe, 3-rail, 2 car, without lights	68-70	70	95
1173/3	51960/51960	blu+gry	BRe, 3-rail, 2 car, with lights	68-73	70	95
1020	51960/51960	blu+gry	BRe, 2 car, without lights	74-84	70	95
1021	51960/51960	blu+gry	BRe, 2 car, with route lights	74-84	70	95
1022	51960/51960	blu+gry	BRe, 2 car, with route lights, 2 motors	74-84	70	95
1025	NE51953/NE51954	green	BRe, 2 car, without lights	74-88	70	95
1025	NE51953/NE51954	green	BRe, 2 car, with route lights	74-88	70	95
1027	NE51953/NE51954	green	BRe, 2 car, with route lights, 2 motors	74-88	70	95
1120	51960/51960	blu+gry	BRe, 2 car, EMS equipment fitted	82-85	70	95
1125	NE51953/NE51954	green	BRc, 2 car, EMS equipment fitted	82-85	70	95

27. Brush-Sulzer Type 4 Class 47 Co-Co

1170		green		not made	NA	NA
1171		blue		not made	NA	NA

28. Class A3 4-6-2

Tooled and manufactured by Liliput of Austria but assembled by Thernglade Ltd at Wrexham in Wales. From 1974 these models were Liliput UK products. Production of 3-rail models ceased in 1970 although they were available by special order until 1972.

1180	4472 'Flying Scotsman'	green	*LNER* very pale apple green	68	50	70
1180DT	4472 'Flying Scotsman'	green	*LNER* 2 tenders, very pale apple green, coal top on both tenders	68	50	100
1180	4472 'Flying Scotsman'	green	*LNER* correct apple green, 2-rail	68-70	50	70
1181	4472 'Flying Scotsman'	green	*LNER* correct apple green, 3-rail	68-70	60	80
1180DT	4472 'Flying Scotsman'	green	*LNER* 2 tenders, correct apple green, coal top on both tenders, 2-rail	68-70	50	100
1181DT	4472 'Flying Scotsman'	green	*LNER* 2 tenders, correct apple green, coal top on both tenders, 3-rail	68-70	50	100
1180DT	4472 'Flying Scotsman'	green	*LNER* 2 tenders, water tender now with correct top and front handrail fitted to both tenders, 2r	70-73	70	90
1181DT	4472 'Flying Scotsman'	green	*LNER* 2 tenders, water tender now with correct top and front handrail fitted to both tenders, 3r	70	70	90
1180	4472 'Flying Scotsman'	green	*LNER* front handrails on tender, 2-rail	70-73	60	80
1181	4472 'Flying Scotsman'	green	*LNER* front handrails on tender, 3-rail	70	70	90
1182	60103 'Flying Scotsman'	green	BRc, 2-rail	70-73	90	110
1182/3	60103 'Flying Scotsman'	green	BRc, 3-rail	70	100	120
1183	- 'Flying Scotsman'	black	red buffer beams and running plate edges, 2-rail	69-73	90	110
1183	4472 'Flying Scotsman'	black	*NER* red buffer beams and running plate edges Ltd Edn	69?	NPG	NPG
1182	60103 'Flying Scotsman'	green	BRc, motor in tender	70-73	90	110
1183	- 'Flying Scotsman'	black	motor in tender	70-73	90	110
1180	4472 'Flying Scotsman'	green	*LNER*, motor in tender	70-73	50	70
1030	60103 'Flying Scotsman'	green	BRc	74-87	90	110
1031	60103 'Flying Scotsman'	green	BRc, without lights	74-75	90	110
1035	4472 'Flying Scotsman'	green	*LNER*, 2 tenders	74-87	50	90
1037	60103 'Flying Scotsman'	green	BRc	74-87	90	110
1038	60103 'Flying Scotsman'	green	BRc, without lights	74-75	90	110
1071	4472 'Flying Scotsman'	green	*LNER* static model	75, 90	NPG	NPG
1075	4472 'Flying Scotsman'	green	*LNER* 2 tenders, static model	75, 90	NPG	NPG
1078	60103 'Flying Scotsman'	green	BRc, static model	75, 90	NPG	NPG
1039	- 'Flying Scotsman'	black	without lights	74-87	90	110
1035T						
1071	4472	black	LNER, water tender in apple green on its own	76, 79	20	30
1070	-	black	water tender fitted with snow plough on its own	78-87	30	45
1130	4472 'Flying Scotsman'	green	*LNER*, EMS equipment fitted	82-84	NPG	NPG
1137	60103 'Flying Scotsman'	green	BRc, EMS equipment fitted	82-84	NPG	NPG

29. Class A4 4-6-2

Tooled and manufactured by Liliput of Austria but assembled by Thernglade Ltd at Wrexham in Wales. From 1974 these models were Liliput UK products. 3-rail versions were not available. **v = with valances down over the wheels**

1190	4468 'Mallard'	blue	*LNER*, v	70-73	60	90
1188	2509 'Silver Link'	grey	*LNER*, v	71-73	60	90
1195	60027 'Merlin'	green	BRc,	71-73	50	80
1045	4468 'Mallard'	blue	*LNER*, v	74-87	60	90
1040	2509 'Silver Link'	grey	*LNER*, v	74-87	60	90
1050	60027 'Merlin'	green	BRc,	74-87	50	80
1085	4468 'Mallard'	blue	*LNER*, v, static model	75, 90	NPG	NPG
1080	2509 'Silver Link'	grey	*LNER*, v, static model	75, 90	NPG	NPG
1090	60027 'Merlin'	green	BRc, static model	75, 90	NPG	NPG
1041	2512 'Silver Fox'	grey	*LNER*, v, optional name to order	74-87	NPG	NPG
1042	2511 'Silver King'	grey	*LNER*, v, optional name to order	74-87	NPG	NPG
1043	2510 'Quicksilver'	grey	*LNER*, v, optional name to order	74-87	NPG	NPG
1047	4498 'Sir Nigel Gresley'	blue	*LNER*, v, optional name to order	74-87	NPG	NPG
1048	7 'Sir Nigel Gresley'	blue	*LNER*, optional name to order	74-87	NPG	NPG
1051	60025 'Falcon'	green	BRc, optional name to order	74-87	NPG	NPG
1052	60030 'Golden Fleece'	green	BRc, optional name to order	74-87	NPG	NPG
1053	'Golden Shuttle'**	green	BRc, optional name to order	74-87	NPG	NPG
1054	'Kestrel'**	green	BRc, optional name to order	74-87	NPG	NPG
1055	60033 'Seagull'	green	BRc, optional name to order	74-87	NPG	NPG
1046	4468 'Mallard'	black	*NE* wartime livery	78-87	120	160

Cat.No.	Name / Number	Colour	Details	Years	£	£
1046	4468 'Mallard'	black	*NE* wartime livery with fire glow	78	120	160
1045	4468 'Mallard'	blue	*LNER*, v, with fire glow	78	80	100
1040	2509 'Silver Link'	grey	*LNER*, v, with fire glow	78	80	100
1050	60027 'Merlin'	green	BRc, with fire glow	78	70	90
1140	4468 'Mallard'	blue	*LNER*, v, EMS equipment fitted	82-84	NPG	NPG
1145	2509 'Silver Link'	grey	*LNER*, v, EMS equipment fitted	82-84	NPG	NPG
1150	60027 'Merlin'	green	BRc, EMS equipment fitted	82-84	NPG	NPG

** No BR liveried real A4s carried these names!

30. Class A2 4-6-2

This used a Trix Express/International chassis made in Germany with other parts manufactured by Liliput of Austria but assembled by Thernglade Ltd at Wrexham in Wales. From 1974 these models were Liliput UK products. The model was not released in 3-rail versions but they could be made to order as too could ones with Trix coarse scale wheels.

Cat.No.	Name / Number	Colour	Details	Years	£	£
1186	525 'A.H.Peppercorn'	green	*LNER*	70-73	90	140
1185	60525 'A.H.Peppercorn'	green	BRc	71-73	100	160
1187	532 'Blue Peter' **	green	*LNER* as preserved loco	?	185	NPG
1060	525 'A.H.Peppercorn'	green	LNER	74-92	90	140
1061	60525 'A.H.Peppercorn'	green	BRc	74-92	100	160
1060	525 'A.H.Peppercorn'	green	*LNER*, tender drive	78-92	90	140
1061	60525 'A.H.Peppercorn'	green	BRc, tender drive	78-92	100	160
1160	525 'A.H.Peppercorn'	green	*LNER*, EMS equipment fitted	82-84	NPG	NPG
1161	60525 'A.H.Peppercorn'	green	BRc, EMS equipment fitted	82-84	NPG	NPG
1064	'A.H.Peppercorn'	black	*NE*, wartime livery	82-92	160	200
1065	'A.H.Peppercorn'	black	*NE*, wartime livery, tender drive	82-92	160	200

** 12 Code 3 models of this exists which were made for the BBC 'Blue Peter' programme.

AN ENTIRELY NEW STATION-BUILDING SYSTEM

TRIX "Many-ways" STATION SETS

TTR - The Greatest Little Train in the World

The Many-ways station leaflet

Coaches

Trix coaches fall into two distinct categories - tinplate and plastic.

Tinplate Coaches

The very first coaches sold in Britain were Trix Express ones. The British range of tinplate coaches, which were made from the start up of Trix Twin Railway production until the early 1960s, came in three sizes. The smallest were short 4-wheeled suburban stock which were shorter than the Trix Express ones, available in LNER or LMS livery and were available in composite and brake versions.

The standard coaches were short bogie main line stock of three types - composite (all 3rd for SR), brake end and restaurant car (in some liveries only). These came in LNER, LMS, Southern and, by the early '50s, BR liveries of crimson and cream, maroon and in small quantities of Southern Region green. They were also available in some overseas liveries. There were also short suburban bogie coaches and a parcels coach in bright red or maroon as well as an Engineer's Department version in black.

For the 'scale' models such as the 'Scotsman', 'Princess' and 'Coronation' there were tinplate bogie coaches of nearer scale length and, again of the three types and in LNER teak and LMS maroon. For the 'Coronation' train set, 'scale' coaches were specially liveried for 'The Royal Scot' but were available in only two forms - 1st and brake end.

The 'scale' coaches in the 1950s adopted BR liveries of crimson and cream as well as maroon. Late in the day there were also some chocolate and cream coaches produced and by now they were being fitted with interiors which greatly improved their appearance. Perhaps the most attractive tinplate coach was the Pullman parlour car which carried 'TRIX TWIN' on its sides in place of a name, although authentic parlour car names were adopted in the early '60s.

Plastic Coaches

With new locomotives like Britannia and the Standard 5 in H0 scale, when it came to designing a range of plastic coaches in the early 1960s H0 was naturally adopted as the scale for them. This proved to be a disastrous decision as it tied Trix to the less popular scale for subsequent models like the Western diesel and Trans-Pennine set. The coaches were very attractive and quickly replaced the tinplate ones. They were also available in kit form.

There were four types based on BR Mk1s. These were a composite, brake end, mini-buffet and Pullman kitchen car. With one exception they were available in maroon, green, chocolate & cream, all blue and blue & grey. The exception was, of course, the Pullman car which was in brown & cream or blue & grey. It was available with a good variety of names. The composite coach was also used as an intermediate coach for the Trans-Pennine DMU and, as such, was released in a number of other liveries.

Less attractive was the later use of the coaches in pre-Nationalisation liveries including GWR and LMS during the Liliput UK period.

Wagons

Like the coaches, the wagons started life as tinplate models and did not change to plastic until the 1960s. Originally most wagons were on a short wheel base with a slightly longer one for brake vans, tanks and cattle wagons. They were initially printed with large company lettering but, even pre-war, changed to small letter in the bottom left hand corner of the wagon side. The open wagon also appeared quite early on in a private owner liveries as well as those of 'Trix' and 'Bassett-Lowke'. Four wheel and bogie timber wagons were common, the load being a grooved wooden block. Bogie wagons also included a brick wagon, flat wagon and steel sided wagon and as with other model railway systems, there was a colourful array of tanker wagons. The most striking wagon was the breakdown crane which consisted of two short four wheel trucks one of which contained a working diecast crane and the other a jib cradle.

After the war the wagon range looked very much the same but now fitted with Peco style couplings. These simple tinplate wagon adopted BR liveries in the early '50s but there was little other wagon development until the 1960s. An exception was the introduction of a very attractive Weltrol wagon in 1953 which was released with a variety of well designed loads. This was diecast as were the lighted brake van and the tipping hopper wagon that were released about the same time.

In the 1960s we saw the introduction of plastic for wagon production but unlike Meccano Ltd with their Hornby Dublo range, Trix did not initially appreciate the possibilities of the new material. The first series of plastic wagons had embossed numbers and looked little better than the tinplate wagons they replaced.

This quickly changed when the first private owner open wagons appeared followed by a series of plastic tank wagons and the BRT bulk grain wagon with a large range of adverts.   Some wagons were also available in kit form. From 1974 the wagon range was reintroduced under the Liliput UK name and many remained available until the mid '80s.

Accessories

The first lineside buildings were made of wood and painted cream with grey roofs and red bases. most impressive of these was a terminus station with all-over glazed cover. The footbridges had very steep steps. The buildings developed into the Many-Ways station system which reflected W.J.Bassett-Lowke's interest in modern architecture. The building was modular, allowing the modeller to make up any one of a number of complex designs. Some parts were diecast and heavy, especially the central clock tower. Others, including water towers, gantry signal boxes, engine and carriage sheds, remained in wood until they were dropped from the range. The stations over-all roof and windows were printed acetate sheet.

Trix bought in some items including station figures, luggage and platform accessories from Britains and containers for trucks from Kenlow who manufactured similar ones for MasterModels. An attractive and popular lineside accessory in pre- and post-war years was the derelict coach hut which used the body of the 4-wheel coach, in either teak or maroon finish, mounted on a base.   Other small accessories included diecast signs, telegraph poles and yard lamps; the last two being mounted on similar large square bases. Single, double and junction signals were made and a tinplate signal box which concealed a whistle.

The most famous of all the Trix lineside accessories was the working coal conveyor which allowed tipping hopper wagons to dump coal in a bin from which it was carried up an elevator onto a conveyor belt and emptied into another waiting truck - all operated electrically. The largest accessory came in the '50s and was a ready wired table top, which was covered with green flock and made by the furniture manufacturers Vono Ltd.

Sets

The first train sets were copies of the German Trix Express sets but with British coloured coaches. These had long shiny red boxes in which trains included either three coaches or four wagons. They also contained an oval of bakerlite track and a square power controller. Another feature was the bottle of Trix Shell oil and the brass plugs for fitting onto the end of your connecting wire to attach the controller to the track.

The near square hinged lid set box came in after the war and survived through the 1950s . A feature of it was the space marked as being for you second train. They were really train packs rather than train sets as they contained no track or controls. This would have kept the cost down making an otherwise expensive system look better against rival makes which did include track etc.

At the end of the '50s the sets changed again to include track and incorporate cheaper boxes with lift-off lids and a more attractive printed top. These were redesigned in the '60s with the introduction of plastic coaches; the box top picture showing 'family involvement'.

There was a large range of train sets and train packs made over a period of 35 years and these are sought by some collectors. The most common, and therefore the least interesting, are those in the red hinged top boxes of the 1950s.

Trix short bogie coach produced in SR green for the Schools set

Trix Peppercorn A2 as 532 'Blue Peter', produced for the BBC   [table 30]

Trix
tinplate wagons

Trix mobile crane

WRENN RAILWAYS COLLECTORS CLUB

Are you a Wrenn collector or enthusiast? Need more information about Wrenn models?
Then why not join the **Wrenn Railways Collectors Club!**
Simply telephone 01628-488455 and ask for a membership form!

WRCC Details

The Club now has over 230 members, including members from Australia, Canada & USA. Limited Edition Wagons are commissioned on a regular basis. So far, a J Bly Coal Wagon and 2 different Geest Banana Vans have been produced.
The WRCC has issued 3 guides known as "Wrenn Seekers". These cover the Locomotives, Coaches and Wagons produced by G & R Wrenn Ltd.

"The Wrenn Tracker" - A newsletter issued every 2 months. Features include:
- The history of the G & R Wrenn Company
- A Sales & Wants column
- Any Wrenn related developments at Dapol Limited
- Member's articles for both the enthusiast and collector
- Member's letters, comments and frustrations!
- Details about other products made or sold by Wrenn: e.g., Trackwork, Ephemera, Lima, Formula 152 Cars, Horn Sets, Tri-ang Minix Cars, Electric Model Boats, Master Mariner Boats, Hornby-Dublo and Tri-ang TT !
- Details about forthcoming Train-related events.

The WRCC holds an annual Fair called **"Wrenn F.E.D."** "Wrenn F.E.D. 2000" takes place at Marlow in Bucks on Sunday 22nd October. Wrenn F.E.D. 2001 will be in October 2001. See Press for details.

WRENN RAILWAYS COLLECTORS CLUB

The **Wrenn Railways Collectors Club** exists to provide a forum for all
Wrenn enthusiasts to learn more by the exchange of information.
E-mail: barry@wrennrail.freeserve.co.uk   *Web Site available*
The Club founder, Barry Fentiman, would be pleased to provide any more information and answer any queries from both new collectors and existing enthusiasts. Tel: 01628-488455, Fax: 01628-440515.

WHY NOT JOIN THE
WRENN RAILWAY COLLECTORS CLUB TODAY !

Send for a membership form to: Barry Fentiman, 31 Oak Tree Avenue, Marlow, Bucks SL7 3EN

Wrenn

History

George and Richard Wrenn established their company, G&R Wrenn, at Lee Green at Blackheath, London, in the 1950s and there made track for railway modellers not satisfied with existing proprietary brands. In 1955 they moved to an industrial unit at 11 Honeywood Road, Basildon, Essex where they had room to expand their activities. By the early 1960s they were offering at least 120 items of 00 and TT track and had developed their own slot-car racing system called Formular 152 which had been launched in 1960.

They had developed a number of other mechanical toys and one in particular caught the eye of a representative of the giant toy makers, Lines Bros Ltd., better known for their Tri-ang trade mark. Lines bought a controlling interest in G&R Wrenn in the early 1960s and thus it became part of the Lines Bros. Group and was placed under the wing of Rovex Scale Models Ltd who made Tri-ang Railways.

Following the takeover of Meccano Ltd. by Lines Bros. in 1964, George Wrenn successfully purchased the redundant Hornby-Dublo tools from the Meccano factory in Liverpool. He relaunched the system under the name Tri-ang Wrenn. On the breakup of the Lines Bros. empire in 1971, he bought back from the receiver the shares in his company that had been held by Lines and changed the name of his railway system to Wrenn Railways.

The range of models produced over the next 20 years was quite considerable and included four new model locomotive designs. In 1992 George Wrenn retired and sold his equipment, stock and the Wrenn intellectual assets to Dapol. No new Wrenn locomotive models have been produced since then except, perhaps, from the stock of parts acquired with the Company.

Collecting Club

We are indebted to the Wrenn Railways Collectors Club for their considerable help with advice and proof reading during the preparation of this section. The Club publishes a bimonthly newsletter, called Wrenn Tracker, and also commissions the occasional special edition wagon. Anyone interested in further information about this organisation should contact Barry Fentiman on Tel: 01628 488455 or visit the Club's Web site at http//www.wrennrail.freeserve.co.uk

Milestones

1950s	G&R Wrenn established as track makers.
1955	The Company moves to Basildon.
1960	Formula 152 racing system launched.
1964	Lines Bros. take over Meccano Ltd.
1965	Lines Bros. buy control of the Company.
1966	Wrenn purchase former Hornby Dublo tools.
1966	Wrenn advertise their first ex-Hornby Dublo product – 'Cardiff Castle'.
1967	First Tri-ang Wrenn locos released.
1967	Wrenn enter into an agreement to market Lima N gauge in Britain.
1968	First Tri-ang Wrenn wagons released.
1968	The Company sells-off remainder Tri-ang TT stock.
1972	Wrenn now an independent company again and the product renamed Wrenn Railways.
1973	Wrenn take over the marketing of their own products from Rovex Ltd.
1973	First Wrenn full-colour catalogue published.
1980	Wrenn release the parallel boiler Scot – their first 'original' locomotive.
1984	Their last 'original' locomotive, the streamlined Coronation, is released.
1992	George Wrenn retires and sells his business to Dapol.

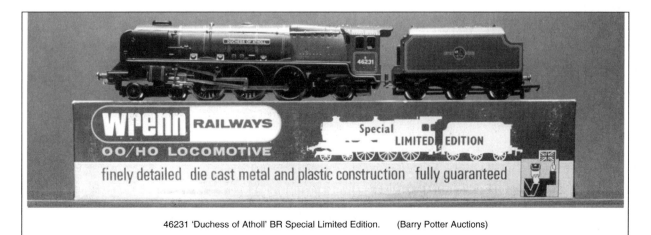

46231 'Duchess of Atholl' BR Special Limited Edition.   (Barry Potter Auctions)

Locomotives

Dates – Providing dates to indicate availability of Wrenn locomotives has always been difficult as they were produced in batches sometimes with gaps between. Introduction dates were also convoluted as new models were frequently added to the catalogue and price list several years before they were ready for release. Dates quoted here should therefore be taken for guidance only.

Suffixes – Some models were later fitted with 5-pole motors and these generally received a 'M2' or '5P' suffix to their catalogue number and, on the whole, at auction fetch a higher price. 'AM2' and 'M2' versions have flanged centre driving wheels and cab detail, as well as 5-pole motors.

1. Castle Class 4-6-0

Cat.No.	Name / Number	Colour	Details	Years	£	£
W2221	4075 'Cardiff Castle'	green	BRc	67-71, 76-89	80	100
W2221	4075 'Cardiff Castle'	green	BRc, in white temporary packaging	67?	180	220
W2221K	4075 'Cardiff Castle'	green	BRc, kit	69-70	400	500
W2222	7002 'Devizes Castle'	green	G(crest)W	71-77,84	80	100
W2221B	5023 'Brecon Castle'	lt.green	BRb	74-75, 79-81	120	150
W2223	4082 'Windsor Castle'	blue	BRb	75-82	100	120
W2247	7029 'Clun Castle'	green	Great(crest)Western	78-80, 83-92	85	110
W2221A	7013 'Bristol Castle'	green	BRc, improved lining	80-84	160	190
W2222	7002 'Devizes Castle'	green	G(crest)W, improved lining	82-84	80	100
W2247A	7029 'Clun Castle'	green	BR	86-87, 91-92	350	410
W2284	5090 'Neath Abbey'	green	BR	89-92	330	390
W2400	7007 'Great Western'	green	BRb, Ltd Edn 250 with stand	85-87	360	425
W2417	5034 'Corfe Castle'	green	BR, Ltd Edn 250 with stand	91-92	360	425
W2221	4075 'Ludlow Castle'	green	BRc, Cardiff Castle number, (an error but about 50 made)	69?	400	500

2. Class 8F 2-8-0

Cat.No.	Name / Number	Colour	Details	Years	£	£
W2224	48073	black	BRc	67-81	60	75
W2225	8042	black	LMS	70-80	70	85
W2240	3144	black	LNER	77-80	75	90
W2225A	8233	black	LMS	84-88	200	250
W2224A	48290	black	BR	82-88	160	200
W2224	48109	black	BR	67-69	440	540
W2272	8016	maroon	LMS	83-87	240	300
W2281	302	grey	WD	86-91	240	300
W2308	48290	green	BRc	90-92	520	650
W2308	48102	green	BRc	91-92	640	800
W2409	48102	black	BRc, Ltd Edn 250 with stand	89-92	320	400

3. 4MT Standard Tank 2-6-4T

Cat.No.	Name / Number	Colour	Details	Years	£	£
W2218	80033	black	BRc	67-84?	60	70
W2219	2679	maroon	LMS	72-84?	65	80
W2220	8230	green	GWR	74-75, 84-?	65	80
W2245	1927	green	Southern	78-84?	145	180
W2245	1927	green	Southern, unlined	?	1050	1300
W2245	1927	green	Southern, olive green	?	625	780
W2246	2085	blue	CR	79-82?	160	200
W2270	80135	green	BRc	83-?	125	160
W2271	9025	green	LNER	83-?	240	300
W2271	9025	green	LNER, unlined	?	1360	1700
-	2679 (on smokebox door)	maroon	Silver Jubilee 1977, Basildon, Sp Edn 25 (Basildon Development Corporation)	77	2000	2500
W2218A	80064	black	BR	85-?	120	150
W2218A	80079	black	BR	?	135	170
W2307	80079	black	BRb, unlined	?	760	920
W2279/5P	80151	black	BRb	?	145	180
W2406	80120	black	BR, Ltd Edn 350 with stand	?	250	310

4. Class R1 Tank 0-6-0T

Cat.No.	Name / Number	Colour	Details	Years	£	£
W2206B/ W2205	31337	black	BRc	68-76, 79-?	35	40
W2206C	-	-	chassis only	69-71	80	100

W2206/						
W2206	31340	green	BRc	69-71, 77-78	40	50
W2205	31340	black	BRc	72-?	40	50
W2207	1127	green	*Southern*	72-82	35	40
W2204	7420	red	*LMS*	74-82	35	40
W2203	-	silver	*SHELL*	78-82	60	75
W2202	56	yellow	*N.T.G.*	79-80	60	75
W2202	56	yellow	*N.T.G.*, yellow smokebox	?	250	320
W2201	38	blue	*Esso*	80-82	80	100
W2201	38	blue	*Esso*, blue smokebox	?	250	320
W2201A	69	green	*SE&CR*	85-89	95	120
W2205A	31047	black	*BRb*	85-88	225	270
W2206	31337	green	BR	?	40	50
W2206A	31128	green	BR	85-90	240	300
W2207A	1152	green	*Southern*	85-90	240	300
W2410	1047	green	*Southern*, Ltd Edn 60? with stand	90-21	640	800
W2408	-	gold	non-powered 24ct gold plated Jubilee tank, Ltd Edn 500 with stand	89-92	160	200
W2206	-	dk.green	*BRb*	?	240	300
-	-	clear	*GWR*, clear plastic body, Sp Edn as display item	?	400	500

5. Rebuilt West Country Class 4-6-2

W2235	34005 'Barnstaple'	green	BRc	68-71, 78	100	130
W2236	34042 'Dorchester'	green	BRc	70-76	135	170
W2237	21C109 'Lyme Regis'	green	*Southern*	73-78, 81-92?	120	150
W2237	21C109 'Lyme Regis'	blue	*Southern*, blue over green	?	320	400
W2238	35028 'Clan Line'	green	BRc	77-88	160	200
W2238	35028 'Clan Line'	green	BRc, etched brass nameplates	91-92	280	350
W2239	34028 'Eddystone'	green	BRc	79-88	175	220
W2236A	34016 'Bodmin'	green	BRc, black nameplates	80-84	330	410
W2236A	34016 'Bodmin'	green	BRc, red nameplates	80-84	310	380
W2269	34053 'Sir Keith Park'	green	BRc, Golden Arrow	86-92	280	350
W2269X	34053 'Sir Keith Park'	green	BRc	86-89	360	400
W2287	34036 'Westward Ho!'	green	BRc	90-92	360	400
W2309	34036 'Westward Ho!'	green	BRc, unlined	?	600	750
W2309	34036 'Westward Ho!'	black	BRb, unlined, no smoke deflectors	92	560	700
W2296	34021 'Dartmoor'	green	BR	90-92	440	550
W2297	35010 'Blue Star Line'	green	BRc	90-92	440	550
W2402	34090 'Sir Eustace Missenden'	green	BRc, Ltd Edn 250 with stand	88-89	360	450
W2415	34052 'Lord Dowding'	green	BRc, Ltd Edn 250 with stand	90-92	365	470

6. Class A4 4-6-2

W2211	60022 'Mallard'	green	BRc	69-79 83-91	80	100
W2212	7 'Sir Nigel Gresley'	blue	*LNER*	70-92	75	90
W2213	4903 'Peregrine'	black	*NE*	74-92	85	110
W2209	4482 'Golden Eagle'	green	*LNER*	78-92	80	100
W2212A	4498 'Sir Nigel Gresley'	blue	*LNER*	79-91	120	150
W2212AM2	4498 'Sir Nigel Gresley'	blue	*LNER*	89-92	280	350
W2210	4468 'Mallard'	blue	*LNER*	79-85	120	150
W2209A	4495 'Great Snipe'	green	*LNER*	81-92	200	250
W2209AM2	4495 'Great Snipe'	green	*LNER*	87-92	320	400
W2211A	60014 'Silver Link'	green	BR	81-90	160	200
W2213A	4900 'Gannet'	black	*NE*	81-89	190	240
W2210A	4495 'Golden Fleece'	blue	*LNER*	85-86	480	600
W2210AM2	4495 'Golden Fleece'	blue	*LNER*	87-91	370	460
W2282	4463 'Sparrow Hawk'	black	*NE*	90-92	440	550
W2283	4493 'Woodcock'	grey	*LNER*	89-92	520	650
W2295	4489 'Dominion of Canada'	blue	*LNER*	90-92	520	650
W2295M2	4489 'Dominion of Canada'	blue	*LNER*	90-92	560	700
W2306	60010 'Dominion of Canada'	green	BRc	91-92	600	750
W2310	4498 'Sir Nigel Gresley'	blue	*LNER*	91-92	620	770
W2413	4464 'Bittern'	green	*LNER*, Ltd Edn 250 with stand	90-92	370	460
W2404	4468 'Mallard'	blue	*LNER*, Ltd Edn 250 with stand	88-90	320	400

7. Princess Coronation (Duchess) 4-6-2

W2226	46245 'City of London'	maroon	BRc	69-80, 86-90	80	100
W2226M2	46238 'City of Carlisle'	maroon	BRc	84-87	280	350
W2226	46245 'City of London'	maroon	BRc, lined tender	?	200	250

Four versions of the Wrenn LMS Princess Coronation Class, 6221 'Queen Elizabeth' (W2301) [table 14], 6228 'Duchess of Rutland' (W2302A) [table 14], 6220 'Coronation' (W2301A) [table 14] and 6244 'King George VI' (W2302) [table 14].   (Romsey Auction Rooms)

Wrenn 46159 'The Royal Air Force' (W2273) [table 11] and 21C155 'Fighter Pilot' (W2265A) [table 13].   (Barry Potter Auctions)

Wrenn Class 08 shunters 72 'N.C.B' (W2234) [table 9] and 'Dunlop' (W2243) [table 9], Class R1 tank Southern 1047 (W2410) [table 4],
LMS Class N2 tank 2274 (W2214) [table 8], Class 20 Bo-Bo diesels BR blue non-powered D8015 (W2230NP)
and green D8010 (W2230) [table 10].   (Barry Potter Auctions)

Wrenn 35003
'Royal Mail Line'
(W2411) [table 13],

21C111 'Tavistock'
(W2407) [table 13]

and 34052
'Lord Dowding' (W2415)
[table 5].

(Barry Potter Auctions)

Cat.No.	Name / Number	Colour	Details	Years	£	£
W2226	46245 'City of London'/ 'City of Birmingham'	maroon	BRc, factory error with different name on each side	?	280	350
W2227	6254 'City of Stoke on Trent'	black	*LMS*	70-76, 79-90	55	70
W2227	6254 'City of Stoke on Trent'	black	*LMS*, late version with large wheels	?	400	500
W2228	46235 'City of Birmingham'	green	BRc	73-92	90	110
W2228M2	46235 'City of Birmingham'	green	BRc	85-90	600	750
W2229	46242 'City of Glasgow'	blue	BRb	73-86	100	130
W2241	6229 'Duchess of Hamilton'	black	*LMS*	78-92	80	100
W2241M2	6229 'Duchess of Hamilton'	black	*LMS*	86-90	360	450
W2242	6247 'City of Liverpool'	maroon	*LMS*	80-90	120	150
W2227A	6256 'Sir William Stanier'	black	*LMS*	82-90	180	230
W2227AM2	6256 'Sir William Stanier'	black	*LMS*	86-90	280	450
W2228A	46241 'City of Edinburgh'	green	BRc	81-86	200	250
W2228AM2	46241 'City of Edinburgh'	green	BRc	86-89	480	600
W2229A	46246 'City of Manchester'	blue	BRb	81-86	240	300
W2264	46229 'Duchess of Hamilton'	maroon	BRc	83-85	360	450
W2226A	46238 'City of Carlisle'	maroon	BRc	83-85	250	310
W2226AM2	46238 'City of Carlisle'	maroon	BRc	84-87	280	350
W2241A	6225 'Duchess of Gloucester'	black	*LMS*	82-88	320	400
W2241AM2	6225 'Duchess of Gloucester'	black	*LMS*	86-88	400	500
W2285	6221 'Queen Elizabeth'	maroon	*LMS*	89-92	335	420
W2286	46252 'City of Leicester'	black	BR	89-92	320	400
W2294	6234 'Duchess of Abercorn'	grey	*LMS*	89-92	320	400
W2299	46221 'Queen Elizabeth'	green	BRc	90-92	400	500
W2304	46244 'City of Leeds'	maroon	BRc, with alternative 'King George VI' plates	90-92	400	500
W2311	46244 'City of Leeds'	black	BRc, unlined	91-92	600	750
W2304	46244 'King George VI'	maroon	BRc, with optional 'Leeds City' nameplates	90-92	400	500
W2312	46245 'City of London'	green	BR	91-92	560	700
W2313	46234 'Duchess of Abercorn'	green	BR	91-92	720	900
W2314	46256 'Sir William Stanier'	green	BRc	91-92	720	900
W2315	46242 'City of Glasgow'	maroon	BRc	91-92	360	450
W2316	46242 'City of Glasgow'	green	BR	91-92	680	850
W2401	6223 'Princess Alice'	maroon	*LMS*, Ltd Edn 350 with stand	87-89	360	450
W2405	46231 'Duchess of Athol'	green	BRc, Ltd Edn 250 with stand	88-90	360	450
W2414	46251 'City of Nottingham'	black	BRb, Ltd Edn 250 with stand	90-92	360	450

8. Class N2 Tank 0-6-2T

Cat.No.	Name / Number	Colour	Details	Years	£	£
W2216	69550	black	BRc	69-71, 77-78, 81-85	75	90
W2217	9522	green	*LNER*	70-82	35	40
W2217A	2690 (number on boiler)	black	*LNER*	82-86	320	400
W2217A	2690 (on coal bunker)	black	*LNER*	84-86	480	600
W2215	2385	black	*LMS*	72-76	40	50
W2214	2274	maroon	*LMS*	78-80	60	75
W2216A	69496	black	BRb	85-88	280	350
W2280	8230	green	*GWR*	85-88	280	350
W2216	69550	maroon	BRc	?	500	620
W2292	2752	dk.green	*Southern*	88-91	560	700
W2292	2752	lt.green	*Southern*	90-92	1450	1600

9. Class 08 Diesel Shunter 0-6-0DS

Cat.No.	Name / Number	Colour	Details	Years	£	£
W2231	D3763	green	BRc	74-84?	40	50
W2232	D3464	blue	BRe	74-82	40	50
W2234	72	maroon	*N.C.B.*	78-80?	65	80
W2233	7124	black	*LMS*	76-80?	65	80
W2243	-	yellow	*Dunlop*	80-82?	65	80
W2232A	08 762	blue	BRe	83-?	160	200
W2231NP	D3768	green	BRc, non-powered	82?	400	500
W2232NP	D3523	blue	BRe, non-powered	82?	400	500
W2231NP	-	black	non-powered	?	300	370
W2233	7124	green	*LMS*	?	240	300

10. Class 20 Diesel Bo-Bo

Cat.No.	Name / Number	Colour	Details	Years	£	£
W2230	D8017	green	BRc	77-?	50	60
W2230B	8003	blue	BRe	77-?	50	60
W2230NP	D8010	green	BRc, non-powered	82-?	200	250
W2230BNP	D8015	blue	BRe, non-powered	82-?	200	250
W2230A	20 008	blue	BRe	82-88	160	200
W2230RF	20 132	grey	BReLL, early Railfreight livery	86-90	280	350

11. Class 6P (Royal Scot) 4-6-0

W2260	6100 'Royal Scot'	maroon	*LMS*	80-89	100	130
W2260/5P	6100 'Royal Scot'	maroon	*LMS*	86-89	200	250
W2261	6102 'Black Watch'	black	*LMS*	80-91	120	160
W2261/5P	6102 'Black Watch'	black	*LMS*	86-89	200	250
W2262	46110 'Grenadier Guardsman'	green	BRb	80-89	145	180
W2260A	6141 'Caledonian'	maroon	*LMS*	82-90	360	450
W2261A	6160 'Queen Victoria's Rifleman'	black	*LMS*	82-88	280	360
W2262A	46148 'The Manchester Regiment'	green	BR	82-90	500	620
W2273	46159 'The Royal Air Force'	blue	BRb	83-92	240	300
W2288	46159 'The Royal Air Force'	green	BR	89-92	320	410
W2274	6125 'Lancashire Witch'	maroon	*LMS*	84-92	160	210
W2293	6141 'Caledonian'	black	*LMS*, gloss finish	89-92	560	710
W2293	6141 'Caledonian'	black	*LMS*, matt finish	89-92	680	850
W2298	46110 'Royal Scot'	green	BR	89-92	475	590
W2403	6146 'The Rifle Brigade'	black	*LMS*, Ltd Edn 250 with stand	88-90	250	320

12. Pullman EMU

W3004/5	S290S+S291S	blu+gry	BRe, 2-car set	79-88	140	175
W3005NP	S290S, S291S	blu+gry	non-powered car sold singly in loco style box	91-92	120	150
W3004/5A	S290S+S291S	blu+gry	BRe, 2-car set, 150 Years 1841-1991, Ltd Edn 20?	92	1450	1800
W3006/7	90+91	brn+crm	2-car set	79-88	160	200
W3006/7	88+89	brn+crm	2-car set	82-88	240	300
W3006/7	90+91	brn+crm	2-car set individually packed in coach style boxes	88-92	270	350
W3007NP	90, 91	brn+crm	non-powered car sold singly in loco style box	91-92	160	210
W3006/7A	90+89	brn+crm	2-car set, 150 years 1841-1991, Ltd Edn 100?	91-92	520	650

13. Streamlined Bullied Pacific 4-6-2

W2265	34051 'Winston Churchill"	green	BRc	82-92	220	275
W2265A	21C155 'Fighter Pilot'	green	*Southern, Golden Arrow*	84-92	320	400
W2265AX	21C155 'Fighter Pilot'	green	*Southern*	84-92	320	400
W2266	21C103 'Plymouth'	green	*Southern*	82-92	240	300
W2266A	34092 'City of Wells'	green	BRc, *Golden Arrow*	85-92	280	350
W2266AX	34092 'City of Wells'	green	BRc	85-92	280	350
W2267	35026 'Lamport and Holt Line'	blue	BRb	82-85	300	375
W2267A	35026 'Lamport and Holt Line'	green	BR	88-91	600	750
W2268	34004 'Yeovil'	blue	BRb	83-89	320	400
W2268A	34004 'Yeovil'	green	BR	88-92	520	650
W2275	34065 'Hurricane'	green	BRc	85-92	360	450
W2276	21C101 'Exeter'	green	*Southern*	87	950	1200
W2276/5P	21C101 'Exeter'	green	*Southern*, Golden Arrow	86-89	850	1100
W2276X/5P	21C101 'Exeter'	green	*Southern*	86-89	320	650
W2277	34066 'Spitfire'	green	BR	86-89	360	460
W2278	21C13 'Blue Funnel Line'	black	*Southern*	85-92	320	400
W2278A	21C13 'Blue Funnel Line'	green	*Southern*	88-89	680	850
W2289	21C5 'Canadian Pacific Line'	black	*Southern*	89-92	480	600
W2290	21C5 'Canadian Pacific Line'	green	*Southern*	89-92	600	750
W2291	34010 'Sidmouth'	green	BR	89-92	350	440
W2305	21C107 'Wadebridge'	green	*Southern*	91-92	600	750
W2407	21C111 'Tavistock'	green	*Southern*, Ltd Edn 250 with stand	89-91	360	450
W2411	35003 'Royal Mail Line'	blue	BRb, Ltd Edn 250 with stand	89-92	360	450
W2412	34020 'Seaton'	green	BR, Ltd Edn 250 with stand	90-92	360	450
W2416	34057 'Biggin Hill"	green	BRc, Ltd Edn 250 with stand	90-92	360	450

14. Streamlined Princess Coronation 4-6-2

W2301	6221 'Queen Elizabeth'	blue	*LMS*	84-88?	320	400
W2302	6244 'King George VI'	maroon	*LMS*	84-88?	320	400
W2301A	6220 'Coronation'	blue	*LMS*	86-88?	600	750
W2302A	6228 'Duchess of Rutland'	maroon	*LMS*	86-88?	600	750

Coaches

The Wrenn range of coaches was limited to those that could be produced from the former Hornby-Dublo tools for the Pullman cars. Those produced included some impossible liveries namely those of LMS and the Southern Railway. The coaches sell in mint boxed condition at around £30 each although some limited edition ones such as 'Evadne' and No.83 may cost up to £80 each. There had been the intention to produce come of the tinplate coaches and the Stove was even illustrated in one catalogue but these were not proceeded with.

Wagons

A large range of wagons was produced and these may be quickly distinguished from Hornby-Dublo ones by their tension-lock couplings. The range includes a horse box, blue spot van, long fruit van, small tank wagon, hopper, 5-plank open wagon, ventilated van, Presflo, Prestwin, utility van, gunpowder van, banana van, refrigerator van, small hopper, mineral wagon, grain wagon, Lowmac, six-wheeled tank wagon, cattle wagon, salt wagon and brake vans based on GWR, LMS and LNER designs. Prices of mint examples range between £10 and £20 with later variations and limited editions rising to £50. Higher priced examples include W4315p horse box 'Roydon Stables Brighton Oct 6-11' printed in red and green, W4652p 'Auto Distributors', W5013a 'St Ivel Gold', W5086 'Co-op Milk', W5091 'Unigate' and wagons with catalogue numbers W5103-W5105, W5109-W5113 and W5500-W5504.

Sets

Initially Wrenn made up train sets to use up the remnant stocks of Hornby-Dublo that they acquired in the mid '60s. After that there were three Wrenn sets numbered 001 to 003. The first two sell at around £250 each while 003 could cost you about twice that.

Previously published information

As stated in the introduction, the main objective of this catalogue is to provide comprehensive lists of the locomotives with detailed listings of rolling stock destined to appear in the next edition. As a consequence, the listings of rolling stock which appeared in the first edition have not been included here. However, if this information is required please send £2 in postage stamps and we will be pleased to send you a copy.

34065 'Hurricane' BR, 34092 'City of Wells' BR and 34004 'Yeovil' BR [table 13]   (Barry Potter Auctions)

Wrenn 46256 'Sir William Stanier' (W2314) [table 7], 46244 'City of Leeds' (W2311) [table 7], 21C109 'Lyme Regis' (W2237) [table 5], 4082 'Windsor Castle' (W2223) [table 1], 34092 'City of Wells' (W2266A) [table 13], 35026 'Lamport & Holt Line' (W2267) [table 13], 6100 'Royal Scot' (W2260) [table 11], 6102 'Black Watch' (W2261) [table 11], 4468 'Mallard' (W2210) [table 6] and 34090 'Sir Eustace Missenden' (W2402) [table 5].　　(Barry Potter Auctions)

Wrenn 7007 'Great Western' (W2400) [table 1], Class 8F 48102 (W2409) [table 2], 4464 'Bittern' (W2413) [table 6], 46251 'City of Nottingham' (W2414) [table 7], 6146 'The Rifle Brigade' (W2403) [table 11], 21C111 'Tavistock' (W2407) [table 13], 34051 'Winston Churchill' (W2265) [table 13], 46242 'City of Glasgow' (W2315) [table 7], CR 2-6-4 tank 2085 (W2246) [table 3], Class R1 'N.T.G.' 56 (W2202) [table 4] and SR 2-6-4 tank 1927 (W2245) [table 3].　　(Barry Potter Auctions)

Playcraft packaging

Playcraft

History

Although never developed into a major British range, the appearance of this 12 volt 2-rail system in the market in 1961 sent shivers down the spines of Britain's major model railway manufacturers at the time. The reason: its price! Advertised as 'Build that Big Layout for a Small Price', Playcraft was the cheapest mass-produced electric railway system yet seen.

Throughout the 1950s, the competitive British market, led by Tri-ang Railways, offered comprehensive model railway systems at very attractive prices, but from 1961 the new Playcraft range cut the cost of 'getting started' even further. Sold mainly through F.W.Woolworths, Mettoy were clearly interested in the beginner's market and offered starter sets at £1 each. As a result, two of the major players at the time responded with cheap starter sets of their own and Playcraft's expansion of British models was contained.

The Playcraft trademark was owned by Mettoy of Northampton, who also owned Corgi Toys and distributed Aurora plastic kits in the UK. Playcraft was first used on a re-badged version of the Aurora model highways systems, but was quickly applied to the new railway range and the Aurora kits. Most of the railway models were made in France by Jouef, although elements were also produced by Brawa, Pola, Aurora and at the Mettoy plant at Fforest-fach. To give maximum flexibility, the range was scaled at 3.5mm/ft, HO scale. Some British outline wagons were nearer to 4mm/ft, as were the British designed accessories such as the excellent Signals Kit. It is also true that many of the models were based on French and other Continental prototypes.

Playcraft Railways was launched at the 1961 Toy Fair with the first sets being available by the following Christmas. Throughout their life a mixture of Playcraft Railways and Jouef boxes were used. Larger sets such as the Kangarou and Cockerill crane used standard Jouef packaging with English instructions on a card insert. Production of the British models continued quite actively up until the end of 1968 after which there seems to have been a general run-down so that, by the end of the decade, only models of French prototypes were being offered.

This, however, was not the end of the British range. In the early 1970s a hideous clockwork version of the

Class 29 diesel, fitted to a rigid 4-wheel chassis was produced. Partnered with SNCF day cars re-branded as BR Buffet and Composite coaches, it was sold as a Starter Set. Similar treatment befell the SNCF BB66150 diesel, this time matched with bright red ex-SNCF coaching stock. The 1976 Jouef catalogue shows the Class 29 (D6100) but now fitted with Continental couplings. This was a re-tooled version using a later Jouef M20 motor driving one bogie only, catalogue 8911. All exterior detail is on raised mouldings, including numbers and BR arrows. Re-branded ex-SNCF day cars were matched with it, given correct BR Mk1 numbers for a Buffet, brake 2nd and Composite!

Further Reading

We know of no books specifically about the Playcraft range but there was a series of articles in Model Railway Collector: Volume 7 Nos. 3 and 4 (March and April 2000).

Couplings

Couplings – Playcraft models may be found with three types of coupling. The earliest type, known as 'Lanal', were original Jouef couplings, similar to a type used by Tri-ang. From around 1963/64, the Peco design, used for Hornby-Dublo and Trix models, were fitted to Playcraft stock. After 1968, stock began to appear with European lifting bar couplings as fitted to Jouef items. Despite this, Jouef were using Lanal couplings on starter sets as late as the 1980s.

Coaches

The British coaches were rather short for Mk1s but from the start were available in BR standard maroon and Western Region chocolate and cream. These were quickly followed by a Southern Region green rake. They consisted of a composite, a 2nd class open, a 2nd brake and, later, a restaurant car. A special feature was the early fitting of interiors. These were correctly a light timber colour and the restaurant car even had its kitchen detailed with printed self-adhesive stickers. Thus, the interiors were much better than those of Tri-ang Hornby, the main competitor at the time. The four British Mk1s were issued in blue and grey livery during 1967 together with teak versions. By October 1963, a Royal Mail travelling post office set was being offered; the coach from the set also being available separately as well as a non-operating version. All of the British coaches are quite cheap to buy, although the blue and grey and particularly the teak versions are hard to find.

There were several Continental coaches sold in Playcraft packaging. These included SNCF stock consisting of a post office van, 1st class stainless steel coach, and 1st class and composite versions of the standard green coach. There were also four Wagon-Lits International vehicles in the form of a 1st class Pullman car, Continental sleeper, dining car and a channel ferry sleeping car, branded 'London - Paris'. These initial models had Lanal couplings but soon changed to the Peco type. A Continental luggage van followed with two Trans-European Express stainless steel coaches (one with optional operating tail lights), a centre car for the Budd EMU, Wagon-Lits dining coach in red and a four wheeled heat generator van. The demand for the Continental stock in Britain is quite low, although these last two items are considered to be rare and command premium prices. The 1969 price list shows two 'vintage' SNCF coaches. These would be rare if ever released in Playcraft boxes.

Wagons
Although we tend to think of certain Playcraft wagons as being British, they were, in fact, based largely on French vehicles. The bogie wagons ran on American type diamond bogies typical of the TP stock supplied to France by the USA after the last war. An attractive feature of those wagons that were supposed to represent British prototypes was the use of British Railways names for them such as 'Boplate', 'Weltrol' and 'Walrus' which were on printed data panel labels but later printed directly onto the side of the wagon.

Some wagons were available in more than one colour and rare colours command higher prices. Examples include the BR brake van in green, 21 ton mineral wagon in dark redand yellow, 7-plank coal wagon in bright yellow and the wine barrel wagon in light maroon.

The range included a high sided bogie open wagon, planked high sided wagon, van, steel drop-side wagon, BR brake van, high and low sided bogie open wagons, bogie goods and refrigerator vans, bogie tanker, well wagon, Walrus, bogie bolster wagon with different loads, 'Shell/BP' tanker, steel mineral, 'Blue Circle' bulk cement twin silo wagon and a barrel wagon. The bogie hopper was available with or without working trapdoors and in a set with an under-track hopper and collecting bin. Later issues included the tank wagon in Solonia and Butagaz liveries; both considered scarce.

The European range included a goods wagon with a sliding roof, steel open wagon, 'Evian'/'Badoit' mineral water van, 'Algeco' French cereal hopper, 'Kronenbourg' French beer van, a magnificent operating Cockerill steam powered crane set, French articulated STVA car transporter and the Jouef Kangourou set containing a tractor unit, access ramp, loading area, two Kangourou wagons and two semi-trailers. Again, the Continental wagons have limited appeal in Britain although the Kangourou set has tempted a number of British Railways stalwarts! Rarities include the mineral water van branded Evian on both sides and the rather attractive beer van in the colours of Heineken. Late 1969 issues include long wheel base bogie tanker 'Butagaz' and similarly stretched bogie cattle van, both in Playcraft boxes.

Accessories
There was a good range of accessories with the goods depot and engine shed being particularly popular. The shed was very similar to that offered in the Hornby Dublo range, but was bright red, and also had an extension set. Curiously it was described as having operating smoke vents! The girder bridge set was modelled on the Great Central Railway overbridge at Rugby and designed in the UK.

Sets
There was quite a large range of train sets which took the names of famous stations and goods depots according to whether they were passenger or freight sets. In nice condition the more common sets (Clapham, Stratford, Broad Street and Snowhill) sell for between £25 and £40. The sought after sets are, of course, the London-Paris Night Ferry in its original picture box, the operating crane train set and, interestingly, some of the later starter sets with vehicles in odd colours. Expect to pay around £70 for an early Night Ferry set with a black Nord Pacific.

Locomotives

1. 0-4-0 Tank (Continental)   Early models have silver wheels and later ones have red ones.

P535	708	green	BRc, clockwork	61	5	10
P535	708	green	BRc, electric	61	7	15
P831	708	black	BRc, clockwork	61	5	10
P831	708	black	BRc, electric	61	7	15
-	708	red	BRe, clockwork, from a set	69-70	10	15*

2. Class 29 Diesel Bo-Bo

P837	D6100	green	BRc	61	10	20
P8371	D6100	blue	BRe	68	12	25
-	D6100	blue	BRe, from sets, clockwork with 4 wheels only!	70	10	15*
J8911	D6100	blue	BRe, raised detail, 4-wheel drive	76	15	20*

3. 0-4-0 Diesel Shunter

P838	D2705	green	no decals, hazard stripes	64	10	18
P8381	D2705	blue	BRe, hazard stripes	68	15	20
P536	D2705	green	no decals, clockwork	64	5	10

Locomotives of Continental types also sold in Playcraft boxes with Peco type couplings for the British market included:

Budd stainless steel 2-car EMU (£15-£35)
SNCF 2-8-0 (£20-£40)
SNCF 0-4-0 diesel shunter (£15-£25),
SNCF BB13001 Class electric (£20-£45)
SNCF Panoramic rail car (£15-£35)
SNCF CC 7107 Class electric (£20-£40)
Dutch 1308 electric (£60-£70)

Nord Type 231C Pacific (£20-£35)
SNCF 0-8-0 tank (both open and closed cab versions) (£20-£35)
SNCF BB67001 Class diesel (£12-£28)
TEE CC40101 Trans-Europe Express electric (£20-£40)
SNCF BB 66150 Class diesel (£15-£30)
SNCF CC70000 Class diesel-electric (£15-£35)

Playcraft 0-4-0 diesel shunter (P838)   [table 3]

Playcraft bogie goods van with sliding doors (P653)

Playcraft operating Royal Mail coach (P454)

4th edition
Playcraft catalogue

Tri-ang TT

History

In the 1930s there had been experiments in 2.5 mm : 1 ft scale on 12.2 mm gauge track but, while the gauge was successful, the scale was found to be too cramped.

Following the second world war, HP of America produced a TT system in 2.5 mm scale and in 1950 the German Rokal system was developed in a slightly larger scale. Rokal was imported into Britain in 1951 and this rekindled interest in TT scale in Britain. While Peco produced their Minilay track, few others responded. It needed a major company to show its faith in the scale.

In 1953, Walter Lines, chairman of the toy manufacturing giant Lines Bros. Ltd, returning from a trip to the Continent, brought back a train set manufactured by Wesa of Switzerland. He gave instruction that Rovex Scale Models Ltd., who were manufacturing the Tri-ang Railways 00 system, were to start work immediately on a Tri-ang TT system.

The command from above was not well received at Rovex where management were struggling to keep their heads above water with their staggering success of 00 system. Despite this, someone was put on TT development as soon as the Company moved into its new factory at Margate in the Summer of 1954. Many of the TT tools were made in the factory at Margate and the system was launched at the Toy Fair in the Spring of 1957 where the first two sets were displayed.

All locomotives and rolling stock were fitted with tension-lock couplings which had not yet appeared on the Tri-ang Railways 00 system. To distinguish it from the larger gauge system, the new TT products were packaged in yellow boxes with red printing and these would soon become a very familiar sight in model shops. Sets were available either with a battery box or a mains controller. The latter carried an 'X' suffix to their code.

At last the market had the impetus it needed to see TT taken as a serious scale for modelling. Other manufacturers quickly jumped on the band wagon producing accessories in the scale. For many this meant just producing smaller versions of existing models but track, card buildings, wagon kits and lineside accessories quickly appeared.

As with many of their ventures, Lines Bros. were determined to give their new baby a fighting chance. This meant producing a sizeable range of models to demonstrate their confidence in the system. Only by doing this could they persuade both the public and retailers that Tri-ang TT was here to stay and therefore worth buying.

1962 saw models of French prototypes added to the TT range. In order to access the European Common Market, which Britain had not yet joined, Lines Bros. built a factory in Calais. Various toy ranges were transferred there and one which the Company hoped to introduce to France was Tri-ang Railways TT. While other product lines from the Calais factory succeeded, the TT venture was not a success and the Continental tooling was sent to the Margate factory to be used there.

Tri-ang's eighth edition TT catalogue showed a system in decline with a number of models now missing from the range. Sales of the TT system had been falling sharply since 1960. In just two years the sales figures for sets halved. By 1964, total sales were just one sixth of what they had been in 1960.

By 1968, G&R Wrenn, who were another member of the Lines Group, had acquired the remaining stock of Tri-ang TT and were selling it as Wrenn Table Top Railways. According to a tool inventory, carried out in the early '90s, the bulk of the tools for the TT system stayed at Margate or, at least, those for the British range did.

Thus passed Britain's only TT scale system, but it was not the end of TT. It has remained one of the scales still modelled today and much of its success should be

Milestones

1951	Rokal TT imported into Britain.
1953	Lines Bros. examine a Wesa TT set.
1954	Work on a Tri-ang TT system has started.
1957	Tri-ang TT launched at Toy Fair.
1959	Merchant Navy model launched.
1959	B type track introduced.
1960	'Britannia' released.
1961	Gold plated set appears.
1962	Production of Continental range of Tri-ang TT starts in France.
1963	French tools transferred to Margate.
1964	Last catalogue is released.
1967	A special run of models made.
1967	A few blue and grey coaches made.
1968	Wrenn acquire outstanding TT stock.

laid at the door of the 3 mm Society who have concentrated their energies on the production of models and materials to meet their members' needs.

Further Reading

There is, as yet no definitive book on this subject although there is coverage in the first volume of Pat Hammond's trilogy, 'The Rovex Story'. The book concerned is 'Volume 1 - Tri-ang Railways'. There are a few additional notes in 'Volume 2 – Tri-ang Hornby'. The subject was also covered in a three part article in the 'Model Railway Collector' magazine Volume 7 numbers 2-4 (Feb-Apr 2000).

Collectors Club

We would also like to recommend the Tri-ang Society which caters for collectors of a wide range of Tri-ang toy products. The Society has a quarterly newsletter, called Tri-ang Telegraph, which contains a number of original articles by well known collectors. Details of the Tri-ang Society may be obtained from the Miles Rowland on Tel: 0161 9765059. Tri-ang TT is also sometimes covered in the magazine of the Train Collectors Society (details at the front of the book).

Dates – It is difficult to be completely accurate with production dates and those given should be treated as a guide, only.

Listing – The models are arranged in the order we believe they were available.

Tri-ang Est Continental Pacific (T591)   [table 8]

Tri-ang Class 08 diesel shunter as 13007 (T95)   [table 4]

Locomotives

1.   Jinty 0-6-0T   There were two similar but different body moulds used at the same time.

T90	34171	black	BRc, unlined**	57-61	20	25
T90S	4171	black	BRc, lined - with smoke generator (only 5 made)	62	100	150
T90	4171	black	BRc, lined	62-68	25	30

** The model had plastic centre driving wheels until 1959.

2.   Castle Class 4-6-0

T91/92	4082 'Windsor Castle'	green	BRc, matt and gloss versions	57-61	35	40
T91/92	5011 'Tintagel Castle'	green	BRc**	62-65	40	45

** Both solid and open wheels may be found on these models.

3.   Non-rebuilt Merchant Navy 4-6-2

T93/94	35028 'Clan Line'	green	BRc**	59-64	50	55
(T43)	'Clan Line'	gold	BRc, from Ltd Edn T43 Kays set	61	80	100*

** Lining varies in shade between yellow and orange.

4.   Diesel Shunter 0-6-0DS

T95	13007	green	BRc	59-61	25	30
T95	D3115	green	BRc	62-67	25	30

5.   Class 31 Diesel A1A-A1A

T96	D5500	green	BRc**	59-68	30	35
T96	D5500	blue	BRc, made in France	67?	400	500

** To be found with solid or separate handrails.

6.   'Britannia' Class 4-6-2

T97/98	70000 'Britannia'	green	BRc**	60-61	50	55
T97S/98	70036 'Boadicea'	green	BRc with smoke generator	62-64	70	75
T97/98	70036 'Boadicea'	green	BRc	62-64	55	70

Both solid and open wheels may be found on these models. ** May be found unlined with smoke but this may have resulted from an exchange of chassis.

7.   GWR Prairie 2-6-2T

T99	6157	black	BRc, lined, solid or open wheels	61-67	55	65

8.   Est Class 231D 4-6-2

T591S	1401	black	AL S16, with smoke generator	62-68	80	100
T591	1401	black		62-68	60	80

9.   Diesel Multiple Unit

T190	M50421	green	BRc, power car	63-67	35	40
T137	M59133	green	centre car	63-67	30	35
T136	M50425	green	BRc, trailer car	63-67	25	30

10.   Continental 0-6-0T

T590	-	black		63-64	80	120

11.   Continental EMU

T594/595	silver	not made	-	-

Tri-ang Kays gold set   [table 3]

Coaches

Most of the coaches fall into two categories - suburbans and mainline. Early suburban coaches had roundish windows (£7-9) while late ones had squarer ones and are rarer (£13-15). The rarest mainline coaches are blue and grey (£35-40) but most other colours are quite common (£8-10). There are a lot of minor variations in these, such as different running numbers and class lines etc., amongst which some will be rarer than others. Utility vans and sleeping cars are less common (£13-15) but amongst the most sought after coaches are the three Pullman cars, 'Eagle', 'Falcon' and 'Snipe' (£30-35). The only French coach you are likely to find is the silver coloured T580 (£25-30).

Wagons

The rarest wagons are the five French types, T570-T574, (£25-30). Most other wagons cost between £3 and £5 each but exceptions are the small tank wagon with four Shell transfers (£18-20), track cleaning tar tank (£12-15) and the salt and cement wagons (£10-12). Bogie tank wagons and wagons with original loads generally sell at around £8-10. There are examples of the cattle wagon, bogie well wagon and ore wagon in green plastic but these are very rarely offered for sale and so a value is hard to determine, but £25-30 is suggested. Some wagons, such as the flat wagon, mineral wagon and fruit van, may be found in a number of different shades of plastic however we have no information on scarcity of these.

Accessories

The Tri-ang TT system had the benefit of a good range of attractive lineside accessories. The station was available both as the T31 main set (£30-35) and T32 island set (£25-30) and as loose items (£1 to £10 depending what they are). Other accessories included signal boxes and water towers (£8-10), engine and diesel sheds (£10-12), level crossings (£5-6), fuelling depots (£20-25), goods sheds (£65-70), girder bridges (£15-18), girder bridge presentation sets (£30-35), cattle docks (£28-30), signal gantries (£65-70), track foundations, incline pier sets, high levels supports, telegraph poles (all £2-3), lineside hut sets (£9-10), footbridges (£7-8) and signals (£3-5). Rarest item in the British range is the rubber tunnel (made by associate company Young & Fog) for which we have no example of a price. The French accessories consisted of a signal box, water tower, engine shed and goods depot all of which are rare and for which we have no established prices.

Sets

The rarest sets of all are those produced for the French market. While these can occasionally be bought in France at a reasonable price, at auction in Britain they would command a very high price. The most sought after British one is the 'gold plated' Merchant navy set (T43) made in small quantity for Kays. In good condition this can fetch £500 or more at auction. The next rarest is the T11 Express Passenger Set which commands prices around £150. The T6 Express Passenger Train Set is probably the next rarest. Most other sets sell for between £65 and £85 with the T2 and T10 goods sets, somewhat less – say, £40-45.

Tri-ang Prairie tank 6157 (T99)   [table 7]

Tri-ang TT train set box illustration

Tri-ang Britannia Class 70000 'Britannia' (T97/98) and 70036 'Boadicea' (T97/98)   [table 6]

Tri-ang Castle Class 4082 'Windsor Castle' (T91/92) and 5011 'Tintagel Castle' (T91/92)   [table 2]

4th edition
(1960) catalogue

Tri-ang Continental passenger car (T580)

Large Tri-ang TT layout showing the range of buildings available

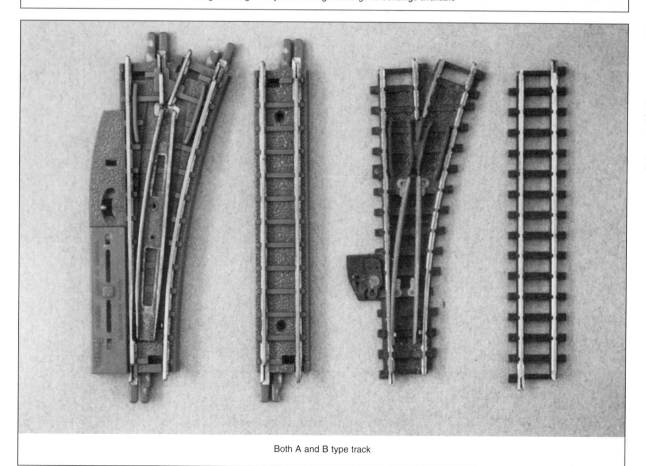

Both A and B type track

Lone Star Treble-O-Lectric catalogue circa 1961

Lone Star

History

Die Casting Machine Tools Ltd (DCMT) was founded by Bob Mills, who worked alone in a garage in Palmers Green, London, in 1940. Here he built a die casting machine and later went into partnership with Sidney Ambridge, developing the business. For a few years they found themselves involved in war work but, when peace came, they found good trade in supplying the blossoming array of new companies that formed to manufacture for the fast growing post-war market.

One of these new companies was founded by an ex-employee of DCMT, Rodney Smith and his partner Leslie Smith who pooled their demob money and bought one of the DCMT machines. The company they founded was Lesney and the product range the machine made for them was Matchbox Toys. Another famous ex-employee of DCMT was Jack Odell who worked for Lesney before setting up his own company Lledo to produce the Days Gone series.

It was not long before DCMT decided to go into manufacturing themselves and one of the first companies they did diecasting work for was Crescent Toys; a company also remembered for their model railway accessories. When they parted company with Crescent Toys in 1950 they decided manufacture and market toys themselves.

The craze with children at the time was the wild west films seen on television and a series particularly popular was 'Riders of the Range'. The writer remembers watching it, half hidden behind the sofa! DCMT cashed in on this craze and produced the first diecast toy revolver and the Lone Star range was born. Lone Star was hugely popular, partly through its links with the television programme but also through other links it developed with the Eagle boy's comic and a serial on Radio Luxembourg.

Lone Star's toy range became considerable and diverse in subject matter. In 1955 they went into the plastic soldier market with the take-over of Harvey's and by the end of the decade had a range of 200 figures. Expansion of the toy business led to the Company moving to a new factory at Hatfield and a series of diecast cars called Road-masters followed. Next came the series for which they are best remembered by model train collectors.

While the idea of an N gauge system had been around for a long time, Lone Star were the first company to attempt producing a commercial range for the British market. It started as a push-along system in 1957 called Lone Star Locos. All items were to 000 scale with a track gauge of 8.25 mm (exactly half 00 gauge). Initially all parts, including the track and buildings, were diecast and roughly based on real prototypes.

At the Harrogate and Brighton toy fairs in 1960, an electric range, known as Treble-O-Lectric, was launched which used many of the push-along castings fitted with plastic wheels to run on a finer scale 9 mm track and with tension-lock couplings. In order to fit a motor inside locomotives, two completely new models were tooled up and these were the Class 23 (Baby Deltic) and the Class 24 diesels.

1962 saw the introduction of an American range of locos and rolling stock which won DCMT a major contract to supply Montgomery Ward of Chicago. This company had a large mail order business and some 600 retail store outlets across North America. Blister packaging was also introduced in 1962. Vinyl was used the following year in the production of a series of buildings called Gulliver County and with these came a set of diecast 000 scale road vehicles. Encouraged by the good sales across the Atlantic, Canadian liveries followed in 1964.

In 1965 however, following an unsuccessful attempt to interest Lines Bros. (Tri-ang) in purchasing the railway

---

Milestones

1940	DCMT formed by A.R.Mills.
1949	DCMT manufacturing for Crescent Toys.
1950	DCMT start their own toy range under the name Slikka Toys.
1955	Takeover of Harvey's hollow-cast figure business.
1956	Move to new factory at Hatfield.
1956	Road-masters car series introduced.
1957	Launch of Lone Star Locos.
1960	Introduction of Treble-O-Lectric
1962	American range.
1962	Arrival of blister packaging.
1963	Gulliver County launched.
1963	Impy cars launched.
1964	Canadian liveries.
1965	Production of Treble-0-Lectric and Lone Star Locos ceases
1967	New range of Treble-0-Trains launched.
1968	Push-along trains renamed 'Impy Treble-0-Trains'
1969	Tuf-Tots launched.
1970	Railway range removed from UK market and renamed 'Lone Star Model Trains'
c1973	Model trains withdrawn.
1978/79	Abortive plan to re-launch railway system.
1983	Lone Star/DCMT in liquidation.
1985	Treble-0-Trains Ltd dissolved
1988	Lone Star sold to Sohni-Esco Group.

system, production of Lone Star Locos and Treble-0-Lectric ceased.

In 1967, many of the passenger and goods stock items from the Treble-0-Lectric range were reissued in bubble-packs as Treble-0-Trains, using locomotives from the electric system, but without motors, and with a new plastic track produced for the series. In 1968, this system was renamed Impy Treble-0-Trains and new bubble-packs were produced.

In 1970 the train system was designated 'for export only', renamed Lone Star Model Trains, the term '000' finally dropped in favour of 'N Gauge' and the bubble-packs were replaced by boxes. It remained available for overseas sales until approximately 1973.

In 1979, Lone Star made plans to re-launch the model railway system. Contemporary subjects, such as the 125 High Speed train were mocked up but the system never reached production.

Meanwhile, the mid '60s had seen the launch of Lone Star's Impy series of small cars to compete with Matchbox and Husky. Tuf-Tots, Roadmaster Majors, Kings of the Road and many other series followed. In 1988 Lone Star was taken over by Sohni-Esco of Germany and production at Hatfield came to an end. However, DCMT continued as an independent company still in the business of manufacturing diecasting machines.

Plastic copies of Lone Star 000 labelled 'Hong Kong' may be found, but whether these were pirated copies or resulted from the sale of moulds is not clear. GEM models have reissued white metal copies of the Lone Star 000 Citroen and articulated lorry and the Tuf-Tots were reissued as Mokes by Microlink of Swansea.

Further Reading
A useful book called 'Lone Star Toys' has been written by Andrew Ralston and published by Auto Review Publications (ISBN: 1 900482 14 2). This provides a useful history of the Company but when it comes to describing the models it has a bias towards the car ranges rather than the railway. A new book, expected soon, should redress the balance. Called 'The Great Book of Lone Star' it is being written by Geoffrey Ambridge whose father was one of the partners who started the whole thing. Geoffrey Ambridge also has a web site for the book at www.lone-star-diecast-bk.com. There were also two articles by Clive Gehle in the January and February 2000 issues of Model Railway Collector which were specifically about the Lone Star railway models.

The Models

Numbering
– As the various train series overlapped it is possible to find a particular model with more than one code number. For example, the signal box appeared as 33, 80, EL.152 and 92 and yet only the packaging changed. In order to keep it simple we have listed below the models as they were presented in series but be aware that if you have an unboxed item you may find it in more than one list.

Colours – Many of the models were produced in a variety of colours and some are rarer than others.

Prices – It is very difficult to give a realistic guide to these as dealers often have little idea of the rarity or otherwise of items they are selling. It is therefore possible to pick up unusual items at bargain prices but it is also possible to find relatively common pieces overpriced.

Lone Star Treble-0-Lectric
Baldwin 0-8-0

[table 3]

1. 'Lone Star Locos' in Boxes (1957-60)

1	0-6-0 Class 3F Tank Loco	5	8
2	2-6-2 Class 3 Tank Loco	5	8
3	Open Goods Wagon (2)	3	5
4	BR Midland Region Coach	3	5
5	Straight Track - metal (3)	2	4
6	Curved Track - metal (3)	2	4
7	0-6-0 Diesel Shunting Loco	4	7
8	4-6-2 Class A4 Gresley Loco	5	8
9	Tender for No.8	3	4
10	4-6-2 Class 8P Loco Princess Royal	5	8
11	Tender for No.10	3	4
12	US Diesel Loco	5	8
13	Brake Van	3	4
14	Cattle Wagon	3	4
15	UD Tank Wagon	3	4
16	BP Tank Wagon	3	4
17	Shell Tank Wagon	3	4
18	Goods Van (2)	5	6
19	BR Mk1 Composite Coach	4	5
20	Points - metal (1LH, 1RH)	4	5
21	Crossovers - metal (2)	3	4
22	Sleeper Built Buffer (3)	3	5
23	Re-railer Track - metal (3)	2	3
24	Station and Platform	7	10
25	Flat Wagon (3)	4	6
26	US Passenger Coach	4	5
27	Girder Bridge with Piers	6	8
28	Incline Piers (6)	3	5
29	Plastic Trees (3)	5	6
30	Telegraph Poles - plastic (12)	5	6
31	Fences and Gates - plastic (12+2)	5	6
32	Semaphore Signal	4	5
33	Signal Box	3	5
34	American flat car	3	5
35	American flat car with cars	17	20
36	American crane car	4	6
37	American tank car	4	6
38	American caboose	3	5
39	American box car	4	6
40	Level crossing	4	6
41	Automobiles (3)	21	25
42	Footbridge	5	8
GS1	Goods Train Set	NA	35
GS2	Mainline Express Set	NA	35
GS3	Mainline Goods Set	NA	35
GS4	American Diesel Set	NA	35

2. 'Lone Star Locos' in Blister Packs (1962-65)

50	0-6-0 Class 3F Tank with Track	5	8
51	2-6-2 Class 3 Tank with Track	5	8
52	0-6-0 Diesel Shunter with Track	4	8
53	4-6-2 Class A4 Gresley Loco	5	8
54	4-6-2 Class Princess Royal	5	8
55	Tender for No.53 with 2 Straight Tracks	3	5
56	Tender for No.54 with 2 Straight Tracks	3	5
57	Midland Region Coach with Track	5	5
58	BR Mk1 Composite Coach	4	5
59	Brake Van with Flat Wagon	4	8
60	Cattle Wagon with Open Goods Wagon	5	8
61	UD Tanker with Straight Track	4	5
62	BP Tanker + Flat Wagon	4	6
63	Shell Tanker with Re-railer Track	4	5
64	Goods Van + Open Wagon	5	8
65	100T Breakdown Crane Wagon	4	5
66	US Diesel Loco	5	6
67	US Passenger Coach	4	5
68	Bogie Flat Wagon with Track	4	6

69	Bogie Tank Wagon	4	6
70	US Caboose	3	5
71	US Box Car	4	6
72	Straight Track (5)	4	5
73	Curved Track (5)	4	5
74	Points (1LH, 1RH) and Track (2)	5	6
75	Re-railer Track (4)	3	4
76	Crossover (1), Buffer (2) and Track (2)	4	6
77	Level Crossing with Re-railer Track	4	5
78	Girder Bridge with Piers	6	8
79	Incline Piers (6)	3	5
80	Signal Box with Signal	5	8
81	Signals (3)	6	10
82	Plastic Trees (5)	5	6
83	Telegraph Poles, Fences, Gates	6	8

3. 'Treble-O-Lectric' (1960-65)

Track and spare parts have been excluded from the following list. For set contents, see end of this section.

EL.50	Standard Goods Set	NA	55
EL.51	Standard Passenger Set	NA	55
EL.52	Goods Set with Accessories	NA	60
EL.53	Passenger Set with Accessories	NA	60
EL.54	Transcontinental Passenger Set	NA	65
EL.55	Transcontinental Goods Set	NA	65
EL.56	BR De-Luxe Scenic Set	NA	80
EL.60	D5000 Diesel Loco	10	12
EL.60A	D5000 Diesel Loco (non-motorised)	5	7
EL.61	D5900 Diesel Loco	10	12
EL.61A	D5900 Diesel Loco (non-motorised)	5	7
EL.62	US F7 Diesel Loco Union Pacific	12	25
EL.62A	US F7 Diesel Loco Union Pacific (non-motorised)	5	7
EL.63	US F7 Diesel Loco New Haven	15	30
EL.63A	US F7 Diesel Loco New Haven (non-motorised) USA & Canada only	20	25
EL.64	US F7 Diesel Loco Chesapeake & Ohio	15	30
EL.64A	US F7 Diesel Loco Chesapeake & Ohio (non-motorised) USA & Canada only	20	25
EL.65	US F7 Diesel Loco Kansas City Southern	15	30
EL.65A	US F7 Diesel Loco Kansas City Southern (non-motorised) USA & Canada only	20	25
EL.66	US 0-8-0 Baldwin Steam Loco + Tender Union Pacific	18	25
EL.66L	US 0-8-0 Baldwin Steam Loco + Tender Union Pacific with headlight	20	30
EL.67	F7 Diesel Loco Canadian Pacific	16	20
EL.67A	F7 Diesel Loco Canadian Pacific (non-motorised) USA & Canada only	20	25
EL.68	F7 Diesel Loco Canadian National	16	20
EL.68A	F7 Diesel Loco Canadian National (non-motorised) USA & Canada only	20	25
EL.70	Mk1 Composite Coach - maroon	4	5
EL.71	Mk1 Brake End Coach - maroon	4	5
EL.72	US Coach Union Pacific	4	6
EL.73	US Vista Dome Coach Union Pacific	4	6
EL.74	Mk1 Composite Coach - green	5	6
EL.75	Mk1 Brake End Coach - green	5	6
EL.76	US Coach New Haven	6	7
EL.77	US Vista Dome Coach New Haven	6	7
EL.78	US Coach Pullman	6	7
EL.79	US Vista Dome Coach Pullman	6	7
EL.80	Brake Van	2	3
EL.81	Shell Tank Wagon	3	4
EL.82	BP Tank Wagon	3	4
EL.83	UD Tank Wagon	3	4
EL.84	Cattle Wagon	3	4
EL.85	Open Goods Wagon	3	4

EL.86	Goods Van	3	4
EL.87	US Box Car Union Pacific	4	6
EL.88	100T Breakdown Crane Wagon	7	10
EL.89	Bogie Flat Wagon with Citroën DS19 and Land Rover	15	20
EL.90	Bogie Tank Wagon Mobilgas	7	9
EL.91	US Caboose Union Pacific	4	6
EL.92	US Box Car Boston & Maine	4	6
EL.93	US Box Car New Haven	4	6
EL.94	US Box Car Santa Fe	4	6
EL.95	Bogie Tank Wagon Texaco	7	9
EL.96	Bogie Flat Wagon with Austin Articulated Lorry	15	25
EL.97	US Caboose New Haven	4	6
EL.98	US Caboose Chesapeake & Ohio	4	6
EL.99	US Caboose Kansas City Southern	4	6
EL.100	Straight Track - nickel silver (9.2")	1	1
EL.101	Half Straight Track - nickel silver (2.6")	1	1
EL.102	Curved Track - nickel silver (12" radius)	1	1
EL.103	Half Curved Track - nickel silver (12" radius)	1	1
EL.104	Left Hand Point - nickel silver	3	4
EL.105	Right Hand Point - nickel silver	3	4
EL.106	Left Hand Diamond Crossing – nickel silver	3	4
EL.107	Right Hand Diamond Crossing – nickel silver	3	4
EL.108	Rerailer 9.2" with track – nickel silver	3	4
EL.109	Rerailer 4.6"	2	3
EL.110	Power Feed Terminal	1	2
EL.111	Uncoupler and Straight Track – nickel silver	1	2
EL.112	Uncoupler	1	2
EL.113	Power Feed Terminal Leads	1	2
EL.114	Point Operating Motor	4	5
EL.115	Electric Point Switch	2	2
EL.116	Left Hand Electric Point	7	10
EL.117	Right Hand Electric Point	7	10
EL.130	Canadian Pacific Coach	8	10
EL.131	Canadian Pacific Vista Dome Coach	8	10
EL.132	Canadian National Coach	8	10
EL.133	Canadian National Vista Dome Coach	8	10
EL.140	Box Car Canadian Pacific	8	10
EL.141	Caboose Canadian Pacific	8	10
EL.142	Refrigerated Box Car Canadian Pacific	8	10
EL.143	Caboose Canadian National	8	10
EL.150	Station and Platform	8	12
EL.151	Platform Extensions with Lamp Standards	10	12
EL.152	Signal Box	5	16
EL.153	Semaphore Signal - Home (2)	5	6
EL.154	Semaphore Signal - Distant (2)	5	6
EL.155	Rail Built Buffer (3)	2	3
EL.156	Girder Bridge with Piers	6	12
EL.157	Incline Piers (6)	3	7
EL.158S	Incline Tray - Straight (4)	8	10
EL.158C	Incline Tray - Curved (4)	8	10
EL.159	Telegraph Poles (28)	4	5
EL.160	Fences (24) and Gates (4)	4	5
EL.161	Trees (plastic) (3)	4	5
EL.162	Tunnel	5	10
EL.163	Footbridge	5	12
EL.164	Level Crossing with Barriers	4	8
EL.165	Loading Gauge (3) (not made)	-	-
EL.166	2-Colour Light Signals (3)	9	12
EL.167	Set of 12 Plastic Figures (unpainted)	10	12
EL.168	Set of Five Road Vehicles (Citroën DS19, Land Rover, Dennis Fire Engine, Austin Articulated Flat Lorry, AEC Regal IV Single Deck Bus)**	35	50
EL.169A	Bridge Girder (trade pack)	NPG	12
EL.169B	Bridge Pier (trade pack)	NPG	12

EL.177	4-Piece Scenic Baseboard (36"x36")	20	25
EL.180	Fish Plates (12)	2	2
EL.181	Spare Band Drives (5)	4	4
EL.182	Battery Controller	5	6
EL.183	Track Clips (10)	4	5
EL.184	Power Control Unit 12V DC	4	5
EL.185	Isolating Fish Plates (12)	3	3
EL.186A	Replacement Motor for Diesels	8	10
EL.186B	Replacement Motor for Baldwin	8	10
EL.187A	D5000 Chassis and Bogies (no wheels)	NPG	5
EL.187B	D5900 Chassis and Bogies (no wheels)	NPG	5
EL.187C	F7 Chassis and Bogies (no wheels)	NPG	5
EL.188A	British Coach Bogie and Wheels	NPG	4
EL.188B	US Coach Bogie and Wheels	NPG	4
EL.188C	US Goods Bogie and Wheels	NPG	4
EL.189	Brass Driving Wheels for Diesels (12)	NPG	5
EL.190A	British Coach Wheels (12)	NPG	5
EL.190B	US Coach Wheels (12)	NPG	5
EL.191A	British Goods Rolling Stock Wheels (12)	NPG	5
EL.191B	US Goods Rolling Stock Wheels (12)	NPG	5
EL.192	Track Fixing Screws (20)	NPG	4
EL.193	Carbon Brushes (2) and Springs (2)	NPG	5
EL.197	Transformer/Rectifier	5	10
EL.198	Controller	10	20

** This set of vehicles was at one time sold in a Gulliver County box.

4. 'Treble-O-Trains' in Blister Packs (1966-68)

74	US Diesel Loco Union Pacific	10	12
75	D5900 Diesel Loco	10	12
76	US Baldwin 0-8-0 (tenderless)	10	15
77	BR Mk1 Composite Coach	4	5
78	US Passenger Coach	4	5
79	US Box Car New Haven	4	6
80	Bogie Tank Wagon Shell	4	5
81	Bogie Flat Wagon with Citroën DS19 and Land Rover	15	20
82	100T Breakdown Crane Wagon	7	10
83	US Caboose New Haven	4	6
84	Cattle Wagon and Brake Van	6	8
85	Curved Track - plastic (6)	4	6
86	Straight Track - plastic (6)	5	7
87	Trees (6)	5	6
88	Level Crossing with Barriers and Track	4	8
89	Figures, Telegraph Poles, Fences, Gates	10	12
90	Footbridge	5	10
91	0-6-0 Tank Loco with Open Goods Wagon	7	12
92	Signal Box with 2 Colour Light Signals	8	10
93	Crossovers - plastic	3	5
94A	Right Hand Point - plastic	4	5
94B	Left Hand Point - plastic	4	5

5. Impy 'Treble-O-Trains' in Blister Packs (1968-69)

With the exception of the five items listed below, this was an identical range to Treble-O-Trains in blister packs. They had the same catalogue numbers and values but different package design.

95	Princess Steam Locomotive	10	20
96	D5000 Diesel Locomotive	10	20
97	Vista Dome Coach	4	6
8020	Union Pacific Goods Set	NA	45
8030	Union Pacific Passenger Set	NA	45

6. Lone Star Model Trains

This was the same range shown in 4 and 5 above but packed in boxes with the new name and with a '7' added to the catalogue number.

7.   'Gulliver County' Buildings
These were vinyl moulded buildings, each a single moulding with features picked out with paint.

1320	Inn	10	18
1321	Church	10	18
1322	Fire Station	10	20
1323	Ranch Style Bungalow	10	18
1324	Shop with Car Park	10	18
1325	Garage Service Station	10	18
1326	Pair of Shops	10	18
1327	Two Storey House with Garage	10	18
1328	Thatched Cottage	10	18
1340	Twin Falls Station	10	18
	Scenic Village Set**	NPG200	

** The Scenic Village Set consisted of two pieces of hardboard painted green with roads marked out on them, one of each of the Gulliver County buildings, several of the N scale road vehicles, fences, telegraph poles and trees.

Sets

The Lone Star Locos sets were called 'Gift Sets' and were packaged in window boxes with card decking and trays. Five were made:

No.1 Goods Train Set – 2-6-2T, box van, UD tanker, Shell tanker, brake van, signal box and two signals.
No.2 Main Line Passenger Set – A4 loco and tender, 3 BR composite coaches and 2 signals.
No.3 Main Line Goods Set – Princess loco and tender, box van, goods truck, flat truck, brake van, signal box and 2 signals.
No.4 American Transcontinental Diesel Set – US diesel, 3 US passenger cars and 2 signals.
No.5 American Transcontinental Goods Set – US diesel, US box car, US tank car, US caboose and 2 signals.

The **Treble-0-Lectric** sets had the models still in their individual blue and yellow boxes which was slotted into spaces in the set box decking. The set box had no window but a lift-off lid. They had the following contents:

EL.50 BR Standard Goods Set – D5000 diesel, a brake van, cattle wagon, goods van and an oval of track.
EL.51 BR Standard Passenger Set – D5900 diesel with two coaches and an oval of track
EL.52 BR Goods & Accessories Set – D5000 diesel, brake van, Shell tanker, cattle wagon, open wagon, an oval of track, a point and siding, buffer stop, signal box, signal, station, fences & gates, trees and telegraph poles.
EL.53 BR Passenger & Accessories Set – This was the same as EL.52 but with the train from EL.51.

EL.54 Transcontinental Passenger Set – Union Pacific F7 diesel, 2 matching coaches and an oval of track. For USA and Canada only, sets were available in all liveries.
EL.55 Transcontinental Goods Set – Union Pacific diesel, Mobilgas tanker, UP box car, UP caboose and an oval of track. For USA and Canada only, sets were available in all liveries.
EL.56 BR De Luxe Scenic Set (2 Levels) – this had an elevated section in the middle and contained 4 vacuum-formed scenic sections which could be bought separately. It included over 90 pieces in all including a diesel passenger train and cost 9 guineas.
EL.57 BR De Luxe Scenic Set (Flat) – this had 4 scenic sections which together made a flat layout with roadways in the middle.
• There was also a version exclusive to the USA that appeared in the Montgomery Ward catalogue, featuring a lake and mountain.

For the Treble-0-Trains sets, in Impy packaging, the models were unboxed and laid in depressions in a vacuum-formed tray in a window set box. The contents of the Baldwin set were most strange consisting of a tender-less loco, bogie Shell tanker, 100 ton crane wagon, American box van, British brake van, signal box, 2 colour light signals, footbridge, level crossing and an oval of track.

Lone Star Impy Treble-0-Trains tanker in blister pack.   [table 5]

Lone Star Locos crane car.   [table 1]

Lone Star Locos boxed station and platform.   [table 1]

Lone Star flat cars with vehicles, station extension and girder bridge.

Lone Star Gulliver County fire stations and fire engines.   [table 6]

Trafford Code 3 Schools Class 938 'St.Olave's' (TMC20) on a Hornby 'Eastbourne' (R2144).   [table TH2]

Trafford
Code 3
Britannia Class 70048
'The Territorial Army 1908-1958'
(TMC12)
on a Hornby
'Firth of Clyde' (R2104).

[table TH4]

Trafford
Code 3
A3 Class 2508
'Brown Jack' (TMC29)
on a Hornby
'Cameronian' (R2103).

[table TH3]

Train Trading Post
Code 3
Merchant Navy Class 35029
'Ellerman Lines'
on a Hornby
'Lord Beaverbrook' (R310).

[table PH1]

Code 3 models

Background

A Code 3 model is one that has been finished (or, as is usually the case, refinished) outside the factory by a secondary 'manufacturer'. These are often retailers who buy a quantity of a certain model and re-release them in modified form. To count as a Code 3, a model has to have been produced in the modified form in quantity and to a common specification. This means that one off modifications do not count. Batches of 50 or more are usual. These should have a numbered certificate to authenticate them and to indicate how many of them were modified.

Code 3 models have their own niche market and this subject is likely to be a minefield for us to list as there has been little recording of Code 3 models until recent times. Consequently, there may be many in existence that we should be listing but of which we know nothing. Obviously, numbered certificates with models are good evidence that a model should be included. Care, however, should be taken not to assume that the maximum production figure quoted was necessarily achieved. As Code 3 models were/are often produced on demand it is possible that the actual number made fell short of the set target.

Ex- Hornby Models

Trafford Model Centre   All have etched brass nameplates and a numbered certificate.

TH1.	**Duchess 4-6-2**					
TMC1	46229 'Duchess of Hamilton'	green	BRc, ex-'City of Hereford' (R2015), Ltd Edn 50	99	100	120
TMC3	46229 'Duchess of Hamilton'	maroon	BRc, ex-'City of Liverpool' (R2041) or 'City of Leeds' (X3705) Ltd Edn 250	99	75	90
TMC38	46238 'City of Carlisle'	green	BRb, ex-'City of Bradford', Ltd Edn 250	00	NPG	90
TMC39	46242 'City of Glasgow'	green	BRc, ex-'City of Bristol' Ltd Edn 250	00	NPG	90
TMC41	46236 'City of Bradford'	green	BRb, ex-'City of Bradford', Ltd Edn 250	00	NPG	90
TMC42	46237 'City of Bristol'	green	BRc, ex-'City of Bristol', Ltd Edn 250	00	NPG	90
TMC45	46245 'City of London'	maroon	BRc, ex-'City of Liverpool' (R2041) or 'City of Leeds' (X3705) Ltd Edn 250	00	NPG	90
TMC46	46246 'City of Manchester'	maroon	BRc, ex-'City of Liverpool' (R2041) or 'City of Leeds' (X3705) Ltd Edn 250	00	NPG	90
TMC49	46249 'City of Sheffield'	maroon	BRc, ex-'City of Liverpool' (R2041) or 'City of Leeds' (X3705) Ltd Edn 250	00	NPG	90
TMC146	46238 'City of Carlisle'	maroon	BRc, ex-'City of Liverpool' (R2041) or 'City of Leeds' (X3705) Ltd Edn 250	00	NPG	90
TMC147	46236 'City of Bradford'	maroon	BRc, ex-'City of Liverpool' (R2041) or 'City of Leeds' (X3705) Ltd Edn 250	00	NPG	90
TMC148	46220 'Coronation'	green	BRc, ex-'City of Bristol', Ltd Edn 250	00	NPG	90
TMC149	46221 'Queen Elizabeth'	green	BRb or BRc, ex-'City of Bradford' or 'City of Bristol', Ltd Edn 250	00	NPG	90
TMC150	46222 'Queen Mary'	green	BRb or BRc, ex-'City of Bradford' or 'City of Bristol', Ltd Edn 250	00	NPG	90
TMC151	46223 'Princess Alice'	green	BRb or BRc, ex-'City of Bradford' or 'City of Bristol', Ltd Edn 250	00	NPG	90
TMC152	46224 'Princess Alexandra'	green	BRb or BRc, ex-'City of Bradford' or 'City of Bristol', Ltd Edn 250	00	NPG	90
TMC153	46235 'City of Birmingham'	green	BRb or BRc, ex-'City of Bradford' or 'City of Bristol', Ltd Edn 250	00	NPG	90
TMC154	46240 'City of Coventry'	green	BRc, ex-'City of Bristol', Ltd Edn 250	00	NPG	90
TMC155	46240 'City of Coventry'	maroon	BRc, ex-'City of Liverpool' (R2041) or 'City of Leeds' (X3705) Ltd Edn 250	00	NPG	90
TMC156	46241 'City of Edinburgh'	green	BRc, ex-'City of Bristol', Ltd Edn 250	00	NPG	90
TMC157	46243 'City of Lancaster'	maroon	BRc, ex-'City of Liverpool' (R2041) or 'City of Leeds' (X3705) Ltd Edn 250	00	NPG	90
TMC158	46244 'King George VI'	green	BRb, ex-'City of Bradford', Ltd Edn 250	00	NPG	90
TMC159	46244 'King George VI'	maroon	BRc, ex-'City of Liverpool' (R2041) or 'City of Leeds' (X3705) Ltd Edn 250	00	NPG	90
TMC160	46247 'City of Liverpool'	maroon	BRc, ex-'City of Liverpool' (R2041) or 'City of Leeds' (X3705) Ltd Edn 250	00	NPG	90
TMC161	46248 'City of Leeds'	green	BRb or BRc, ex-'City of Bradford' or 'City of Bristol', Ltd Edn 250	00	NPG	90

Code 3 models

TMC162	46253 'City of St.Albans'	green	BRb or BRc, ex-'City of Bradford' or 'City of Bristol', Ltd Edn 250	00	NPG	90
TMC163	46255 'City of Hereford'	green	BRb or BRc, ex-'City of Bradford' or 'City of Bristol', Ltd Edn 250	00	NPG	90

TH2. Schools Class 4-4-0

Some of the Schools Class locomotives, besides new names and numbers, have been fitted with large chimneys for the Lemaitre exhaust.

TMC2	922 'Marlborough'	black	*Southern*, ex-'Cheltenham' (R2039), Ltd Edn 50	99	100	120
TMC6	904 'Lancing'	black	*Southern*, ex-'Cheltenham' (R2039), Ltd Edn 250	99	85	100
TMC7	30935 'Sevenoaks'	black	BRb, ex-'Cheltenham' (R2039), Ltd Edn 250	99	80	90
TMC8	907 'Dulwich'	malachite	*Southern*, ex-'Dulwich' (R2124), large chimney, Ltd Edn 250	00	85	95
TMC20	938 'St.Olave's'	malachite	*Southern*, ex-'Dulwich' (R2124) or 'Eastbourne' (R2144), large chimney, Ltd Edn 250	00	NPG	95
TMC30	926 'Repton'	malachite	*Southern*, ex-'Dulwich' (R2124), Ltd Edn 250	00	NPG	95
TMC35	903 'Radley'	malachite	*Southern*, ex-'Dulwich' (R2124), large chimney, Ltd Edn 250	00	NPG	95
TMC36	30903 'Eton'	black	BRb or BRc, ex-'Cheltenham' (R2039) or 'Downside' (X3704), large chimney, Ltd Edn 250	00	NPG	95
TMC37	30933 'King's Canterbury'	black	BRb, ex-'Cheltenham' (R2039) or 'Downside' (X3704) Ltd Edn 250	00	NPG	95
TMC91	30913 'Christ's Hospital'	black	BRb, ex-'Cheltenham' (R2039) or 'Downside' (X3704), Ltd Edn 50	00	NPG	90
TMC102	901 'Winchester'	malachite	*Southern*, ex-'Dulwich' (R2124), large chimney, Ltd Edn 50	00	NPG	95
TMC103	933 'King's Canterbury'	malachite	*Southern*, ex-'Dulwich' (R2124), large chimney, Ltd Edn 50	00	NPG	95
TMC104	920 'Rugby'	malachite	*Southern*, ex-'Dulwich' (R2124), large chimney, Ltd Edn 50	00	NPG	95
TMC105	909 'St.Paul's'	malachite	*Southern*, ex-'Dulwich' (R2124), large chimney, Ltd Edn 50	00	NPG	95
TMC106	915 'Brighton'	malachite	*Southern*, ex-'Dulwich' (R2124), large chimney, Ltd Edn 50	00	NPG	95
TMC107	30916 'Whitgift'	green	BRc, ex-'Sevenoaks' (R2181), Ltd Edn 50	00	NPG	90
TMC108	30911 'Dover'	green	BRc, ex-'Sevenoaks' (R2181), Ltd Edn 50	00	NPG	90
TMC109	30913 'Christ's Hospital'	green	BRc, ex-'Sevenoaks' (R2181), Ltd Edn 100	00	NPG	90
TMC110	30906 'Sherbourne'	green	BRc, ex-'Sevenoaks' (R2181), Ltd Edn 50	00	NPG	90
TMC111	30910 'Merchant Taylors'	green	BRc, ex-'Sevenoaks' (R2181), Ltd Edn 50	00	NPG	90
TMC123	30926 'Repton'	green	BRc, ex-'Sevenoaks' (R2181), Ltd Edn 250	00	NPG	95
TMC136	931 'King's Wimbledon'	black	*Southern*, ex-'Cheltenham' (R2039), large chimney, Ltd Edn 100	00	NPG	100
TMC137	933 'King's Canterbury'	black	*Southern*, ex-'Cheltenham' (R2039), large chimney, Ltd Edn 100	00	NPG	100
TMC138	30933 'King's Canterbury'	green	BRc, ex-'Sevenoaks' (R2181), large chimney, Ltd Edn 250	00	NPG	95
TMC140	913 'Christ's Hospital'	malachite	*Southern*, ex-'Dulwich' (R2124), Ltd Edn 250	00	NPG	95
TMC141	30938 'St Olaves'	black	BRb, ex-'Cheltenham' (R2039), Ltd Edn 250	00	NPG	95
TMC142	30937 'Epsom'	green	BRc, ex-'Sevenoaks' (R2181), large chimney, Ltd Edn 250	00	NPG	95
TMC143	30932 'Blundells'	black	BRb, ex-'Cheltenham' (R2039), Ltd Edn 250	00	NPG	95
TMC145	937 'Epsom'	malachite	*Southern*, ex-'Dulwich' (R2124), large chimney, Ltd Edn 250	00	NPG	95

TH3. A3 Class 4-6-2   sc = single chimney   dc = double chimney

TMC4	60051 'Blink Bonny'	green	BRc, ex-'Flying Scotsman' (R2054), Ltd Edn 250	00	80	95
TMC5	60035 'Windsor Lad'	green	BRc, ex-'Flying Scotsman' (R2054), Ltd Edn 250	00	80	95
TMC19	2506 'Salmon Trout'	green	*LNER*, ex-'Cameronian' (R2103), Ltd Edn 250	00	NPG	95
TMC21	2507 'Singapore'	green	*LNER*, ex-'Cameronian' (R2103), Ltd Edn 250	00	NPG	95
TMC29	2508 'Brown Jack'	green	*LNER*, ex-'Cameronian' (R2103), Ltd Edn 250	00	NPG	95
TMC40	60040 'Cameronian'	green	BRb or BRc, ex-'Flying Scotsman' (R2054), Ltd Edn 250	00	NPG	95
TMC43	60102 'Sir Frederick Banbury'	green	BRb, GN tender, sc, ex-'Doncaster' (R2140), Ltd Edn 250	00	NPG	95
TMC44	60105 'Victor Wild'	green	BRb, GN tender, sc, ex-'Doncaster' (R2140), Ltd Edn 250	00	NPG	95
TMC47	60106 'Flying Fox'	green	BRb, GN tender, sc, ex-'Doncaster' (R2140), Ltd Edn 250	00	NPG	95
TMC48	60110 'Robert the Devil'	green	BRb, GN tender, sc, ex-'Doncaster' (R2140), Ltd Edn 250	00	NPG	95
TMC57	60049 'Galtee More'	green	BRb, GN tender, sc, ex-'Doncaster' (R2140), Ltd Edn 250	00	NPG	95
TMC58	60056 'Centenary'	green	BRb, GN tender, sc, ex-'Doncaster' (R2140), Ltd Edn 250	00	NPG	95
TMC59	60065 'Knight of the Thistle'	green	BRb, GN tender, sc, ex-'Doncaster' (R2140), Ltd Edn 250	00	NPG	95
TMC92	60092 'Fairway'	green	BRb, GN tender, sc, ex-'Doncaster' (R2140), Ltd Edn 50	00	NPG	95

TMC95	60078 'Night Hawk'	green	BRb, GN tender, sc, ex-'Doncaster' (R2140), Ltd Edn 50	00		NPG	95
TMC96	60082 'Neil Gow'	green	BRb, GN tender, sc, ex-'Doncaster' (R2140), Ltd Edn 50	00		NPG	95
TMC97	60090 'Grand Parade'	green	BRb, GN tender, sc, ex-'Doncaster' (R2140), Ltd Edn 50	00		NPG	95
TMC98	60088 'Book Law'	green	BRb, GN tender, sc, ex-'Doncaster' (R2140), Ltd Edn 50	00		NPG	95
TMC99	60037 'Hyperion'	green	BRb, GN tender, sc, ex-'Doncaster' (R2140), Ltd Edn 50	00		NPG	95
TMC100	60041 'Salmon Trout'	green	BRb, GN tender, sc, ex-'Doncaster' (R2140), Ltd Edn 50	00		NPG	95
TMC101	60042 'Singapore'	green	BRb, GN tender, sc, ex-'Doncaster' (R2140), Ltd Edn 50	00		NPG	95
TMC112	60105 'Victor Wild'	green	BRc, GN tender, dc, ex-'Manna' (R2152), Ltd Edn 50	00		NPG	95
TMC113	60106 'Flying Fox'	green	BRc, GN tender, dc, ex-'Manna' (R2152), Ltd Edn 50	00		NPG	95
TMC114	60110 'Robert the Devil'	green	BRc, GN tender, dc, ex-'Manna' (R2152), Ltd Edn 50	00		NPG	95
TMC115	60049 'Galtee More'	green	BRc, GN tender, dc, ex-'Manna' (R2152), Ltd Edn 50	00		NPG	95
TMC116	60056 'Centenary'	green	BRc, GN tender, dc, ex-'Manna' (R2152), Ltd Edn 50	00		NPG	95
TMC117	60078 'Night Hawk'	green	BRc, GN tender, dc, ex-'Manna' (R2152), Ltd Edn 50	00		NPG	95
TMC118	60090 'Grand Parade'	green	BRc, GN tender, dc, ex-'Manna' (R2152), Ltd Edn 50	00		NPG	95
TMC119	60088 'Book Law'	green	BRc, GN tender, dc, ex-'Manna' (R2152), Ltd Edn 50	00		NPG	95
TMC120	60037 'Hyperion'	green	BRc, GN tender, dc, ex-'Manna' (R2152), Ltd Edn 50	00		NPG	95
TMC121	60041 'Salmon Trout'	green	BRc, GN tender, dc, ex-'Manna' (R2152), Ltd Edn 50	00		NPG	95
TMC122	60042 'Singapore'	green	BRc, GN tender, dc, ex-'Manna' (R2152), Ltd Edn 50	00		NPG	95

TH4. Britannia Class 4-6-2

TMC9	70045 'Lord Rowallan'	green	BRc, ex-'Firth of Clyde' (R2104), Ltd Edn 250	00		NPG	90
TMC10	70046 'Anzac'	green	BRc, ex-'Firth of Clyde' (R2104), Ltd Edn 250	00		NPG	90
TMC11	70047	green	BRc, ex-'Firth of Clyde' (R2104), Ltd Edn 250	00		80	90
TMC12	70048 'The Territorial Army 1908-1958'	green	BRc, ex-'Firth of Clyde' (R2104), Ltd Edn 250	99		80	90
TMC13	70049 'Solway Firth'	green	BRc, ex-'Firth of Clyde' (R2104), Ltd Edn 250	00		NPG	90
TMC14	70050 'Firth of Clyde'	green	BRc, ex-'Firth of Clyde' (R2104), Ltd Edn 250	00		NPG	90
TMC15	70051 'Firth of Forth'	green	BRc, ex-'Firth of Clyde' (R2104), Ltd Edn 250	00		NPG	90
TMC16	70052 'Firth of Tay'	green	BRc, ex-'Firth of Clyde' (R2104), Ltd Edn 250	00		NPG	90
TMC17	70053 'Moray Firth'	green	BRc, ex-'Firth of Clyde' (R2104), Ltd Edn 250	00		80	90
TMC18	70054 'Dornoch Firth'	green	BRc, ex-'Firth of Clyde' (R2104), Ltd Edn 250	99		80	90
TMC33	70033 'Charles Dickens'	green	BRb, ex-'Robin Hood' (R2142), Ltd Edn 50	00		NPG	90
TMC69	70004 'William Shakespeare'	green	BRb, ex-'Robin Hood' (R2142), Ltd Edn 50	00		NPG	90
TMC70	700000 'Britannia'	green	BRb, ex-'Robin Hood' (R2142), Ltd Edn 50	00		NPG	90
TMC84	700007 'Coeur de Lion'	green	BRb, ex-'Robin Hood' (R2142), Ltd Edn 50	00		NPG	90
TMC85	700009 'Alfred the Great'	green	BRb, ex-'Robin Hood' (R2142), Ltd Edn 50	00		NPG	90
TMC86	700014 'Iron Duke'	green	BRb, ex-'Robin Hood' (R2142), Ltd Edn 50	00		NPG	90
TMC87	70015 'Apollo'	green	BRb, ex-'Robin Hood' (R2142), Ltd Edn 50	00		NPG	90
TMC88	70024 'Vulcan'	green	BRb, ex-'Robin Hood' (R2142), Ltd Edn 50	00		NPG	90
TMC89	70031 'Byron'	green	BRb, ex-'Robin Hood' (R2142), Ltd Edn 50	00		NPG	90
TMC90	700036 'Boadicea'	green	BRb, ex-'Robin Hood' (R2142), Ltd Edn 50	00		NPG	90
TMC93	700020 'Mercury'	green	BRb, ex-'Robin Hood' (R2142), Ltd Edn 50	00		NPG	90
TMC	70021 'Morning Star'	green	BRb, ex-'Robin Hood' (R2142), Ltd Edn 50	00		NPG	90
TMC	70037 'Hereward the Wake'	green	BRc, ex-'Firth of Clyde' (R2104), Ltd Edn 250	00		NPG	95
TMC	70029 'Shooting Star'	green	BRc, ex-'Firth of Clyde' (R2104), Ltd Edn 250	00		NPG	95
TMC	70017 'Arrow'	green	BRc, ex-'Firth of Clyde' (R2104), Ltd Edn 250	00		NPG	95
TMC	70010 'Owen Glendower'	green	BRc, ex-'Firth of Clyde' (R2104), Ltd Edn 250	00		NPG	95
TMC	70000 'Britannia'	green	BRc, ex-'Firth of Clyde' (R2104), Ltd Edn 250	00		NPG	95

TH5. Princess Royal Class 4-6-2

TMC22	46203 'Princess Margaret Rose'	green	BRb, ex-'Princess Louise' (R2070), Ltd Edn 250	00		NPG	90
TMC129	46207 'Princess Arthur of Connaught'	green	BRb, ex-'Princess Louise' (R2070), Ltd Edn 50	00		NPG	90

TH6. A4 Class 4-6-2 All have corridor tenders and darkened metalwork. dc = double chimney sc = single chimney

TMC23	60031 'Golden Plover'	green	BRc, ex-'Golden Fleece' (R2101), dc, Ltd Edn 250	00		NPG	95
TMC24	60003 'Andrew K McCosh'	green	BRc, ex-'Silver Link', sc, Ltd Edn 250	00		NPG	95
TMC25	60007 'Sir Nigel Gresley'	green	BRb or BRc, ex-'Silver Link' or 'Golden Fleece' (R2101), sc or dc, Ltd Edn 250	00		NPG	95
TMC26	60008 'Dwight D Eisenhower'	green	BRc, ex-'Silver Link', sc, Ltd Edn 250	00		NPG	95
TMC28	60004 'William Whitelaw'	green	BRb or BRc, ex-'Silver Link' or 'Golden Fleece' (R2101), sc or dc, Ltd Edn 250	00		NPG	95
TMC31	60032 'Gannet'	green	BRb or BRc, ex-'Silver Link' or 'Golden Fleece' (R2101), sc or dc, Ltd Edn 250	00		NPG	95
TMC34	60034 'Lord Farringdon'	green	BRb or BRc, ex-'Silver Link' or 'Golden Fleece' (R2101), sc or dc, Ltd Edn 250	00		NPG	95

TMC71	60001 'Sir Ronald Mathews'	green	BRc, non-corridor tender, Ltd Edn 250	00	NPG	95
TMC72	60011 'Empire of India'	green	BRb or BRc, ex-'Silver Link' or 'Golden Fleece' (R2101), sc or dc, Ltd Edn 250	00	NPG	95
TMC73	60024 'Kingfisher'	green	BRb or BRc, ex-'Silver Link' or 'Golden Fleece' (R2101), sc or dc, Ltd Edn 250	00	NPG	95
TMC74	60025 'Falcon'	green	BRb or BRc, ex-'Silver Link' or 'Golden Fleece' (R2101), sc or dc, Ltd Edn 250	00	NPG	95
TMC75	60027 'Merlin'	green	BRb or BRc, ex-'Silver Link' or 'Golden Fleece' (R2101), sc or dc, Ltd Edn 250	00	NPG	95
TMC76	60028 'Walter K.Wigham'	green	BRb or BRc, ex-'Silver Link' or 'Golden Fleece' (R2101), sc or dc, Ltd Edn 250	00	NPG	95
TMC77	60029 'Woodcock'	green	BRb or BRc, ex-'Silver Link' or 'Golden Fleece' (R2101), sc or dc, Ltd Edn 250	00	NPG	95
TMC78	60032 'Gannet'	green	BRb or BRc, ex-'Silver Link' or 'Golden Fleece' (R2101), sc or dc, Ltd Edn 250	00	NPG	95
TMC139	4488 'Kingfisher'	blue	BRc, ex-'Kestrel' (R2154), sc, Ltd Edn 250	00	NPG	95
TMC173	60019 'Bittern'	green	BRc, ex-'Silver Link' or 'Golden Fleece' (R2101), sc or dc, Ltd Edn	00	NPG	95

TH7. Rebuilt Merchant Navy 4-6-2   Darkened metalwork

TMC63	35021 'New Zealand Line'	green	BRc, ex-'Clan Line' (R2169), Ltd Edn 250	00	NPG	100
TMC64	35022 'Holland America Line'	green	BRc, ex-'Clan Line' (R2169), Ltd Edn 250	00	NPG	100
TMC65	35024 'East Asiatic Company'	green	BRc, ex-'Clan Line' (R2169), Ltd Edn 250	00	NPG	100
TMC66	35025 'Brocklebank Line'	green	BRc, ex-'Clan Line' (R2169), Ltd Edn 250	00	NPG	100
TMC67	35028 'Clan Line'	green	BRc, ex-'Clan Line' (R2169), Ltd Edn 250	00	NPG	100
TMC68	35030 'Elder Dempster Lines'	green	BRc, ex-'Clan Line' (R2169), Ltd Edn 250	00	NPG	100

TH8. Streamlined Coronation 4-6-2   Darkened metalwork

TMC79	6225 'Duchess of Gloucester'	maroon	LMS, ex-'Duchess of Hamilton' (R2179), Ltd Edn 250	00	NPG	90
TMC80	6226 'Duchess of Norfolk'	maroon	LMS, ex-'Duchess of Hamilton' (R2179), Ltd Edn 250	00	NPG	90
TMC81	6227 'Duchess of Devonshire'	maroon	LMS, ex-'Duchess of Hamilton' (R2179), Ltd Edn 250	00	NPG	90
TMC82	6228 'Duchess of Rutland'	maroon	LMS, ex-'Duchess of Hamilton' (R2179), Ltd Edn 250	00	NPG	90
TMC83	6229 'Duchess of Hamilton'	maroon	LMS, ex-'Duchess of Hamilton' (R2179), Ltd Edn 250	00	NPG	90

TH9. Castle Class 4-6-0   Darkened metalwork

TMC61	5014 'Goodrich Castle'	green	BRc, Ltd Edn 250	00	NPG	90
TMC62	5087 'Tintern Abbey'	green	BRc, Ltd Edn 250	00	NPG	90

TH10. King Class 4-6-0

TMC60	6000 'King George V'	green	GWR, ex-'King Henry VII' (R2119), Ltd Edn 250	00	NPG	90

Train Trading Post

PH1. Bullied Pacific   Repainted with engraved brass nameplates and numbered certificate.

-	35029 'Ellerman Lines'	blue	BRb, ex- 'Lord Beaverbrook' (R310), Ltd Edn 50	95	120	150

Frizinghall Model Railways   All come fitted with etched brass nameplates (where named) and renumbered and issued with a certificate.

FH1. J94 0-6-0ST

FMR12A	118 'Brussels'	blue	LMR, ex- R2151, Ltd Edn 100	00	NPG	50
FMR12B	196 'Errol Lonsdale'	blue	LMR, ex- R2151, Ltd Edn 100	00	NPG	50

FH2. Class 56 Diesel Co-Co

FMR14A	56074 'Kellingley Colliery'	blk+org	LoadHaul, ex-R2074	00	NPG	55
FMR14B	56110 'Croft'	blk+org	LoadHaul, ex-R2074	00	NPG	55

FH3. Classes 41XX, 51XX and 61XX Prairie Tank 2-6-2T   Sprayed black

FMR13A	various	black	BRb, Class 41XX, ex-R2098A	00	NPG	60
FMR13B	various	black	BRb, Class 51XX, ex-R2098A	00	NPG	60
FMR13C	various	black	BRb, Class 61XX, ex-R2098A	00	NPG	60

Miscellaneous

MH1. **Class 86**

-	86220 'The Round Tabler'	grey	InterCity, ex-R333, (Round Table), Ltd Edn 1267, etched nameplates	90	50	75
-	86102 'Robert A Riddles'	grey	BRe InterCity ex-R289, (IWPA)	88?	50	75

MH2. **Holden 0-4-0T**

-	30	blue	ex-R796, (Pendle Forest Model Railway Society)**, Ltd Edn 150	94	40	50

** Transfers

MH3. **Patriot 4-6-0**

-	45538 'Giggleswick'	green	BR, (Giggleswick School), Ltd Edn 50	99	NPG	NPG

Ex- Bachmann Models

Trafford Model Centre   All have etched brass nameplates and a numbered certificate.

TB1. **WD 2-8-0**   Blackened metalwork. Shed plates fitted to customer's choice.

TMC32	90732 'Vulcan'	black	BRb or BRc, Ltd Edn 1000	00	NPG	100
TMC50	90245	black	BRb or BRc, Ltd Edn 100	00	NPG	95
TMC51	90503	black	BRb or BRc, Ltd Edn 100	00	NPG	95
TMC52	90146	black	BRb or BRc, Ltd Edn 100	00	NPG	95
TMC53	90000	black	BRb or BRc, Ltd Edn 100	00	NPG	95
TMC54	90085	black	BRb or BRc, Ltd Edn 100	00	NPG	95
TMC55	90566	black	BRb or BRc, Ltd Edn 100	00	NPG	95
TMC56	90464	black	BRb or BRc, Ltd Edn 100	00	NPG	95
TMC127	90266	black	BRb or BRc, Ltd Edn 100	00	NPG	95

TB2. **A4 Class 4-6-2**   All have the double chimney and darkened metalwork.   **ct = corridor tender**   **nct = non-corridor tender**

TMC27	60022 'Mallard'	green	BRb or BRc, ex-'Seagull' (31-957), ct, Ltd Edn 250	00	NPG	95
TMC31	60032 'Gannet'	green	BRb or BRc, ex-'Seagull' (31-957), ct, Ltd Edn 250	00	NPG	95
TMC124	60004 'William Whitelaw'	green	BRc, ex-'Seagull' (31-957), ct, Ltd Edn 250	00	NPG	95
TMC125	60031 'Golden Plover'	green	BRc, ex-'Seagull' (31-957), ct, Ltd Edn 250	00	NPG	95
TMC126	60003 'Andrew K McCosh'	green	BRc, ex-'Seagull' (31-957), nct, Ltd Edn 250	00	NPG	95
TMC164	60024 'Kingfisher'	green	BRc, ex-'Seagull' (31-957), ct, Ltd Edn 250	00	NPG	95
TMC165	60027 'Merlin'	green	BRc, ex-'Seagull' (31-957), ct, Ltd Edn 250	00	NPG	95
TMC166	60025 'Falcon'	green	BRc, ex-'Seagull' (31-957), ct, Ltd Edn 250	00	NPG	95
TMC167	60028 'Walter K Wigham'	green	BRc, ex-'Seagull' (31-957), ct, Ltd Edn 250	00	NPG	95
TMC168	60029 'Woodcock'	green	BRc, ex-'Seagull' (31-957), ct, Ltd Edn 250	00	NPG	95
TMC169	60018 'Sparrow Hawk'	green	BRc, ex-'Seagull' (31-957), nct, Ltd Edn 250	00	NPG	95
TMC170	60016 'Silver King'	green	BRc, ex-'Seagull' (31-957), nct, Ltd Edn 250	00	NPG	95
TMC171	60026 'Miles Beevor'	green	BRc, ex-'Seagull' (31-957), nct, Ltd Edn 250	00	NPG	95
TMC172	60023 'Golden Eagle'	green	BRc, ex-'Seagull' (31-957), nct, Ltd Edn 250	00	NPG	95

Frizinghall Model Railways   All come fitted with etched brass nameplates and renumbered and issued with a certificate.

FB1. **A4 Class 4-6-2**   Repainted

FMR10A	60003 'Andrew K.McCosh'	garter blue	BRa, cream lettering, Ltd Edn 100	00	NPG	90
FMR10B	60004 'William Whitelaw'	garter blue	BRa, cream lettering, Ltd Edn 100	00	NPG	90

FB2. **Class B1 4-6-0**   Repainted

FMR11A	8302 'Eland'	black	NE, Ltd Edn 100	00	NPG	70
FMR11B	8306 'Bongo'	black	NE, Ltd Edn 100	00	NPG	70

Ex-Trix Models   *Miscellaneous*

MT1. **A2 Class 4-6-2**

These were supplied to a Mr Fox who was responsible for the BBC 'Blue Peter' model railway layout. It is understood that the new number transfers were applied at the factory and Mr Fox had the nameplates and double chimney done. In the spring of 1998, 7 of these came on the market.

-	532 'Blue Peter'	green	LNER, double chimney, Ltd Edn 12?	00	150	NPG

Scales and Gauges

'Scale' refers to the linear scale of the model,
for example: 4mm to 1 foot (the 'OO' scale measurement).
'Gauge' refers to the distance between the running rails of the track.
Listed here are a few of the more common scales and gauges.

Gauge name	Scale	Gauge distance
'N' (British)	2 mm to 1 foot	9 mm
'OOO'	2 mm to 1 foot	9.5 mm
'TT' (British)	3 mm to 1 foot	12 mm
'HO'	3.5 mm to 1 foot	16.5 mm
OO'	4 mm to 1 foot	16.5 mm
'EM'	4 mm to 1 foot	18 mm
'O' (British)	7 mm to 1 foot	32 mm
'No.1'	10 mm to 1 foot	45.45 mm
'No.2'	7/16 inch to 1 foot	51 mm
'No.3'	17/32", 1/2" or 14 mm to 1 foot!	63.5 mm

> *The illustrations below are only approximately to scale but serve to give some idea of the difference in size between the various gauges.*

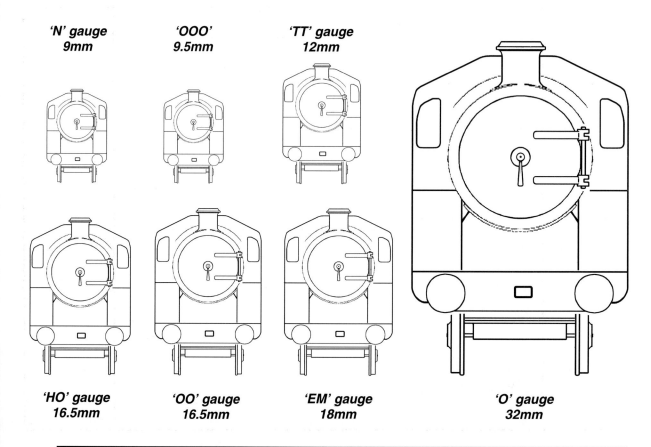

'N' gauge
9mm

'OOO'
9.5mm

'TT' gauge
12mm

'HO' gauge
16.5mm

'OO' gauge
16.5mm

'EM' gauge
18mm

'O' gauge
32mm

Sale and Purchase Record

Date	Models bought or sold	Price

Swapmeet Publications Reader Service

2nd Edition
'British Model Trains Catalogue'
Reader Survey

Whether you are a collector or trader, we would greatly value your views on this new Edition and would ask you to kindly complete and return this questionnaire.

We hope to publish the results of this survey, and for the three most constructive and helpful replies that we receive, we shall be giving a year's **free subscription** to the collecting magazine or newspaper of their choice. If necessary, do please use a photocopy of this form or a separate sheet of paper for your response. Thank you.

1   What do you like MOST about the Catalogue? _____
_____

2   What do you like LEAST about the Catalogue? _____
_____

3   What improvements or additions would you like to see? _____
_____

4   Would you like the Catalogue to be published yearly or every two years?
_____

If you have model information not currently included in the Catalogue – do please send it to us. Your costs will be fully refunded.

Name and Address (BLOCK CAPITALS, please) _____
_____
_____
_____

Kindly send your response to:
Swapmeet Publications, PO Box 47, Felixstowe, Suffolk, IP11 7LP.

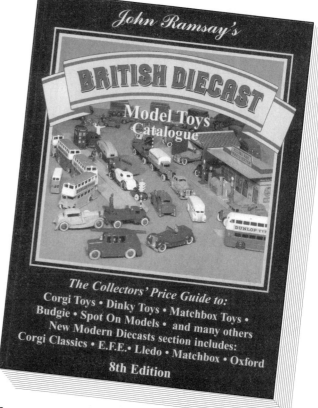

Guide to Advertisers

The Guide to Advertisers has been compiled as an extra service for Catalogue users. Whilst every care has been taken in compiling the listing, the publishers cannot accept responsibility for any errors or omissions. Similarly, the publishers cannot accept responsibility for errors in the advertisements or for unsolicited photographs or illustrations.

Notes